EMBRYOLOGY OF THE VIVIPAROUS INSECTS

By

HAROLD R. HAGAN

ASSOCIATE PROFESSOR OF BIOLOGY, THE CITY COLLEGE OF
THE COLLEGE OF THE CITY OF NEW YORK

AWARDED AN

A. CRESSY MORRISON PRIZE IN NATURAL SCIENCE

BY THE NEW YORK ACADEMY OF SCIENCES

THE RONALD PRESS COMPANY ⟋ NEW YORK

DEDICATED TO
DOCTOR JOHN ANDREAS WIDTSOE
AND TO THE LATE
PROFESSOR WILLIAM MORTON WHEELER

PREFACE

This pioneer monograph on the embryology of the viviparous insects has been designed to fulfill three functions: as a text for the student entomologist, as a source book for the professional entomologist or general zoologist, and as a reference tool for public health and applied research workers who desire a knowledge of the embryogenies of viviparous hexapods. For the first time, the book presents a comprehensive survey of earlier papers on viviparity, a historical introduction to each species or group, a thorough treatment of the known embryogenies, and a very comprehensive bibliography which covers all essential references to date. Moreover, it includes historical accounts of several species whose viviparity remains uncertain or has recently been disproved.

The embryogenies have been treated separately and fully. Since the reproductive system of a viviparous insect nearly always presents some anatomical peculiarities fitted to the type of viviparity shown, their descriptions have often been included. Brief historical summaries bring into review the preceding work on each insect discussed, and theories concerning them, while gaps in our present knowledge are often indicated and suggestions are offered for further investigations. The book includes much hitherto unpublished research by the author. The species concerned are *Glossina tachinoides, Diploptera dytiscoides,* and *Arixenia jacobsoni.*

The author is deeply conscious of his indebtedness to the many scientists who have contributed the fruits of their labors to this compilation, and he is grateful for the encouragement he has received from a multitude of sources. Professor W. M. Wheeler suggested the title and scope of the work, which Harvard University aided by providing a research fellowship. Professors Leigh Hoadley, A. B. Dawson, C. T. Brues, and Joseph Bequaert at the Biological Laboratories, and W. J. Clench, Curator of Molluscs, Museum of Comparative Zoology, offered laboratory and library facilities, specimens, and much helpful advice. The American Museum of Natural History, through the late Dr. Frank E. Lutz, made available space and literature for completing the work in

New York City. Additional specimens of *Diploptera dytiscoides* were received from Mr. Francis Yap, a former assistant in the Hawaiian Islands, and from Mr. Yoshio Kondo of the Bishop Museum at Honolulu. Dr. K. W. Dammerman, Director, and Dr. M. A. Lieftinck, Entomologist, of the Zoological Museum at Buitenzorg, Java, sent specimens of *Arixenia jacobsoni*. Dr. Karl Jordan of the British Museum contributed a few specimens of *Hemimerus*, Dr. T. A. M. Nash forwarded *Glossina* from Africa, and Dr. G. M. Turner, Wood Conversion Laboratory, Madison, Wisconsin, sent specimens of *Micromalthus* larvae.

A colleague, Professor J. I. Kendall, obtained a copy of a rare paper which is apparently unavailable in the United States, while Professor A. Glen Richards, University of Minnesota, and Mr. J. C. Crawford, of the U. S. D. A. Bureau of Entomology and Plant Quarantine, supplied several references. Certain papers were translated from the Scandinavian languages by Dr. Elizabeth Deichmann, Curator of Echinodermata, Museum of Comparative Zoology; from the Russian by Miss Tatyana Podruskya; and from the Italian by Miss Rina Orcesi.

Mr. R. E. Snodgrass, U. S. D. A. Bureau of Entomology and Plant Quarantine, offered friendly and constructive advice. I am especially indebted to him for reading and criticizing the manuscript. Finally, the author wishes to pay tribute to the untiring assistance of his wife, Dolly C. Hagan, in translating many of the German articles, typing the manuscript, reading proof, and helping with the index.

All illustrations from earlier papers have been redrawn, some with modifications to better elucidate the text. Sources are acknowledged in the explanations accompanying the drawings. A few of them are purely diagrammatic to make clear descriptions which are not easily visualized by the reader.

HAROLD R. HAGAN

New York
June, 1951

CONTENTS

PART I

GENERAL CONSIDERATIONS

PART II

EMBRYOGENIES

ILLUSTRATIONS

PART I

GENERAL CONSIDERATIONS

Chapter 1

INTRODUCTION

The study of the processes of reproduction, the direct steps which enable new generations of a species to arise and eventually to supplant the older in regular succession, is relatively young. It had to await the arrival of certain technical advances in other branches of science involving, among other things, the perfection of microscopes, the advent of the microtome, and adequate physicochemical fixation of tissues coupled with proper staining methods. Kowalevsky (1871) was the founder of modern insect embryology, for, aside from his material contributions, he was apparently the first to employ such aids in his field. The favorable spirit of inquiry attained in our present state of civilization also has become a most important stimulus to the detailed and often tedious study of specific problems.

Some Fundamental Concepts and Terms

Several terms have been employed with various limitations by different authors. To avoid ambiguity in their usage here, an attempt has been made to explain their general scope.

Embryology Defined.—The investigation of the problems of reproduction is embraced in the term *embryology,* while *embryogeny* is simply a factual record of developmental processes. More fully defined, embryology may be described as the theoretical study of the significance of morphological and physiological factors involved in the origin of a reproductive element, its fertilization when this is an essential step, its parental care and protection, and the various stages involved in its gradual development into a mature organism capable of reproducing another generation in turn.

In a more restricted sense, embryology is limited to an analysis of the physiological and morphological changes by which a fertilized egg evolves into an independent organism, though sometimes this inquiry is continued to the point where the individual becomes at least sexually mature. The latter definition is partly followed here because reproductive maturity sometimes precedes physical maturity, as Giard (1900) and Uichanco (1924) have so ably called to our attention through their discussions. In such cases, where reproductive and physical maturity do not coincide, further physical development is commonly considered only a part of the individual's ontogeny. In most cases embryological details are followed only to the point where the rudiments of the various organs are fairly well established, usually some time prior to the hatching or birth of the offspring. The majority of the embryogenies herein described are similarly restricted.

The Embryo Defined.—For purposes of convenience in treatment, the term *embryo* has, at times, been quite definitely limited, especially in insects where various metamorphic stages have frequently been recognized in the growth preceding maturity. The concept of an embryo should not be confined solely to that stage of development which runs its course within the egg; in its widest application it covers all stages of immaturity in an animal. There are certain species whose ova lack egg covering; thus it becomes increasingly difficult to differentiate the earliest postnatal forms of such individuals from their prenatal embryos, or from the egg-stage embryos of other insects.

The Birth Product.—The maternal sexual unit of reproduction is the ovum or egg. Ova are always fertilized by the corresponding paternal element, the spermatozoon, except in those species capable of parthenogenetic development. Impregnation of the egg is invariably internal. It stimulates activation phenomena which lead to fertilization. The development of parthenogenetic ova is caused by the influence of a less obvious agent than the sperm. In either case, a series of mitoses and cell divisions follows, which is the first direct step in embryo formation.

Insect birth products leave the parent under two entirely different sets of conditions, each of which may be considerably modified. Most insects extrude ova that are invariably enclosed in choria, or shells; others give birth to naked offspring which lack the chorion. Since the latter type of birth product is the subject of most of this text, further discussion of it will appear later.

Modifications of the ovum may also be two in number. The first modification relates to the chorion and its organization. It may range from a very thin, delicate membrane through various degrees of toughness to a hard, brittle, and thick covering. Numerous contrivances for insuring atmospheric oxygen, rigidity, concealment, and attachment may be visible superficially. In any case, the chorion is the characteristic covering.

The second type of variability in eggs refers to their internal organization. Many eggs, when deposited, have not commenced development at all, while others may contain the first cleavage nuclei. On the other hand, the egg shell may enclose a completely formed larva ready to hatch shortly after deposition. Examples of such eggs are to be found particularly abundantly among flies, chrysomelid beetles, and scale insects. The embryos in their eggs closely approximate the developmental age of the active naked offspring of other species just after hatching from eggs that were deposited before much development had occurred in them. Thus a selected list of insects could easily include species whose birth products, apparent to us as eggs, would, at deposition, actually show their contents to be embryos in almost every stage of growth between the extremes just mentioned. Each species, of course, would typically lay eggs whose contents represent some one of the various stages.

The foregoing discussion has emphasized the presence of only two visible birth products. One is an egg identified by the superficial chorion; the other an embryo without such a covering. Insects depositing ova are said to be *oviparous,* while those giving birth to embryos devoid of such covering are termed *viviparous.* The application of these or corresponding terms is necessary for the proper discrimination between birth products, with regard to the presence or absence of an egg shell. No reference to the developmental age of the contents of the egg when laid is intended. Viviparity has stimulated the use of additional terms to define the type of product issuing at birth. *Larviparity* is commonly applied to the production of offspring that appear as larvae; *nymphiparity,* on the other hand, refers to the birth of species with incomplete metamorphosis. *Pupiparity,* apparently first applied to the birth of offspring of the family Hippoboscidae by Latreille (1805), has been found to be untenable since larviparity occurs in these species. Nevertheless, the word is still used to indicate a group of Diptera (Hippoboscidae, Streblidae, Nycteribiidae) whose reproduction is similar throughout.

The Significance of the Chorion.—The viviparously produced offspring is apparently able to cope with its environment from birth just as efficiently as is the individual that emerges from the deposited egg. The only visible difference between them when leaving the mother lies not in ontogenetic variations but in the fact that the egg possesses an intact chorion. The young, viviparously born insect either had none or hatched from it before birth. Since the chorionic covering is purely an accessory, or extraembryonic, device that is discarded by the embryo after it has served its purpose, some authorities have assumed that there is no point in distinguishing between certain species whose young lack this structure at birth and others, almost as well developed, yet born within it. Two somewhat divergent views have been expressed upon this subject. In classifying groups of flies, in part by the class of reproductive system shown, Townsend (1934a, p. 144), clearly disregards the degree of development attained by the embryo in the egg and ignores the presence or absence of the egg shell. He classifies reproduction as viviparous, whether the larva has hatched or not, if deposition results in its immediate activity. Oviposition occurs, he maintains, if the deposited birth product, regardless of development which may be indistinguishable in age from the former class, rests quietly for "a longer or shorter" time before becoming independently active. This author, it must be pointed out, takes a most extreme view of the conditions constituting oviparity and viviparity, assuming that larval activity at deposition is the dipteran expression of viviparity just as Réaumur (1737) spoke of nymphiparous Hippoboscidae in contrast to oviparous forms. But the above citation well illustrates the difficulty of judiciously treating these borderline cases.

For the opinion of one who is more concerned with the philosophical treatment of the problem, let us turn to Lankester (1919, p. 534), who writes as follows:

Animals which pass a large part of their embryonic growth within the mother's body and are born naked and with much the shape and locomotive capacity of the adult are called "viviparous." But really all animals are viviparous, for the birth product is a living thing whether it is a naked egg-cell or more or less advanced in development. The enclosure of the birth product in a shell or case, which has given rise to the term "oviparous," is not of any value as indicating the real degree of development of the young at birth, for in some cases unfertilized egg-cells, in others mere disks of developing embryonic cells (as in birds, etc.), and in yet other cases well-shaped young ranging from the early larva up to the completely formed miniature of the adult, as in some of the shell-bearing snails, may be enclosed within an egg-shell when "laid" by the mother. There is accordingly no great general importance to be attached to the distinction between "viviparous" and "oviparous" animals. The egg-shell has, of course, its protective value, but the exact phase and nature of the living thing within it must be considered in any comparison of the reproductive processes of different animals.*

In viewing the embryonic histories of viviparous insects in the following chapters, one will no doubt arrive at the conclusion that the presence or absence of the chorion may not be so unimportant as it seems from this citation. Indeed, its absence is probably associated with several highly significant new adjustments on the part of both mother and offspring, adjustments that warrant a clear distinction being made between the two sorts of birth product: the chorionic egg or embryo and the achorionic embryo. Detailed consideration of such factors must be deferred until the concluding chapter for, obviously, the embryogenies must be presented first. Mention might be made, however, of some of the important factors related to the embryo lacking a chorion, as compared with one enclosed by an egg shell; differences in the amount and kind of food supply, the diverse structures present to insure food supplies for the embryo, extent of maternal care, and the relative length of time the offspring remain in intimate association with their mother before each must shift for itself. Ova are individually enclosed in a chorion or egg shell for their protection from ecological factors otherwise inimical to them. The chorion thus appears to be a most important accessory of the birth product in that it probably repels certain predators and other destructive organisms, acts as a permeable membrane for respiratory purposes, and prevents too rapid alteration of the moisture content of the egg. In fact, in most cases if not in all, the chorion is the essential structure concerned in maintaining the physical integrity of the egg.

Regardless of the known or unknown factors involved in the provision of a chorion over the egg, another phase of the importance of a shell has, perhaps, received less attention in the past than it deserves. This refers to the hazards involved in the escape of the embryo from the chorion at hatching. Occasional authors have mentioned this crisis in the life of the embryo which is the first of a series to be encountered; the insect faces similar crises whenever ecdyses occur, when a pupa forms, and when it emerges as an adult. According to Imms (1931), Berlese recognizes the

* The above quotation is given with the courteous permission of the Editors of the Clarendon Press and the Quarterly Journal of Microscopical Science.

hatching crisis and Wigglesworth (1939) lists the means available to various embryos in meeting this problem.

Ovoviviparity.—This term has suffered so much mutilation in meaning in earlier literature that one sometimes doubts the wisdom of employing it at all. A few authors, nevertheless, include the word with appropriate limitations. Borradaile (1923, p. 140) and Shull (1924, p. 182), for example, agree that it is a form of viviparity resulting from the retention of a yolk-laden ovum within the maternal uterus. No nutriment is provided for the embryo other than the original yolk in the egg. Birth follows hatching, occurring when the embryo is at a developmental stage practically equivalent to that of offspring hatching from deposited eggs. In this sense, ovoviviparity is used in the present text, where it will serve to designate a specific type of viviparity.

The confusion concerning the use of the term *ovoviviparity* arose after it became evident that various ova, upon deposition, may conceal within their choria any condition from unfertilized eggs through a gradually ascending series to offspring practically ready to hatch upon deposition, a situation discussed in the preceding section and aptly illustrated by the oviposition of certain Ephemeridae. The term was gradually expanded to include more and more of these stages until its precise application seemed lost. According to Geddes and Thomson (1889, p. 248), for example, "the term is of little use, however, for the cases to which it is applied shade off towards the two other forms of birth."

Ovoviviparity is used uniformly throughout these pages to distinguish one type of viviparity from three other definite types. Specifically, it is that type of viviparity in which an egg with a chorion develops in the maternal oviduct into an embryo which hatches before deposition. Prior to birth, the yolk of the egg is its only food supply.

The Age of Embryonic Stages.—The time interval basis alone has conspicuously failed as a measure of developmental age in insects because the environment, which determines the approximate temperature of the egg, fluctuates constantly. Time can be used as a measure only in relation to temperature, humidity, etc., and different species of insects have been found to exhibit individual requirements with regard to these factors. Such relationships offer a wide field for experimental exploration, and promise most valuable practical application in the work of the agricultural experiment station entomologist, the ecologist, and the embryologist.

Because of the difficulties involved in determining the developmental age of an insect in relation to time and other factors, it has been customary to arbitrarily describe succeeding stages of the embryo as they appear, and to refer to them by descriptive terms. This has often resulted in emphasis being placed on stages of widely varying duration in time and of unequal importance in this part of the ontogeny.

Certain parasitic forms among oviparous as well as viviparous species may provide developmental stages capable of being measured by time intervals, due to their intimate association with a rather uniform environment. It may be true, for example, of the viviparous Polyctenidae lying buried in the fur of bats and of the oviparous orders Mallophaga and Anoplura in similar situations or of larvae of the bot and warble flies. Here, it might be suspected, the temperature may approach the constancy of that surrounding the mammalian embryo.

Influence of Metamorphosis.—The birth product of oviparous species has been shown to be an egg with a more or less developed embryo enclosed in a chorion, while immature, naked offspring are produced viviparously. In either event the offspring have been called nymphs or larvae, as the case may be, without any explanation of the embryological significance of these terms.

One realizes that as the evolutionary history of any selected group lengthens, the most recent survivors encounter conditions usually far different from those presented to the earliest ancestors. The physical and biological environments have, in a real sense, also evolved. Or the normal spread of radiating nascent species forces the emigrants to contend with new conditions. We usually conceive of the species involved as adding to their ontogeny during this process and are accustomed to finding ever more of their life history relegated to premature stages before the contemporary standards of maturity are attained. As a result, the more or less independent life of an organism occurs at a later period than formerly prevailed in the ancestors, and protective maternal care plays a far more important part in the survival of specialized species among higher groups of animals.

Insects show these changes, too, but it seems that very little has been added to the egg or prenatal stages, while the immature insect nearly always reveals most conspicuous alterations. Such accumulated modifications have helped to produce those stages now included under the term *metamorphosis.*

Some insects, hatching from eggs, are from the first so similar to their parents in structure and organization that, in addition to growth, only very slight changes after each ecdysis are necessary to duplicate the parent. As would be expected, such species are the most primitive members of the existing hexapods. They are said to be *ametabolous.*

The vast majority of insects fall into another class with two types of metamorphosis. The members of the first type, the *hemimetabola,* emerge as immature insects or nymphs which, while usually specifically recognizable, nevertheless differ materially in bodily proportions from the adult and possess many of the adult structures only in a relatively rudimentary form. During succeeding instars growth and maturity are gradually attained by increase in size and altered bodily proportions, the specific development of external imaginal structures from the existing rudiments, and the formation of the complete reproductive and other internal organs which are characteristic of the adult. Most of the orders are hemimetabolous.

Several orders exhibit complete metamorphosis and are, therefore, *holometabolous.* The offspring is a larva that in no way resembles the adult insect. Nor does it succeed in attaining the adult form as simply as the hemimetabolous nymph. Instead, at the end of larval growth it submits to a period of apparent quiescence (pupal stage) while its imaginal rudiments (imaginal discs) develop, disintegration and histolysis remove the purely larval tissues, and a complete reorganization of the soma finally produces the adult form.

If the theories regarding metamorphosis, as presented by Berlese and summarized so well by Imms (1931, p. 47 *et seq.*), prove of interest to the taxonomist and morphologist, how much more suggestive are they to the embryologist. If eggs hatch prematurely so that the offspring are actually in earlier stages of development when they appear, it forces one to appreciate more clearly the great diversity that has enabled each species to cope successfully with new environments. The nymph and the larva have absorbed many of the adaptive modifications of the species, feeding and growth, and have left to the adult the burden of reproduction and seeking favorable situations for the offspring. The prenatal embryo, whether oviparous or viviparous, has also probably condensed its ontogenetic history, which may account for its accelerated development to the partial or entire exclusion of certain phylogenetic factors. Among these may be the obscuring of primitive cleavage stages, gastrulation, entodermal rudiments, and the true significance of blastokinesis.

In all of these prenatal and metamorphic changes the viviparous species, as they have appeared, conform closely to their oviparous relatives. But it must be at once apparent that the hatched offspring of the ametamorphic and the metamorphic series may all represent different embryonic stages. No ametabolous insects are known to be viviparous.

Derivatives of the Germ Layers.—The derivation of the various tissues and organs from the primary germ layers, as shown in the following lists, reveals the extent to which the ectoderm and mesoderm suffice to supply these parts. The entoderm is very poorly represented, a situation quite in contrast with similar tabulations usually presented in vertebrate texts. Vertebrates have the digestive tract, portions of the urinary system, lungs, liver, pancreas, thyroid, and other glands of entodermal origin. In Table 1, below, entoderm refers to a functional tissue without reference to its genesis.

TABLE 1

DERIVATIVES OF THE THREE GERM LAYERS IN INSECTS

ECTODERM	MESODERM	ENTODERM
bursa copulatrix	blood	epithelium of mid-intestine and the attached caeca, when present
chitinous secretions forming skeleton, wings, and setae	chorion of ovum	
	fat body	
common oviduct	follicular yolk	
common spermaduct	heart	
corpora allata	muscles	
epithelium of apodemes	paired oviducts	
epithelium of procto-daeum	paired spermaducts	
	tissues encapsulating germ cells	
epithelium of stomo-daeum	tissues supporting all organs	
hypodermis		
Malpighian tubules		
nervous system		
oenocytes		
salivary glands		
trachea		
uterus		
vagina		

In the preceding discussion, no attempt has been made to show the origin of the primary layers, since this point will be brought up later. The origin of the entoderm has long been a subject of wide differences of opinion. Supporting mesodermal elements surround various organs and in some instances the term *connective tissue* has been applied to them. However, no connective tissues corresponding to those recognized by the vertebrate histologist can be said to occur in insects. The germ cells arise very early in the ontogeny, probably from cleavage nuclei before the primary germ layers have been formed. Their early recognition in the developing embryo is sometimes difficult or, perchance, has hitherto been overlooked in specific instances.

Influence of the Study of Viviparity on Entomology

Now that some years have elapsed since the majority of the viviparous insects have had their embryogenies revealed, one may with propriety briefly enumerate those phases of the subject which seem to have benefited the field of entomology as a whole, or, indeed, may have been influential in furthering general zoological thought. It is believed that studies of viviparous insects have made valuable contributions to science though some, unfortunately, have not withstood sustained investigation. Nevertheless even the latter, though now useless, have frequently provoked more thorough investigation of the facts. Only brief mention need be made of these points, for they are all of common knowledge and to treat each one separately and adequately would require much space. Most of the authorities mentioned in this section are cited later in the literature with which their contributions are most closely associated.

Viviparity.—Viviparity in insects was one of the important contributions to entomological literature. Its earliest discovery probably never will be known and in the succeeding chapters only observations gleaned from the literature can be presented. However, since Lister's communication in 1671, the list of known viviparous species has constantly enlarged. In later years, the detailed studies of several species have brought to light many pecularities of embryonic structure and of maternal functions not common to oviparous forms.

Parthenogenesis.—It is said that Aristotle suspected the honey bee of being, at times, capable of producing offspring from unfertilized eggs. Goedart in 1667 also recorded the hatching of eggs deposited by a virgin moth, and Albrecht in 1701 observed the same thing in an unmated adult female silkworm. These are, apparently, among the earliest records of parthenogenesis in insects, and all are oviparous species. The concept of parthenogenesis in biological thought first arose, however, from the investigations of Leeuwenhoek, Réaumur, and Bonnet, whose work, reviewed in a later chapter, was confined to the viviparous aphids. Leeuwenhoek discovered the young within the reproductive tract of the agamic female; Réaumur expressed great interest in determining the facts and presented the problem to Bonnet for solution. Universal controversy and a suddenly aroused curiosity regarding this unusual method of reproduction in animals resulted from Bonnet's report in 1745. Had the latter given this matter his continued attention instead of engaging in a lengthy controversy with Friedrich Kaspar Wolff on the relative merits of epigenesis and preformation, much of the later work on parthenogenetic reproduction might not have been left to Dzierzon and Von Siebold in the middle of the nineteenth century. In the final analysis, it must be conceded that Bonnet's work on viviparous aphids introduced a new concept of insect reproduction that Owen (1849) later termed parthenogenesis.

Paedogenesis.—Another new entomological concept appeared when Wagner (1862) announced that larvae of a species of fly produced living offspring. Bonnet's presentation of parthenogenesis in aphids created no greater excitement among zoologists than this incredible revelation. Von Baer (1866) applied the term *paedogenesis* to this sort of reproduction. Subsequent investigations have not only verified Wagner's observations but at least three American species also have been found to be paedogenetic. One, reported by Felt (1911) in New York, is a species closely related to the original example as is also another described by Johannsen (1910), while the third, a coleopteran of the genus *Micromalthus*, was discovered by Barber (1913). Furthermore, Wheeler came to the conclusion that the viviparous aphids must be considered paedogenetic, in a sense, for their earliest embryos begin development before the mother insect is mature. His student, Uichanco, confirmed this recently, and the author found a similar condition existing in the Polyctenidae.

Insect Cytology and Genetics.—The discovery of paedogenesis and of parthenogenesis eventually added materially to the study of genetics as well. *Miastor* larviparity revealed for the first time the entire germ track—the complete, detailed history of the germ cells from one generation to the next. Kahle, in 1908, had already called attention to their prominence and the ease with which they could be followed throughout the life cycle, and Hegner, in 1912, gave their activity special consideration. Kahle also observed peculiarities in the chromosomal reduction in *Miastor* and this promises to be a fertile field for further investigation of other insects too. Another clarification of genetic data came from a study of meiosis in parthenogenetic aphids. This insect produces agamic males and females by means of diploid ova instead of haploid males and diploid females as occurs, for example, in bees.

Hermaphroditism.—The viviparous aphids gave origin to an hypothesis of hermaphroditism when their peculiar method of reproduction first attracted attention. Balbiani (1869 *et seq.*) unfortunately became convinced of the truth of this when he examined the mycetom in the haemocoele of the female insect and mistook this organ for part of the reproductive system. Consistent adherence to this belief undoubtedly marred the otherwise excellent study he made of the aphids, and adversely influenced the opinions and investigations of many entomologists for some time. From the ensuing discussions, however, arose an early and more comprehensive grasp of the nature of the mycetom and its symbiotic functions. Hermaphroditism is not unknown in insects, for in recent years Hughes-Schrader (1924) has reported its presence in *Icerya,* an oviparous species.

Heterogamy.—Finally, the ideas involved in Steenstrup's alternation of generations should be mentioned in connection with viviparity in insects. Steenstrup (1842) immediately included the aphids among his examples of organisms exhibiting alternation, but he was at that time, of course, unable to differentiate between several expressions of this phenomenon. The concept of the botanist with regard to the alternation of generations includes the alternation of the haploid gametophyte generation of a plant with the diploid sporophyte. In animals a somewhat similar situation is known, for example, among the Coelenterata where an asexually budded generation alternates with the amphigonous generation. But the plant and animal differ profoundly in that the latter is not haploid in either generation but only in its gametes. This condition in animals is more precisely known as metagenesis. Among insects no budding occurs, nor is any generation haploid except for males of certain species, and even they do not alternate with diploid males.

The viviparous insects possessing two forms of reproductive individuals often present a generation of parthenogenetic females at one time and an amphigonous at another. This condition is cyclic and differs considerably from the preceding cases in other organisms; it is actually a cyclic alteration of generations rather than an alternation of generations. Indeed, the two forms, frequently do not strictly alternate, since parthenogenetic generations are often repeated several times before the amphigonous form again appears. The term *heterogamy* was proposed long ago to indicate this cyclic condition in insects.

LITERATURE CITED

Von Baer (1866), Balbiani (1869 *et seq.*), Barber (1913), Bonnet (1745), Borradaile (1923), Felt (1911), Geddes and Thomson (1889), Giard (1900), Hegner (1912), Hughes-Schrader (1924), Imms (1931), Johannsen (1910), Kahle (1908), Kowalevsky (1871), Lankester (1919), Latreille (1805), Lister (1671), Owen (1849), Réaumur (1737), Shull (1924), Steenstrup (1842), Townsend (1934), Uichanco (1924), Wagner (1862), Wigglesworth (1939).

Chapter 2

FEMALE ANATOMY AND EMBRYOGENY

Before outlining the specific embryonic histories of the viviparous insects it will be desirable to review briefly the structure of the female reproductive system and the principal steps in the development of all insects. Such a résumé will provide basic material for comparisons with some of the modifications in form and function exhibited by viviparous insects, for it must be at once apparent that the latter have not only survived the evolutionary changes of related species, and the insects as a whole, but have also become specifically adjusted to many new functions not possessed by oviparous species. More extended and detailed treatment may be had by consulting such authors as Berlese (1909), Dawydoff (1928), Henneguy (1904), Hirschler (1924), Johannsen and Butt (1941), and Korschelt and Heider (1899). Imms (1925) gives less space to this subject, yet his presentation is quite adequate. Finally, Snodgrass (1926) should be mentioned for his excellent paper which, while elementary, is clear but sufficiently generalized to apply to the major steps in the embryogeny of most insects. One of his later contributions to insect morphology, Snodgrass (1935), furnishes a comprehensive chapter on this subject.

Although embryonic development in insects is a continuous and smoothly integrated process, with no sharply distinguishable epochs present in which new parts abruptly arise, one can nevertheless recognize certain trends in the embryological sequence. These may be rather arbitrarily divided into the following phases: (1) a period of nuclear multiplication and cellular organization, (2) a period of cellular rearrangement and a differentiation of tissues, (3) a period of tissue specialization and the formation of the rudiments of organs, and (4) a period of definitive formation of the embryo and its organ systems.

These advances in development are sometimes abbreviated under the main headings of "tissue differentiation" and "organology." This classification corresponds rather closely to one proposed by Seidel (1929, p. 331) in his studies on *Platycnemis* and

16

the reader may find the latter more satisfactory, even though Seidel considers the end products marking the finish of each stage rather than the particular nature of the processes carried on in each case. He lists the stages thus: (1) formation of the blastoderm, (2) germ layer formation, (3) differentiation of organ systems, and (4) histological differentiation of parts. The agreement in these two opinions at least confirms the assertion that distinct advances in embryonic development proceed in an orderly, unvarying sequence.

The successive stages described in the following pages are simply selected from the embryonic history to permit the reader to visualize, at least in part, the embryo and its differentiations at these periods. The descriptions treat these stages when the particular degree of development of the parts it is desirable to discuss is clearly evident, and it is to be understood that the evolution of the different tissues and organs has arisen by almost imperceptible steps to the point where it is called to attention.

Female Reproductive System

The Ovary.—The ovaries are paired mesodermal organs lying in the haemocoele on either side of the alimentary tract. Each consists of several similar tubules, called ovarioles, their number varying according to the species (Figs. 1, 15, 99). According to Grassi (1887), there is only a single ovariole in each ovary of *Campodea* and the same condition obtains in *Miastor* (Kahle, 1908). *Glossina* and *Termitoxenia* also have but one ovariole in each ovary while Imms (1925) gives the number in the hymenopteran, *Doryctes,* as two. Hagen (1858), on the other hand, reports the presence of two or three thousand ovarioles in the ovary of the termite (*T. nigricans*) and they must also be very numerous in certain Diptera, for Townsend (1934) says that the female of one species possibly lays about 15,000 eggs. Réaumur (1738) estimated the number of eggs to be approximately 30,000 in the same species or one closely related to it.

Three distinct regions may be recognized in a tubule, or ovariole. At the end, or distal portion, a slender terminal filament extends forward in the body, usually uniting with others from the tubules of the same ovary. This common filament then sometimes fuses with a similar filament from the second ovary, thus forming the suspensory ligament. The common filament of each ovary or the ligament continues anteriorly and serves to retain the ovaries in their approximate positions in the body cavity. They may be attached distally to the dorsal body wall, to the pericardial diaphragm, to the fatty tissue, or they may lie unattached in the haemocoele. In certain species, filaments may be

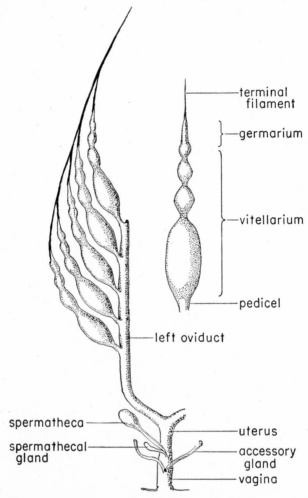

terminal filament

germarium

vitellarium

pedicel

left oviduct

spermatheca

spermathecal gland

uterus

accessory gland

vagina

FIG. 1.—Female reproductive tract with right oviduct and ovary omitted; one ovariole further enlarged. Diagrammatic, dorsal views.

greatly reduced and almost functionless, or absent. The second portion of the ovariole is known as the end-chamber, or germarium, which is the most essential portion of the reproductive system because it contains the primary germ cells and, often, specialized descendants of the primary germ cells which have lost their reproductive function and now serve as nurse cells for the remaining oöcytes. These cells trace their origin back to the primordial germ cells which usually appear at a very early stage in the embryonic development of the individual, before the ovarioles are differentiated. The germarium begins immediately at the base of the terminal filament and extends posteriorly in the body for a short distance, where it unites with the third portion of the tubule.

The vitellarium, the third section of the ovariole, is usually the largest part of the tubule and serves as a duct through whose lumen the oöcytes pass eventually into the oviduct. Frequently the lower end of the ovariole becomes modified into a stalk or pedicel at its junction with the oviduct. In other cases, the pedicel is a branch of the paired oviduct which extends upward to meet the ovariole. It is often closed at its junction with the latter by the epithelial cells at its distal, blind end. A common lumen leading from the ovariole through the pedicel to the body of the paired oviduct is established temporarily by the dissolution of these occluding cells just prior to the passage of an egg or embryo into the oviducts, as, for example, in *Hemimerus*. While in the vitellarium, the oöcytes usually become invested with a single layer of epithelial cells, the ovarian follicle, which secretes on its internal surface the chorion that surrounds and protects the egg after deposition. Here, too, before the chorion appears, the oöcytes acquire most of their stored nutriment, of which the follicular epithelium often contributes the major portion, or the nutriment may be derived mainly from special nurse cells when these are present. Mollison's (1904) excellent illustrations furnish us an example of the first case, and the nurse cells shown in later discussions of *Melophagus*, *Miastor*, and *Aphis* supply examples of the second. In either case, the oöcyte becomes very greatly enlarged during its descent in the vitellarium because of the rapid accumulation of yolk required for the subsequent development of the embryo. This is one of the important distinctions which can differentiate the embryonic development of oviparous insects from many viviparous species; the latter, as will be shown later, are often yolk-poor and frequently derive additional nutriment from other sources. Sometimes, too, in viviparous species the follicular epithelium does not secrete a chorion around the oöcyte.

The Oviducts and Vagina.—After the egg leaves the ovariole it enters the paired oviduct. There is one such duct for each ovary which serves as a collection tube for the eggs, or products of the ovarioles. If the ovarioles are grouped into a mass as a compact ovary, their union with the paired oviduct will be at approximately the same place. If they are distributed serially along the oviduct, as in the more primitive orders of insects, the junctions of the different ovarioles will naturally be correspondingly dispersed and the eggs from certain ovarioles may traverse only a portion of the paired oviduct before arriving at its union with the common oviduct. Often an egg-calyx will be found at the end of the paired oviduct. It is a dilated portion of the duct in which ova are stored temporarily, although storage of eggs may also occur in various other portions of the reproductive tract. As a rule, the paired oviducts are mesodermal extensions of the gonads but exceptions occur where the latter arise as lateral evaginations from the common oviduct, hence are of ectodermal derivation. In this case a chitinous intima is present in the lumen.

The paired oviducts unite with the common oviduct beneath the alimentary canal in the posterior portion of the body. This region arises as an ectodermal invagination, is usually rather short, and connects proximally with the vagina when this organ is present; otherwise, it opens directly outside of the body. The vagina is a secondarily invaginated portion of the body wall, hence also ectodermal in origin. Upon examination it will be found to contain in its lumen a chitinous lining, secreted by its cells and continuous with the intima of the common oviduct. This portion of the reproductive system often varies in size and shape, due to its function as a storage reservoir in many insects which retain the eggs for a time before deposition. The distal portion, when enlarged, is called the uterus. Its proximal end is attached firmly to the body wall, of which it is a part, and from it the offspring are extruded.

Accessory Organs.—When a receptaculum seminalis, or spermatheca, is present for the storage of spermatozoa from the male, it will usually be found attached to the dorsal side of the vagina near the union of the latter with the common oviduct. It may vary from spherical to tubular in shape or even be branched, and more than one may be present. A spermathecal gland may lie just posterior to it.

Another pair of accessory glands may also be present. They usually open either into the vagina near the spermatheca, or posterior to this organ. The functions of accessory glands differ in various insects, but for the most part their secretions serve to cement the eggs to objects upon which they are deposited or to form the oötheca which protects the egg mass until the hatching of the young.

Since these glands are diverticula from the vagina they may be considered as ectodermal derivatives. Other special organs sometimes appear in certain species but they hold little of concern in this treatment and therefore may be ignored for the present. Later discussions will introduce some of them at appropriate places.

For one who is interested in the general comparative structure of the reproductive systems of insects, their physiology, and phylogenetic significance, the recent contributions to this subject by Heberdey (1931) and Snodgrass (1935, 1936) are especially recommended.

The Early Development of the Embryo

For convenience, the general embryological sequence has been divided into two broad subdivisions. The first, tissue differentiation, covers the period utilized by the embryo to establish the primary germ layers from which specific organs may be derived. The second subdivision emphasizes the evolution of the various organ systems from these fundamental tissues (see Chapter 3).

Some consideration of the egg prior to any trace of development has been included under this heading. There is ample justification for this because the embryo utilizes the egg as a vehicle for development after fertilization and some interesting general facts regarding it should therefore be noted.

The Egg.—Fundamentally, the insectan egg consists of a small amount of cytoplasm and a nucleus. These two substances form the protoplasmic content of the egg. However, since the egg must generally provide nutriment for the future embryo, quantities of other substances are found in it (Figs. 2, 148). These enclosed materials may exhibit specific arrangement with relation to the cytoplasm, and because they are present, evidences of polarity within the egg are frequently recognizable. Interspersed in the meshes of the cytoplasm are to be found yolk spheres, fat globules, symbiotic organisms in eggs of some species, and granular substances whose nature is practically unknown.

A large mass of literature exists bearing on the contents of eggs, and there is much difference of opinion regarding their probable nature and utility to the embryo. An excellent paper on such cytoplasmic inclusions is that of Payne (1932), which reveals some of the difficulties involved in their study. The yolk spheres are the largest of these secondary inclusions and, because of their great numbers, are the major factor in determining the size of the egg. Their typical, more or less uniform distribution throughout the egg, as is the case also with the fat globules, causes the cytoplasm to assume the form of a reticulum.

Eggs vary in size, as was stated in the preceding paragraph, according to the quantity of yolk stored within them. The difference in bulk seems, therefore, to depend almost entirely upon the requirements of the embryo destined to feed upon the yolk. Species whose eggs produce endoparasitic embryos are often practically devoid of yolk. Small ova are typical of Diptera whose eggs are to be ingested by other leaf-feeding insects. Townsend (1934) has given the measurements of a few such eggs and has compared them to related species whose eggs are rich in yolk. *Clemelis* deposits an egg, according to him, that measures 27 x 20 x 20 microns; it is invisible to the human eye. By comparison, a species of *Hypodermodes* lays eggs whose dimensions are 5,000 x 2,500 x 2,500 microns. The bulk of the smaller egg totals about 4,800 cubic microns while the other contains approximately 25,000,000 cubic microns!

While the cytoplasm consists of a network of fine strands ramifying through the interior of the egg, a slight accumulation of it, without yolk, is to be found in the area immediately surrounding the nucleus. In most insects it also forms a distinct homogeneous layer over the egg surface. When perceptible, this peripheral layer is distinguished as the perivitelline layer, periplasm, cortical layer, or the "Keimhautblastem" of German authors.

The nucleus is large and enclosed in a very delicate nuclear membrane. Besides the chromatin within it, from one to several nucleoli may be visible. Its location before fertilization usually is near the center of the egg, but it shifts its position during the maturation and fertilization processes.

Hegner (1914, 1917) has extensively treated the organization of the insect egg and has been able to show that certain types of polarity exist in it at a very early stage of development. His studies chiefly concern egg polarity in relation to germ cell formation in the developing embryo, and attention is called to his papers here because some specific examples of polarity will appear in the later chapters.

'The coverings of the egg consist first of a delicate and structureless vitelline membrane outside of the periplasm from which it arises. It has not been demonstrated in some insect eggs. Outside of this is the chorion, which may frequently be seen to consist of two distinct layers, the endochorion and the exochorion. The two are firmly united by trabeculae. The chorionic layers often appear to be laminate, especially when rather thick, and the exochorion usually presents, on its surface, a sculptured appearance due to the position and shape of the cells of the follicular epithelium which secreted it. It may be extremely thin and delicate or surprisingly hard, more or less brittle, smooth or curiously ribbed, or possess spines and other appendages. Its surface is usually interrupted by one or more tiny openings which form the micropylar area. The micropyle presumably exists to facilitate the entrance of spermatozoa into the egg, which otherwise is enclosed in an impenetrable chorion. The location of the micropyle varies in different insects but will generally be found at the anterior pole of elongate eggs. In the micropylar area the periplasm of the egg usually is considerably thicker, extending cone-shaped for a short distance toward the center of the egg. The vitelline membrane also appears to be attached to the endochorion at this point. Lécaillon (1898a) considers these matters at length in his paper on the chorion of the eggs of Chrysomelidae, and an older paper by Korschelt (1887) is also very useful (Figs. 20, 105).

Many insect eggs are elongate and subcylindrical, but ovate and spherical shapes are frequently encountered, while in some species they are pedunculate or otherwise modified in shape. However, they usually exhibit external polarity, as well as internal, with anteroposterior, dorsoventral, and lateral axes. Within the maternal reproductive tract their orientation is the same as that of the mother, as is also the position of the embryo which develops eventually within them. This general law of orientation was first formulated by Hallez (1885, 1886) and has repeatedly been verified by subsequent observers.

Fertilization.—As the egg leaves the common oviduct it passes the opening of the duct leading from the spermatheca. Here it presumably receives on its surface a discharge from this organ containing a supply of spermatozoa. One or more spermatozoa penetrate into the egg through the microplyar area, for poly-spermy is common in insects.

Usually prior to egg deposition the egg nucleus has migrated toward the periphery and has undergone the maturation divisions. Actually the egg is in the oöcyte stage until after maturation, when it becomes a mature ovum. The male pronucleus from the sperm head of one of the spermatozoa fuses with the pronucleus of the egg, and the surplus spermatozoa, as well as the polar bodies, disintegrate and are absorbed into the egg cytoplasm. In fertilization, the sperm and ovum restore the original quantity of chromatin on the fertilization spindle, and the egg again contains a complete diploid nucleus.

Parthenogenetic reproduction affords an exception to the preceding statements, for two kinds of maturation have been discovered in this method of propagation. In diploid parthenogenesis only one maturation mitosis takes place and the number of chromosomes is not reduced. The offspring produced this way are all females as, for example, the agamic summer aphids. In haploid parthenogenesis there is a reduction division in maturation, therefore the ovum contains qualitatively only the haploid chromosome constitution. This condition results in the production of males as, for example, drone bees. Being parthenogenetic, there is no contribution to the egg in the form of a spermatozoon with its hereditary potentiality from the male parent.

Cleavage and Blastoderm Formation.—Upon the completion of fertilization, or only maturation in the case of parthenogenesis, the egg proceeds with its development into an embryo. The zygote nucleus moves toward the center of the egg and initiates a series of mitoses that are commonly called cleavage divisions. Three types of cleavages may be distinguished, whose products at first appear quite different, a fact due entirely to the relative amount of yolk present in the egg. The first is superficial cleavage, which occurs in most insects; the second is total cleavage; and the third is incomplete cleavage.

In superficial cleavage the nucleus undergoes mitosis and the daughter nuclei continue this process until, at last, a large number of cleavage nuclei is formed within the egg. Each nucleus isolates itself from the others by migration. Surrounding each nucleus is a small, stellate mass of cytoplasm, whose extensions, ramifying through the egg, presumably are in contact with the rest of the cytoplasm as well as joining similar processes from sister nuclei (Fig. 2). Thus, since there appear to be no cell membranes at this time, the egg cytoplasm is really a syncytium. Yet it is probable that each nucleus directly affects the cytoplasm in its own immediate vicinity more than in any other. Sachs (1892) proposed the term *energid* to distinguish nucleated cytoplasmic aggregations of this type and it appears that its use

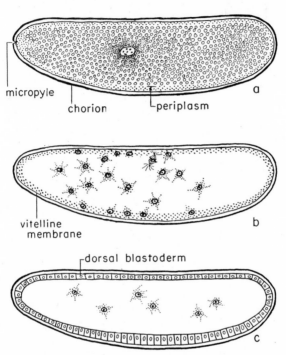

Fig. 2.—Sagittal sections of eggs, yolk represented only in upper figure. *a,* unfertilized ovum with nucleus centrally situated in cytoplasm. *b,* cleavage nuclei central, blastodermic nuclei in peripheral cytoplasm. *c,* yolk cells central, peripheral blastoderm complete; ventral plate forming. Ventral side is down and posterior end is to the left. Diagrammatic.

is pertinent here, although practically everyone has adopted the term *cleavage nucleus,* thus tacitly ignoring the fact that these bodies answer every criterion of a cell except for the absent cellular membrane. Korschelt and Heider (1899) also called attention to the inaccuracy of the original term "cleavage cells" used for these nucleated masses. Sometimes these cells, or their nuclei, at least, migrate independently to the periplasm; in other species they seem to acquire a definite spatial arrangement in their migration and move outward simultaneously. In many eggs the nuclei first arrive at the surface in the anterior portion. Eventually they reach the peripheral layer of cytoplasm, the periplasm, and there arrange themselves approximately equidistantly over the surface (Fig. 38).

This appearance of nuclei in the periplasm is followed by the formation of superficial cleavage furrows in the latter, which separate the nuclei from each other laterally. Each cytoplasmic area, however, is still continuous with its fellows and with the interior cytoplasm on the inner surface. Finally the bases are separated from the inner cytoplasm and definite superficial cells, the blastodermic cells, cover the egg.

During the migration of the nuclei a few of them may remain within the egg and never enter directly into blastoderm formation. Again, the superficial cells of the blastoderm may wander back into the yolk area or they may divide and return daughter nuclei to the interior cytoplasm. Such amoeboid cells are usually spoken of as yolk cells or vitellophags and may be distinguished as primary yolk cells in the first case, or as secondary yolk cells if they arise from blastoderm cells. But it should be remembered that they do not form distinct cells, as they retain their extended syncytial cytoplasmic processes and form no cell membranes. Their present function probably is to resolve the deutoplasmic material into nutrient substances for assimilation by other cells, and later by the embryonic tissues.

The second type of cleavage appears in some of the more primitive insects, and also in a few species which are highly specialized when the eggs are poorly supplied with yolk. In these cases the mitoses are accompanied by cleavage planes that cut directly through the egg so that complete cells are immediately constricted off; hence we may speak of total cleavage in these forms. *Anurida* and *Isotoma* show total cleavage and the condition has been secondarily acquired in certain parasitic Hymenoptera.

Investigators have called attention to a third type of cleavage in the eggs of insects with somewhat more yolk within them. Here the daughter cells are at once distinctly separated from the others at the time of cleavage except for their inner ends at the center of the egg which, for a time, are open and confluent at their bases. Later, all blastomeres are separated by cell membranes. This is called incomplete cleavage and may be recognized as a compromise between the first and second classes, due perhaps to the amount of yolk present which prevents the full expression of either of the other two types. The viviparous Strepsiptera exhibit incomplete cleavage, though others may look upon this type as a much delayed example of one of the preceding types.

The Ventral Plate.—When the blastoderm is completely formed the cells on the ventral side of the egg become columnar in shape, in marked contrast with the remaining cells, especially those in the anterior and dorsal portions. Marginally, however, they gradually decrease in height farther from the center until they merge into the typical, more or less cuboidal, blastodermal type of cell (Fig. 2). This area of columnar cells comprises the ventral plate, or embryonic area, while the extraembryonic area is composed of the rest of the blastoderm. This plate varies in different species with regard to its relative size and position on the ventral side of the egg. In yolk-rich insects the ventral plate is usually comparatively small and, at first, may even be ovate rather than elongate. However, in all insects it commences to lengthen further with considerable rapidity. It may often be found nearer to the posterior end of the egg than to the anterior, or it may extend the entire length of the egg.

The Germ Band.—Graber (1890) urged the application of the term *germ band* to the embryonic rudiment whenever it becomes clearly delimited regardless of its histological composition. Since then the terms *ventral plate* and *germ band* are often employed without any distinction in application, yet it is thought a real difference exists between two stages of development which may conveniently be distinguished by the employment of these terms in the sense discriminating writers use them. For one thing, the ventral plate consists of a single tissue while the germ band possesses more. Again, many germ bands are covered by protective membranes that are lacking over ventral plates. Finally, germ bands often pass to other positions in the egg, movements which are not experienced by the ventral plate.

The first step in germ band formation occurs when the ventral plate undergoes mesentoderm formation, a phenomenon repeatedly, but not universally, homologized with true gastrulation. The two-layered condition is achieved in three ways which will be described in the following paragraphs.

Gastrulation.—A longitudinal furrow appears in the mid-line of the ventral plate of many embryos which causes an inpushing of the cells involved. The crest of each longitudinal ridge approaches the one opposite and they finally fuse over the furrow

(Fig. 3a-c), again forming an unbroken exterior ventral surface. This area may now be spoken of as presumptive ectoderm, from which the true ectoderm of the embryo, and all of its derivatives, will arise. At this time its cells are large, comparatively few in number, and columnar. The interior cellular portion, which was cut off by this operation, quickly flattens out and becomes closely applied to the inner surface of the ectoderm. It includes cells of the formative mesoderm and its derivatives, as well as limited portions which most investigators believe will later give rise to entoderm. This layer may well be called the mesentoderm at this stage.

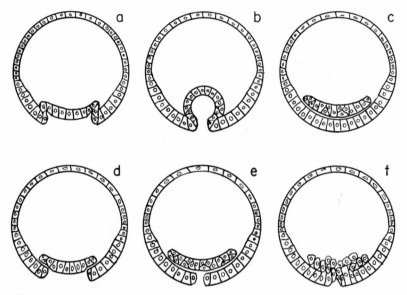

Fig. 3.—Cross sections of eggs showing three methods of mesoderm formation; yolk omitted. a–c, invagination or involution; d–e, overgrowth; f, delamination. Diagrammatic. (From Snodgrass, Smithsonian Annual Report, 1925.)

In other species the gastrular furrow may not appear as outlined above. In this modification of the process, the two longitudinal lateral areas of the ventral plate simply push outward and grow over the median longitudinal portion. The lateral plates finally meet and fuse along the ventral mid-line, gradually covering a narrow central strip, or middle portion, of the ventral plate, leaving it all the time practically flat along its central axis (Fig. 3d-e). This operation results in the same formation of the mesentoderm as before and cannot be said to be essentially different except in the displacement of the middle plate toward the interior without the distinct prefolding of the latter. This method of mesenteron formation may be spoken of as overgrowth followed by confluence of the lateral plates.

A third type of mesentoderm formation, and one least often encountered in hexapod embryogeny, is due to the appearance of horizontal cleavage in the cells along the main axis, or portions of it, in the ventral plate. A limited area of presumptive ectoderm thus gives rise to cells in the interior of the egg which proceed to arrange themselves into a mesentoderm strip (Fig. 3f). From these cells a definitive layer of mesoderm is derived and from restricted areas of the latter a few of the cells are said to form entoderm. This will be discussed later.

Several different opinions have been offered to harmonize the apparent contradictions found in hexapod gastrulation. All are agreed, however, that the primitive, simpler operation has become highly involved due to the abundant yolk in the egg. Roonwal (1936) has recently endeavored to show that the gastrulation covers a much longer portion of early embryonic history than was commonly recognized by earlier authors. Further comments on certain phases of the matter are deferred until the formation of the entoderm is discussed.

Blastokinesis.—Wheeler (1893, p. 68) proposed to classify two migrations of the embryo in the egg as blastokinesis, and for convenience anatrepsis was suggested to designate the movement of the germ band into, or through, the yolk, while katatrepsis indicates the return, or compensatory, passage of the older embryo to its original position. The first term is frequently substituted for the last (Fig. 5).

Anatrepsis, or the shifting of the embryo to other portions of the yolk at this early stage, before the internal organs are developed, is very frequently observed in embryos. In studying this movement and in seeking for its probable cause, Wheeler (1893, p. 69) was led to the conclusion that it must enable the embryo to get away for a time from its accumulated waste products. He pointed out that their presence perhaps interferes with the embryo's ready assimilation of the adjacent yolk, and suggested that migration to a new location avoids continued contact with it. This is a physiological or chemical theory to account for blastokinesis, a view that has been quite generally although not universally adopted to explain this curious behavior.

Tirelli (1931) has objected to this theory on the ground that, following katatrepsis, the embryos of some insects, for example *Bombyx mori*, are so disposed in the egg that the developing dorsal side is turned from the yolk supply and separated from it by the fully formed ventral surface of the embryo. He contends that such an arrangement adds to the difficulties of yolk absorption by those very parts of the embryonic body most pressingly in need of nutriment for their growth and completion. He is firmly convinced that katatrepsis, at least, is a purely mechanical shifting of the embryo so that undeveloped portions of it may find room for growth. His contention, unfortunately, is somewhat weakened by use of the silkworm embryo which is much too long for the egg and is thus obliged to fold its body, perhaps masking the physiological need for reversal. Short embryos of other insect species also exhibit katatrepsis yet never exceed the length of the egg and always lie straightened out within it. There seems to be no mechanical necessity for revolution in such cases. Slifer (1932) has commented on the various alternate explanations offered by other writers. She also has furnished a most interesting description of katatrepsis of a living grasshopper embryo.

Anatrepsis provides one method of forming the embryonic envelopes and will be described in connection with the latter. Katatrepsis will be treated later, in conjunction with the destruction of the amnion and serosa.

Embryonic Envelopes.—The formation of the amnion occurs simultaneously with the further growth and extension of the germ band. It provides a protective covering directly over the enlarging germ band and unites with the latter along its margins. The process may take place in one of the following ways: by overgrowth of the amniotic folds as the embryonic rudiment lies superficially on the yolk, or by anatrepsis, that is, the invagination of the embryo into the yolk.

In the first case, formation of the amnion by overgrowth, the earliest evidence of the production of the amniotic fold, is found at the posterior end of the embryo. Here a slight crescentic depression appears at the margin of the germ band which gradually extends around its posterior end and eventually involves the lateral margins as well. The distal edge of the depression now begins to elevate, perhaps by a proliferation of new cells, but more especially by the continued flattening and extension in surface area of the extraembryonic cells already present (Fig. 4).

The raised portion folds medianly over the outer, or ventral, surface of the germ band. Either shortly after this, or simultaneously, a similar folding takes place anteriorly. The posterior, anterior, and lateral folds gradually cover the entire embryo and fuse as they meet over its ventral surface. Upon completion of the process, the upper and lower layers of the fold usually separate. In this manner the inner layer of tissue, with comparatively small and flattened nuclei, is united to the embryo all along its border, covering only the ventral surface of the latter. This inner envelope is now known as the amnion and the space between it and the embryo is the amniotic cavity.

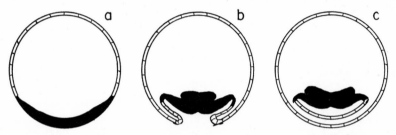

Fig. 4.—Formation of the amnion and serosa by overgrowth. Embryo represented in black, blastoderm and envelopes light. Diagrammatic cross sections.

The outer layer of the fold concerned in amnion formation has always been part of the blastoderm. The cells of the latter now form a continuous layer over the egg, enclosing the yolk and the embryo with its amniotic covering. Its cells gradually flatten and the nuclei become rather widely spaced. In this condition it is spoken of as the serosa, or outer embryonic envelope.

In anatrepsis, a second method of amnion formation, the embryo sinks into the yolk, posterior end first, as it migrates to a new position in the egg. At first the caudal end of the germ band gradually bends backward toward the interior of the egg (Fig. 5a-e). It penetrates farther, and projects anteriorly as more of the embryo becomes involved until, finally, the latter either comes to lie entirely submerged within the interior of the egg, or continues to the opposite surface where it then appears dorsally situated. During the movement, the connection of the margins of the germ band with the blastoderm cells is maintained and no rupture of this tissue occurs. The additional cells required to preserve continuity are furnished in the form of typical amniotic cells again supplied, as in the first example,

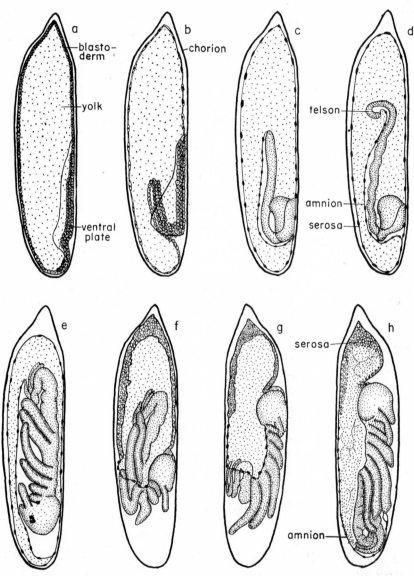

FIG. 5.—Stages of blastokinesis in sagittal sections of the *Calopteryx* egg.
a–e, anatrepsis; *f–h*, katatrepsis. *a*, posterior end of ventral plate sinks into the
yolk; *b, c*, ventral plate migrates anteriorly and dorsally; blastoderm thins out to
form the serosa, the junction between embryo and serosa is the amniotic rudiment. *c*, germ band invaginated except for the anterior portion of the head.
d, metamerism visible. *e*, embryonic appendages developed, amniotic cavity is
ventral to embryo. *f, g, h*, well-developed embryo migrating to ventral surface of
the egg; amnion ruptured and abandoned by embryo as serosa contracts dorsally.
Diagrammatic. (Modified from Brandt, 1869.)

by the continued proliferation of cells, or by the flattening and stretching in surface area of the blastodermal cells drawn in by the invaginating embryo. The fusion of the edges of the amnion occurs over the procephalic end of the embryo as the latter leaves the egg surface. After fusion, separation may take place between amnion and serosa, leaving the two envelopes quite independent of one another. In anatrepsis, of course, the embryo has reversed its orientation so that its head now lies directed posteriorly in the egg. The ventral surface of the embryo has also turned toward the dorsal side of the egg, whereas formerly it faced ventrally.

Segmentation.—The germ band consists of a superficial layer of tissue, the ectoderm, and a somewhat thicker, inner mesentodermal rudiment lying between the ectoderm and the yolk. The mesentodermal cells suffer considerable realignment with the initiation of segmentation. Along either side of the longitudinal axis of the embryo the tissue becomes multilaminar. By continued rearrangement the cells increase in numbers in certain places, corresponding to the future intrasegmental areas, while the layer becomes very thin in the intervening zones. These thin portions mark the positions of the intersegmental areas. Since they occur, in general, in anteroposterior sequence on both right and left sides of the germ band the latter appears in surface view to be transversely segmented. The ectoderm slowly undergoes a change as well. The layer becomes unilaminar and maintains close contact with the inner layer of mesentoderm. As the mesentoderm has developed shallow, transverse intersegmental areas alternating with much thickened intrasegmental regions, its surface will be a succession of swellings and depressions which the ectoderm follows.

Anteriorly, part of the head is prominent because of the two lateral procephalic lobes which have broadened extensively. Two succeeding narrow segments, the antennal and intercalary, abut closely behind the lobes and three more, the mandibular, the first maxillary, and the labial segments, are spaced farther apart posterior to them. These six segments, the first three of which cannot be separately identified in most species, comprise the head region. Following these are three segments which from their first appearance usually are wider laterally than the more posterior segments or the three immediately anterior to them (Fig 6). These three belong to the future thoracic portion of the body.

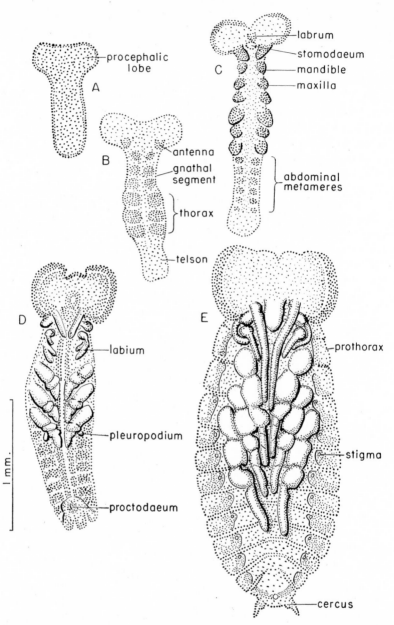

Fig. 6.—*Tenodera sinensis.* Ventral views of developing embryos removed from eggs and drawn to same scale of magnification. *A,* ventral plate with rudiments of procephalic lobes. *B,* germ band with gnathal and thoracic segments defined. *C,* same with rudiments of some appendages, labrum, and stomodaeal invagination. *D,* embryo after revolution to dorsal yolk; appendages formed, proctodaeal invagination in telson. *E,* embryo three-fifths egg length; abdomen straightened and lateral body walls encompass most of the yolk. (From Jour. Morph. and Physiol., **30**, 1, by H. R. Hagan.)

The remainder, never more than twelve segments including the telson, or terminal area, constitute the segments of the abdomen. It should be noted that the newly formed metameres are invariably intercalated just cephalad to the undifferentiated rudiment of the telson. The maximum number of segments does not exceed 21 in the early stages of development, and older embryos have fewer, due to the coalescence of several of them with adjacent segments. Hence the hatched insect exhibits fewer distinct body segments than were present in its embryonic stages within the egg.

Summary.—The egg now contains not only the elongated and segmented germ band which will form the entire insect, but a number of extraembryonic portions, namely: (1) the yolk, (2) a large number of vitellophags, often visibly derived in two ways, with their cytoplasmic processes ramifying throughout the egg and enclosing the nutrient substances, and generally, (3) two embryonic envelopes, the amnion and the serosa. It should be recalled, too, that gastrulation has resulted in a definitely two-layered embryo as in other animals. But one of these two layers, the mesentoderm, is not the same as that typical for other animals. It consists primarily of presumptive mesoderm with, perhaps, some entodermal primordia, while, to follow the usual course of embryology, this layer should be entirely, or almost wholly, formative entoderm. Further reference to entodermal origins will be made when the formation of the mid-intestine is described.

The literature cited at the end of Chapter 3 applies here, also.

Chapter 3

ORGANOLOGY IN THE OLDER EMBRYO

The embryo has become a large and conspicuous part of the egg content, with two very definitely arranged and segmented germ layers and a less apparent entoderm. It is prepared to organize these tissues into various appendages and organs in a manner peculiar to the order to which it belongs. Adequate comparisons of parts in embryos of various orders have not appeared, yet much of phylogenetic interest would come from such treatment. For example, the embryonic external appendages of the holometabolous insects vary widely in different orders and also from those of heterometabolous embryos. Internally, pronounced variations likewise occur, for the former group of insects acquires rudiments of several imaginal organs in the larval portion of embryonic development, long after eclosion. This generalized account, like others, will be influenced by the simpler treatment of the less specialized orders since these have been more thoroughly investigated.

External Appendages.—The rudiments of the anterior appendages are evident before segmentation extends far into the abdominal portion of the germ band (Fig. 6). Normally, the early embryo may exhibit a pair of appendages on each segment of the body, but not on the ocular segment and not on the telson. The ocular segment, however, will eventually develop the optic centers from its broad lateral lobes, which were prominent at a very early stage in germ band formation. The labrum, which now appears between the lobes, is not considered as an appendage although it sometimes begins its development as a bilobed organ. The succeeding segments, to the telson, may each have a pair of appendages, the second cephalic segment bearing the antennae; the third (tritocerebral, intercalary) occasionally shows a second pair of rudimentary and evanescent antennae which shortly disappear; the fourth develops the mandibles and the next two segments form the first and second maxillae, the last partially fusing to form the labium in insects.

The three thoracic segments bear appendages which eventually develop into the legs of the insect. On the first abdominal segment (the tenth in serial order) a pair of appendages arises which will be of especial interest to our discussion in later chapters. These are the pleuropodia which, in many insect embryos, are quite prominent and often very curiously developed both internally and externally. They, too, normally disappear sometime prior to the birth of the embryo. Of the remaining abdominal appendages none are of unusual significance here, but it should be observed that some of them, according to various authors, persist after birth. For example, the appendages of the eighth and ninth segments are said to form the gonapophyses, while those of the tenth or eleventh develop into cerci. It is possible that the appendages of certain segments form into the larval prolegs of holometabolous insects, also the jointed abdominal larval legs of the primitive lepidopteran family Micropterygidae, similar legs in certain larval Mecoptera (scorpion flies), and perhaps the abdominal gills which appear in the third instar of the genus *Cloëon* according to Heymons (1896), although this, too, is disputed. It might finally be mentioned that Folsom (1922, pp. 61–62) places the ventral tube, tenaculum, and furcula of the Collembola among those structures which develop from the first, third, and fourth pairs respectively of the embryonic abdominal appendages.

These appendages in general arise in serial order but many exceptions are known where some of those more posteriorly situated appear earlier. At first they are all simple, shallow evaginations of the ectoderm of which the cephalic, thoracic, and certain posterior abdominal rudiments later continue to elongate into definite segmented appendages. During their growth the mesoderm cells of the inner layer invade the interior cavity of each appendage to form the muscle tissue within them. Those which fail to continue with their growth and development into useful or permanent appendages of the embryo are slowly eliminated through resorption into the body. Meanwhile the embryo grows until it often becomes as long as the egg. Sometimes it attains a length much greater than that of the egg, in which case it is often flexed dorsally anteriorly and either ventrally or dorsally in the posterior region so that it continues to occupy the limited space enclosed by the chorion.

Katatrepsis and the Formation of the Dorsal Body Wall.— Those embryos which have previously migrated to other positions in the egg, and have reversed their anteroposterior axes in relation to the polarity of the egg during the operation, now resume their initial position in which the head again is at the anterior end of the egg. This movement of the embryo is called by various authors, revolution, reversal, orientation, blastokinesis, or kata-trepsis. Usually the migration of the embryo follows the same general course it took in the process of invagination or anatrepsis (Figs. 5, 146). These two migrations are included in the term blastokinesis, as discussed previously.

At the close of katatrepsis the embryo usually shortens in the anteroposterior axis but widens through lateral and dorsal growth. The telson often is flexed ventrally over the most posterior segments and only later tends to straighten out. When the embryo is shorter than the egg it will ordinarily be found, at the conclusion of blastokinesis, on the posterior ventral surface of the egg, extending forward its full length, with the uncovered yolk visible anteriorly and dorsally.

Growth of the body walls now seems to be accelerated. The lateral margins of the germ band extend dorsally most rapidly in the posterior end of the embryo. Dorsal growth of the lateral body wall is slower anteriorly, especially in the anterior thoracic and posterior cephalic regions. The protocephalic portion, nevertheless, advances almost as rapidly anteriorly as do the postero-lateral walls. As a result, the anterior and lateral protocephalic regions quickly form the definitive head with the eyes pushed upwards into their final positions, the antennae shift above the labrum, and the mandibular, maxillary, and labial segments are drawn forward in the formation of the lower posterior parts of the head.

Simultaneously with this katatreptic activity the embryonic envelopes, the amnion, and the serosa assume less significant functions in the embryogeny, or they may be entirely destroyed. According to Korschelt and Heider (1899), they are disposed of in one of the following ways:

1. The two membranes rupture over the ventral surface and are pulled, or by contraction finally arrive, over the dorsal midline of the embryo, where they are enclosed in the embryonic body cavity when the yolk is being circumscribed by its lateral walls (Fig. 7). In the final stages of the dorsal aggregation of the embryonic membranes, a more or less distinct dorsal organ is often formed in them, due to this contraction. Hagan (1917) has shown that in the mantid studied by him two such organs appear, one

with a spherical lumen whose opening is toward the chorion and another which opens toward the embryo.

2. The amnion ruptures and forms a dorsal organ while the serosa remains intact through at least a portion of the future development of the embryo.

3. This is the reverse of the second method in that the serosal membrane is the one destroyed while the amnion forms a continuous envelope around the embryo.

4. Neither envelope is ruptured or destroyed until the time of hatching.

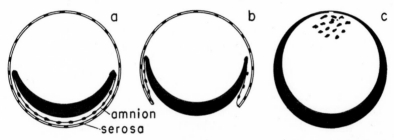

Fig. 7.—Egg and embryo illustrating the fate of the embryonic membranes, cross sections. *a*, membranes intact; *b*, membranes ruptured and being drawn dorsally before upward growth of body walls; *c*, membranes enclosed with the yolk for digestion. Diagrammatic.

It will be noted that in the first three types of disposal of these membranes, one or both of them finally will be converted into nutrient material. In the instances where they continue to persist, or at least one does, the intact envelopes remain rather passively as delicate embryonic coverings. The serosa sometimes secretes one or two membranes at an earlier stage but, apparently, from now on serves no other definite function. In any event, from this point in development both of them may be dropped from subsequent consideration in the embryonic history. The further dorsal growth of the embryonic body wall, and the fusion of its right and left halves along the dorsal mid-line, is accompanied by the gradual inclusion of the ruptured envelopes within the body together with the remaining yolk. An exception to this statement exists when both envelopes persist unbroken, for in this case a small amount of yolk sometimes is left unused between the amnion and the serosa.

The appendages have continued their active growth throughout this period. Those which are to form ultimately into definite extremities have gradually assumed the appearance characteristic of their final form and structure, the segmentation and differentiation of parts becoming quite visible on the surface of each one (Figs. 6, 72, 124, 125). On the other hand, those with no future function have slowly been resorbed into the general body ectoderm and have disappeared. Thus the embryo shows externally well-defined head, thoracic, and abdominal regions, with their appendages folded closely against the body. In the latest stages of embryonic history a definite cuticula covers the hypodermis with spines and setae distributed over its surface.

Internal Organs.—It is unnecessary for our purpose to trace the succeeding steps of all of the internal organs in detail, and impractical to treat them simultaneously. Therefore, each system of organs will be very briefly considered. Developmental time will occasionally be indicated simply by reference to the comparative perfection of the external form of the embryo at any particular interval, or by the degree of development attained by

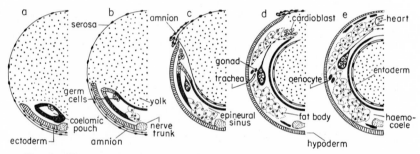

Fig. 8.—Illustrations of growth of the principal tissues and organs in the embryo. Selected stages in cross section with splanchnopleural and somatopleural muscles suggested in black, chorion omitted. Schematic.

other internal organs (Fig. 8). Each system otherwise will be described as a unit. The principal ones are: circulatory, digestive, muscular, nervous, reproductive, and respiratory. The excretory system, in part, is an integral portion of the digestive tract in its embryogeny and will be described with it; the fat bodies and nephrocytes are mesodermic derivatives. A consideration of the excretory functions of these organs and of the intestines, tracheoles, oenocytes, and hypodermis lies in another field.

The Mesoderm and the Coelomic Sacs.—The origin of the mesentoderm has already been described because this tissue arose when the embryo existed only as a ventral plate. Most of the mesentoderm enters into the formation of mesenchyme and its derivatives, although a portion of it is usually thought to give rise to entoderm. This question is more closely examined in connection with the formation of the mid-intestine.

The mesentoderm rapidly enlarges by delamination into a multilayered mass of cells extending beneath the ventral portion of the germ band. As segmentation appears superficially the cells of the inner layer are seen to be multiplying most actively in areas corresponding with the intrasegmental portions of the ectoderm, the thickest masses, or mesoblastic somites, being intrasegmentally arranged and joined to each succeeding somite by thin layers of formative mesoderm. It will be found also that the mesoderm has assumed definite ventrolateral positions in the embryo with very little of this tissue now remaining in a median position. The mesoblastic somites soon begin to show paired internal cavities within them, as they become larger. The outer side of each cavity is to form somatic mesoderm while the inner, or more medianly placed surface, gives rise to the splanchnic mesoderm. The enclosed space between the two layers is the intrasegmental rudiment of the coelomic cavity. Eventually these may open into each other due to the disintegration of the anterior and posterior septa between them. As the ectoderm grows dorsally and finally fuses along the back of the embryo, the mesoblast cells of both somatic and splanchnic layers, by proliferation, follow it. At the same time the lateral coelomic spaces are largely obliterated by invading mesodermic cells which tend partially to fill the lower portion of the space between the somatic and splanchnic layers with mesenchymatous tissue.

The Body Cavity.—The slight withdrawal of the yolk from the ventral portion of the embryo, accompanied by the segregation of the mesoderm into lateral strands in which the coelomic cavities are formed, leaves a space occupied by the forming nerve cord and a few scattered mesodermal elements. This is the epineural sinus or haemal cavity. As the inner walls of the coelomic cavities rupture, these spaces become confluent. Later on the yolk is entirely circumscribed by the mid-intestine (Fig. 8 c–e) and simultaneously reduced in amount so that the body cavity constantly enlarges with further embryonic development. This space, the haemocoele, is eventually bounded externally by the somatopleural musculature and internally by the intestinal muscles of the splanchnopleure. Hence the haemocoele descends from the fusion of the coelomic cavities with a haemal sinus.

Beginning with an early stage in the formation of the ecto-dermal prolongations of the evaginations which mark out the future permanent appendages, somatopleural mesenchyme cells migrate into their cavities. From these cells the muscles activat-ing the extremities will be developed.

The somatic portion of the mesoderm finally becomes closely applied against the ectodermal body wall, where it forms the intrasegmental muscles of the body, pericardial cells, the dorsal diaphragm, and a portion of the fat body (Snodgrass, 1926). The splanchnic layer, on the contrary, firmly unites with the intestinal tract, when the latter is formed, producing its musculature. In addition, it gives rise to part of the reproductive system and the greater part of the fat body (Imms, 1925). Splanchnic muscles show no evidence of metamerism.

The Digestive System.—The earliest rudiments of the di-gestive tract appear at a very early embryonic stage when the external appendages first evaginate. Just posterior to the devel-oping labrum on the protocephalic mid-line, a slight ectodermal depression occurs which rapidly becomes a deep invagination as it pushes dorsally through the mesoderm of the embryo as a blind tube. This is the stomodaeum. The stomodaeal invagination, by differentiation, will give rise to the pharynx and oesophagus, together with the tissue layer connecting it to the mesenteron which develops later. At the same time another invagination, posterior to the stomodaeal invagination, forms the rudiment of the salivary glands. This invagination is carried into the stomo-daeum and later is found to open at, or near, the base of the hypopharynx. Very early it may be seen to be surrounded by a few cells from the mesentoderm tissue which accompany it on its further dorsal and posterior elongation.

At the posterior end of the embryo an invagination similar to the stomodaeum arises in the telson and proceeds anteriorly as the proctodaeum. At it grows forward it draws in a portion of the superficial ectoderm surrounding its external opening at the pos-terior end of the embryo. This area differentiates into the anal opening, rectum, and the hind-intestine proper. In many species, the Malpighian tubules invaginate into the superficial ectoderm on the surface of the embryo, and are carried in with the fore part of the proctodaeum so that they are to be found, finally, as diver-ticula from the internal end of the latter. In other species they seem to arise from the proctodaeal invagination. The proctodaeum will finally connect with the mesenteron at the latter's posterior end. The epithelium of the fore- and hind-intestines, with their accessory structures, are purely ectoderm in origin. After coming in contact with the enteron or mid-intestine they fuse with the latter and the lumen of each opens into the interior of the mid-intestine so that a continuous passage is established.

From the first studies in insect embryology, the nature of the primary cells first entering into the formation of the mesenteron has been a matter of wide differences of opinion among various workers. Very excellent summaries of the alternative views have been presented by Nelson (1915) and Eastham (1930), together with résumés of their own observations. Other recent discussions of the subject have been presented by Hirschler (1912), Paterson (1932), Richards (1932), Snodgrass (1933, 1935), Johannsen and Butt (1941), and Henson (1932, 1946). Three primary theories regarding the source of the cells forming the stomach have been widely discussed. Some investigators believe that the mesenteron arises purely from cells situated at the inner ends of the stomodaeum and proctodaeum and that the mid-intestine therefore is ectodermal in origin; others claim that yolk cells give rise to the mesenteron, thus yolk cells are remnants of a primitive entoderm. Another view is maintained in which it is claimed that cells, originally derived from portions of the mesentodermal tissue, are early set aside to become associated later with the blind ends of the stomodaeum and the proctodaeum, or in other locations, from which positions they finally become active in the formation of the mesenteron.

The great difficulty in definitely ascertaining the facts in mesenteron development may be referred to the obscurity surrounding the primary entodermal layer in its earliest form and in the great diversity exhibited by the various species of insects in this phase of their embryogeny.

Snodgrass seeks to harmonize these three conflicting views by freely admitting the great variability in insects as to the locations in which mesenteron formation is first visible. This does not conflict with his concept of its origin from true entodermal cells. According to him, the formation of the inner layer, commonly spoken of as the mesentoderm, is really all that remains of a typical gastrulation formerly present in more primitive hexapods with less yolk. Large accumulation of yolk has materially altered the appearance of the process in eggs of existing insects. The present gastrulation, which accentuates mesoderm derivation, nevertheless contains true entodermal cells as well, but they are more obscurely represented. When gastrulation begins, the first cells which are cut off, or those most centrally situated, are true entoderm. Instead of at once forming a large and conspicuous gastral cavity, as in other typical metazoans, the cells are suppressed in this activity. They detach themselves from the mesoderm for the most part and wander through the yolk as vitellophags, leaving only remnants of entodermal tissue (represented by small groups of cells), at various locations on the inner surface of the mesodermal rudiment, or in the vicinity of the future stomodaeal and proctodaeal invaginations. Therefore, descriptions of the formation of the mesenteron from any of these situations are readily understood.

In most cases the first indication of mesenteron formation appears in the posterior extension of cellular elements as two narrow bands of tissue from the inner end of the stomodaeal invagination, and two bands directed forward from the proctodaeum. These continue to grow backward from the first point of origin and anteriorly from the second until they finally fuse into two continuous strands bridging the gap still present between the stomodaeum and proctodaeum. Each gradually extends laterally around the yolk as a unilaminar tissue until it encounters the other. Their edges then fuse, forming a tube within which the yolk is enclosed.

Just prior to the final closure of the entodermal portion dorsally, the remnants of the embryonic envelopes, in those instances where one or both have been destroyed, are now also surrounded by the fusing entoderm. Thus the embryonic membranes which were ruptured during katatrepsis finally are taken into the midintestine to be converted into nutrient material.

After the mesenteron has been definitely established, further consumption of the enclosed yolk permits it to reduce its diameter to that more nearly corresponding to its ultimate condition. This is not an extensive reduction, for the embryo meanwhile is enlarging both in length and diameter so that the disparity between its dimensions and that of its mesenteron is already largely eliminated. The splanchnic layer of mesoderm now forms into the definitive musculature of the digestive tract.

From the above description we find that the digestive tract consists essentially of a simple tube composed of a single layer of epithelium throughout. Diverticula arising from it, or in its immediate vicinity, form certain organs accessory to its proper functioning, as the salivary glands, caeca, Malpighian tubules, etc. Except for the mesenteron with its caeca, all are probably of ecto-dermal origin and the lumens of some of them will, at a later stage, be lined with chitin derived from the surface of the cells. The mesenteron or primary absorptive portion of the alimentary tract has arisen from cellular tissue originating directly from within the embryo and is considered to be entodermal in function. It is further distinguished by possessing no chitinous intima of its own.

The Mycetom.—Certain cells in the haemocoele of many spe-cies of insects harbor yeastlike microorganisms whose functional relationship to their host is as yet only partially solved. The gen-eral consensus, supported by the excellent observations of Sulc (1911) and Pierantoni (1913), seems to regard them as metabolic symbionts. Others believe the relationship is mutualistic, para-sitic, etc.

Their emigration from the mother through the follicular epi-thelium into the egg occurs usually, but not universally, before the chorion is secreted or, as in the viviparous offspring of aphids, during blastoderm formation. Entrance is followed by their ulti-mate localization in fat body cells or in vitellophags. In his studies, Pierantoni (1913) has classified the insects possessing them as those which form special organs for retention of micro-organisms and those which do not. An example of the former con-dition came to the attention of Leydig (1850) in his examination of aphid embryos. He discovered a conspicuous greenish organ in the abdominal region and suggested that it might be a nutritive body. Several names have been applied to this body but Sulc (1911) called it a mycetom and the cells composing the organ were termed mycetocytes. Uichanco (1924) has traced the origin of the mycetocytes to the vitellophags derived from lagging cleavage cells, a relationship Wheeler (1893) thought quite pos-sible. The smaller vitellophags of aphids, formed by later migra-tions from the blastodermic layer, apparently never become mycetocytes.

The second class of insects, those providing no symbiotic organ or mycetom, offer security to the symbionts in various portions of the body. Blochmann (1886) discovered microorganisms within both the body tissues and the ova of insects. In most cases resi-dence is apparently confined to mesodermal cells of the insect.

Besides yeasts, bacteria, rickettsiae, and other organisms may be present.

Buchner (1930) and Steinhaus (1946) have shown the widespread distribution of microorganisms in several orders of insects. They usually appear in lobulated masses of cells in the abdominal haemocoele. They are present throughout the ontogeny of the individual and, in the case of the female, some always pass to the next generation, most frequently through the egg. A knowledge of their precise function in the body and physiological influence on the insects protecting them is an undeveloped field for investigation, and nothing has been learned of the stimuli causing them to accumulate in such dense masses in the vicinity of the oöcytes and ova.

The Excretory System.—This consists functionally of several independent units: the tracheal system for the elimination of gases; the Malpighian tubules for the discharge of liquid substances from the body; and the hypodermis, whose excretions usually precipitate in the cuticle. In addition there may be specialized storage cells within the body but their functions are not fully recognized. Only the Malpighian tubules will be considered here.

From a point just posterior to the blind end of the invaginating proctodaeum in a very early stage of its development, two or three pairs of invaginations strike off at angles from it. This may, in some species, occur on the surface of the telson, whereupon their openings are later carried into the interior during the further invaginations of the proctodaeum. These lateral diverticula are the rudiments of the Malpighian tubules. As the proctodaeum continues to invaginate and finally fuse with the mid-intestine, the Malpighian tubules are found to be attached to the proctodaeum just posterior to its junction with the mesenteron. Thus the tubules would be ectodermal in origin but Henson (1932, 1946) believes them to be entodermal in conformity with his theory of entoderm formation. The tubules elongate greatly and ramify freely throughout the haemocoele but several are usually rather closely applied to the mid-intestine. They end blindly distally but their proximal ends open directly into the lumen of the hind-intestine at their points of attachment. From their earliest development, a lumen is present within each. In some species there may be present a very great number of Malpighian tubules, the extra tubules often being simply separate branches of the original two or three pairs and fusing with them anteriorly before the junction of the latter to the proctodaeum.

The Nervous System.—Shortly after the formation of the primitive groove, when the ventral plate first becomes two-layered, a pair of longitudinal ectodermal swellings, the neural ridges, appear and extend the entire length of the embryo. They are separated from one another by a furrow in the same position earlier occupied by the primitive groove. This is the neural groove. The neural ridges separate in the cephalic region to pass around a space which is left for the formation of the labrum and the stomodaeal invagination. These swellings are uniform in external appearance at first but later show a segmental arrangement. Cross sections of this portion of the germ band stage permit us to determine that the swellings are caused by the formation of groups of large cells, the neuroblasts, beneath each neural ridge with a smaller group between them above the neural groove. All were derived from the ectoderm. Sometimes the cells are composed simply of irregularly disposed cells, while in other instances they are quite regularly arranged and, according to Graber (1890), Viallanes (1890), and Wheeler (1891), they consist of a definite number of strands of cells horizontally placed on each side directly beneath the ectoderm. These neuroblasts will give rise to the ganglionic cells and nerves, the median strand supplying the transverse commissures. Paired connectives, derived from the intersegmental areas, will unite them into the ventral nerve chain for purposes of coordination of activity. Anteriorly, the optic centers and the brain, with its three pairs of lobes, have their origin in the head. As differentiation proceeds, a marked reduction in the number of ganglia follows through the coalescence of some of them. For example, the suboesophageal ganglion is composed of the fused ganglia from at least the mandibular, maxillary, and labial segments which are also in the head of the older embryo. The three thoracic ganglia often fuse to form one large ganglion and, in the abdomen, there is often a very pronounced aggregation of most of the ganglia into a relatively small number situated in the anterior segments. The stomatogastric system arises from the ectoderm of the stomodaeum and serves to govern the aorta, salivary ducts, some of the mouth parts, and especially the stomodaeal portion of the digestive system.

The Respiratory System.—This consists of the trachea and the tracheoles. Tracheal invaginations arise in the ectoderm near the distal margin of the base of the last two thoracic and the first eight or nine abdominal segments. The invaginations produce anterior and posterior branches which fuse with those in adjacent segments so that they finally unite into the main longitudinal tracheal trunks. Later, cross connectives and smaller ramifying tracheal branches extend throughout the body. The finest branches of the system are the tracheoles which are in contact with the cells of the body for the purpose of gaseous exchange.

The Heart.—This organ is said to be formed from mesoderm cells, called cardioblasts, which earlier were lying in the dorsal wall of the coelomic cavities (Fig. 8). As the yolk is withdrawn from the embryo through the gradual formation of the entoderm, a space appears ventrally at first, the epineural sinus, which spreads laterally and dorsally upward between the enteron and the body wall. The lateral and dorsal extensions of the mesoderm occupy this region and grow dorsally between the ectoderm and the entoderm with its enclosed yolk, carrying the cells which formerly composed the dorsal coelomic wall along with it. The cells of the original coelomic spaces of the two sides eventually unite over the yolk. These cells, now known as the cardioblasts, form a hollow tube, the rudiment of the heart. The dorsal diaphragm is composed of a sheet of cells which serves to support the heart. The aorta is similarly derived anteriorly and it unites with the heart by a posterior extension of its lumen. Blood cells arise from the residual mesodermal cells remaining in the epineural sinus.

The Reproductive System.—In some species the primordial germ cells are distinctly segregated very early in the cleavage of the egg, while in many others they are not distinguished until later stages. They are usually relatively few in number and, in instances where their early presence has been detected, lie in two masses in the posterior part of the embryo, apparently adjacent to that portion of the mesoderm which will later form the splanchnic layer and immediately below the cardioblasts (Wheeler, 1889). They are invested at an early stage by a layer of mesoderm, this tissue eventually differentiating into the ovarioles and the paired oviducts in the case of the female, or into the corresponding tissues and organs of the male. The primordial cells will give rise to the primary germ cells and, apparently in most instances, to the nurse cells.

Summary.—The female reproductive system consists of paired ovaries in which the oöcytes acquire their yolk supply and paired oviducts, all of mesodermal origin. The common oviduct is of ectodermal derivation, together with any accessory organs it may possess. It conveys ova from the paired oviducts to the exterior environment. Deposited eggs vary widely in size, shape, and number. They consist largely of yolk, pronucleus, periplasm, a little dispersed cytoplasm, and a chorionic covering which serves as protection. Fertilization or, at least, egg penetration is invariably internal. Embryonic development may be conveniently divided into general periods of tissue differentiation and organology. Ectoderm, mesoderm, and segmentation clearly arise early to form the ventral rudiment of the embryo, the dorsal body walls being completed during middle or late stages of organology. The ventral nervous system also appears early, as do rudiments of external appendages. These, in general, show progressive development in an anteroposterior sequence through the thoracic and abdominal regions.

Gastrulation and the origin of entoderm have been the subject of much controversy. It appears a waste of time to speculate further on the subject until more definite evidence is forthcoming. The embryo usually shifts its position once or twice during its development in the egg; the functional advantages of blastokinesis are not clear. Also, at an early point in development the germ band stage gives rise to one or two embryonic envelopes which are termed, through analogy with vertebrate structures, the amnion and serosa. No doubt they are protective as cushions and suspend the embryo in fluid, at least along the ventral surface. Upon their destruction, they are generally consumed by the embryo. The coelomic pouches arise as lateral paired cavities in the mesoderm of most of the segments. Their subsequent partial opening and upward migration before the somatopleure cause their cavities to join with the epineural sinus to form the haemocoele. Where their distal margins meet and fuse in the dorsal midline, the heart and aorta are formed from their cells.

The digestive tract is mostly ectodermal and only the origin of the cells forming the mid-intestine is obscure. Malpighian tubules arise from, or in the vicinity of, the hind-intestine and, in either case, are carried in with the invaginating proctodaeum. Very many embryos receive symbionts from the mother. These are frequently harbored in a paired mycetom consisting of cells derived from early vitellophags. The external hypodermis, Malpighian tubules, the tracheal system, oenocytes, etc., provide for excretion of metabolic wastes; all are ectodermal derivatives. The other details of development require no summation.

LITERATURE CITED

Berlese (1909), Blochmann (1886), Buchner (1930), Dawydoff (1928), Eastham (1930), Folsom (1922), Graber (1890), Grassi (1887), Hagan (1917), Hagen (1858), Hallez (1885, 1886), Heberdey (1931), Hegner (1914, 1917), Henneguy (1904), Henson (1932, 1946), Heymons (1896), Hirschler (1912, 1924), Imms (1925), Johannsen and Butt (1941), Kahle (1908), Korschelt (1887), Korschelt and Heider (1899), Lécaillon (1898a), Leydig (1850), Mollison (1904), Nelson (1915), Paterson (1932), Payne (1932), Pierantoni (1913), Réaumur (1738), Richards (1932), Roonwal (1936), Sachs (1892), Seidel (1929), Slifer (1932), Snodgrass (1926, 1933, 1935, 1936), Steinhaus (1946), Sulc (1911), Tirelli (1931), Townsend (1934), Uichanco (1924), Viallanes (1890), Wheeler (1889, 1891, 1893).

Chapter 4

THE TYPES OF VIVIPARITY

There seems to be no doubt that the viviparous species at present known to us arose from oviparous ancestral stock. Some, such as many of the ovoviviparous forms, apparently have assumed this trait comparatively recently. Indeed, some species are even said to be viviparous under unusual circumstances yet oviparous most of the time; in their ontogeny, viviparity may be just developing as a permanent fixture. Other species exist whose adaptations to the viviparous condition are so highly specialized that their evolution in the production of living young must represent the accumulation of a long series of modifications, spread over a great time interval.

One is immediately impressed by the seemingly endless assortment of variations employed by viviparous species whose members must still furnish nutriment to embryos within their influence, care, and protection. No less amazing are the varied uses made of organs whose present important development and functions in many embryos have solved the problem of acquiring nutriment from the mother under new and peculiar conditions. Such organs, in most cases, are ephemeral in related oviparous forms, or extraembryonic structures to be discarded or resorbed early by them as no longer essential to life.

Yet there does appear to be a definite limitation to the classes of these remarkable contrivances for nourishing the embryo. They follow only a few patterns, in spite of their great variety of expression. This chapter attempts to set the different types in orderly array.

Historical Classifications

The classification of viviparous species has been a gradual process following slowly upon the contributions of investigators in the developmental history of various species. As more recent data have become available and the number of viviparous species has increased, later classifications have, quite naturally, been expanded to include divergent aspects of such reproduction.

An attempt to classify insects on the basis of embryological characters was made by Agassiz (1851) with no very great degree of success. However, his effort was mainly concerned with taxonomic relationships and his data were designed to supplement existing morphological characters already taken into account. In his studies, immature stages of insects were examined subsequent to hatching, hence, since they were not mature they could, from a liberal viewpoint, consistently be classed as late embryonic forms. Dohrn (1870) had the same faith in the taxonomic utility of embryological data when he found that the orders of insects could be divided into two main groups, one having a superficial germ band and the other an immersed germ band. His system, too, proved unsatisfactory in practical application.

Graber (1889) summarized the literature relating especially to the embryonic envelopes and the overgrowth of the dorsal body walls of insect embryos. From these data he constructed a table in which development is classified according to the relationships exhibited between these two mutually interdependent phenomena. Certain interesting observations resulted from his study of the factors involved; namely, systematically related insects often behave quite differently with regard to the formation of the embryonic envelopes, and, conversely, widely different groups may present quite similar conditions in the development of these parts. The conclusion is reached that in considering insect phylogeny one must take into account not only the larval stages but also the earlier embryonal history of insects. With the subsequent accumulation of embryological data the classification, as presented, is impractical, for it would require continual revision and realignment of its groupings in order to keep abreast of later discoveries. It has further been found that the embryonic membranes are extremely plastic structures and lend themselves to a variety of functional accessory modifications. They are not usually considered as parts of the embryo itself. For these reasons, Graber's classification of insect embryos, based upon such characters alone, cannot be considered as an important or practical contribution to the subject.

Several other workers, engrossed in the peculiarities of parthenogenetic development, sought to segregate insects into classes based upon the presence or absence of fertilization phenomena, and examples of these ideas are found in the writings of Lemoine (1893) and Henneguy (1899). The former made a distinction between species based on four main types of reproduction in Hemiptera: (1) essentially viviparous, the aphids proper, (2) oviparous type without fertilization of the egg, represented by the so-called agamic *Phylloxera,* (3) oviparous type with fertilization of the egg including the bisexual forms of aphids and *Phylloxera,* and (4) oviparous type with or without fertilization of the eggs, such as the scale insects.

However, it appears to have been Hansen (1894) who first appreciated the fact that matters of fundamental physiological significance might underlie the modes of reproduction which are found exclusively in the viviparous insects. In discussing the unusual conditions quite evidently surrounding the embryonic life of the dermapteran, *Hemimerus talpoides* Walker, and comparing it with the situation known to exist in other viviparous species, he comments as follows: "This curious propagation places the Hemimerus totally isolated from all known insects, as far as I know, for the propagation of the Pupiparous Diptera differs very much from this, and the other viviparous insects always bear several or many young at a time." It would be expected, perhaps, that this observation might prove stimulating and lead to an attempt on the part of subsequent workers to recognize the desirability of classifying viviparous reproduction on a new basis in which the relationship existing between the embryo, its embryonic history, and specific physiologic adjustments would be taken into account. But such procedure was not followed, probably because the older concept of the supposed importance of parthenogenetic development in eggs still received so much attention in the study of reproduction.

Recent Classifications

More recently, the variations observed in viviparity have convinced investigators that this means of reproduction was amenable to a classification in which certain types could be definitely segregated from others. Where earlier efforts had been directed toward the utilization of embryonic peculiarities in segregating species, or larger taxonomic subdivisions, from one another attention was now focused on the more valuable recognition of possible kinds of viviparity as a part of the phenomena of reproduction.

Holmgren's Classification.—Holmgren (1904) was the earliest investigator who definitely sought to erect a classification of the types of embryology found only among viviparous insects. He possessed adequate examples of several kinds of modifications in both maternal reproductive systems and in embryonic histories to make them the basis for a new and improved scheme of classification. Instead of employing these modifications as the primary basis of his classification, he became convinced that parthenogenesis was fundamental in determining the kinds of viviparity displayed. Assorting the known viviparous insects according to this idea he presented the following divisions, from which a few details have been omitted here.

TABLE 2

CLASSIFICATION OF VIVIPARITY, FORMULATED BY HOLMGREN (1904)

A. Viviparity with parthenogenetic development
  1. Aphidae, Chermetidae, Phylloxeridae, and some Coccidae
  2. Larvae of the cecidomyid, *Miastor*

B. Viviparity with amphigonous development
  1. Neuroptera: *Notanatolica vivipara* and *Cloëon dipterum* (occasionally viviparous)
  2. Orthoptera: Blattidae: *Panchlora viridis, Blabera, Eutegaster,* and *Oxyhaloa*
                Hemimeridae: *Hemimerus*
  3. Coleoptera: Aleocharidae: *Carotoca melantho, C. phylo,* and *Spirachtha eurymedusa*
                Chrysomelidae: *Orina superba, speciosa, vittigera, cacaliae, gloriosa, alpestris* var. *polymorpha, speciocissima, venusta, hyperici*
  4. Hemiptera: Most Coccidae
  5. Diptera: Oestridae: *Oestrus, Cephalemyia*
                Tachinidae: *Tachina* spp., *Gonia, Siphona*
                Dexiidae: *Dexia, Prosena*
                Sarcophagidae: *Sarcophaga*
                Scatophagidae: *Scatophaga* (mentioned in an article by Champion and Chapman [1901] but of which Holmgren can find no further record)
                Muscidae: *Musca sepulcralis, Mesembrina meridiana, Musca vomitoria* (occasionally viviparous)
                Pupipara
                Termitoxenidae: *Termitomyia*
  6. Lepidoptera: a Brazilian micro-lepidopteran concerning whose development nothing is known.
  7. Strepsiptera.

Holmgren's classification was the only one available to subsequent workers for several years and its wide influence is shown by the frequent references to his paper in more recent literature. Nevertheless, later investigators have at times offered new groupings, or have modified his classification under the impetus of freshly acquired facts. A discussion of his arrangement of viviparous insects into classes will be deferred until Comstock's (1925) classification is considered, since the discussion of the latter's presentation of the subject will apply to both.

Keilin's Classification.—In treating the subject of viviparity in the Diptera, Keilin (1916) eliminated from his discussion those species which are only occasionally viviparous due to some abnormal experience suffered by the insect. By way of explanation it may be stated here that many species of flies, which are usually oviparous, may upon occasion be capable of extruding larvae which have happened to hatch from the eggs within the maternal reproductive tract. Such cases have been cited by Lowne (1895), Roubaud (1909), Guyénot (1913), Keilin (1916), and others. Of those species which are constantly viviparous, Keilin presents most instructively certain facts concerning their viviparous condition. He logically divides them into two main groups, based entirely upon physical and physiological factors in the embryonic history. His groups may be arranged as follows:

TABLE 3

CLASSIFICATION OF VIVIPARITY IN DIPTERA, FORMULATED BY KEILIN (1916)

A. Those insects that incubate the offspring only during the embryonic phase; that is, whose larvae are never nourished in the uterus. They are, rather, those ovoviviparous or ovolarviparous forms laying mature eggs, or recently hatched larvae, and are separable into three subtypes as follows:
   1. Modification of the maternal uterus into a storage reservoir: Tachinidae, Dixiidae
   2. Eggs large but generally few in number: Sarcophagidae, Oestridae, Gastrophilidae
   3. Eggs greatly limited in number and of extraordinary size: *Mesembrina meridiana, M. mystacea, Hylemyia strigosa* F., *H. variata* Fall., *Hydrophoria divisa* Mg., *Musca larvipara* Portsh., *Dasyphora pratorum* Mg., *Theria muscaria* Mg.

B. Those insects that continue to incubate the larvae beyond the embryonic stage; that is, those forms which nourish the hatched offspring in the maternal uterus by means of certain special adaptations.
   1. Larviparous species of *Glossina*
   2. Pupiparous species of *Hippobosca, Melophagus, Ornithomyia*

In his excellent discussion of the species and their internal modifications for the viviparous condition, Keilin clearly recognized the necessity for a thorough consideration of the physiological functions involved in certain types of incubation. Under Group A he is able to show a series of gradations in complexity up to his third category, which appears to justify his three subdivisions. However, there is no place for the paedogenetic Diptera, which lack most of the reproductive system.

Comstock's Classification.—In his textbook, Comstock (1925) gives a grouping of viviparous insects in which he uses the same major divisions employed by his predecessors, and shows especially the favorable impression Holmgren's (1904) paper made upon him. His groups, too, are distinguished according to the presence or absence of the biparental condition of the eggs. His classification is extensive and differs in certain details from the others included herein. It is quite difficult to understand why *C. grimmii*, a paedogenetic pupa which was said to deposit eggs, should have been included as a viviparous insect. His classification is presented in summary form, rather than in full, for comparison with those preceding.

TABLE 4

CLASSIFICATION OF VIVIPARITY, FORMULATED BY COMSTOCK (1925)

A. Viviparity with parthenogenetic reproduction
   1. Paedogenetic larvae: Cecidomyidae and Micromalthidae
   2. Paedogenetic pupae: *Chironomus grimmii*, which deposits eggs
   3. Viviparous agamic females: Aphids

B. Viviparity with sexual reproduction
   1. Sexual viviparous insects giving birth to nymphs or larvae: Ephemeridae, Orthoptera, Hemiptera, Lepidoptera, Coleoptera, Strepsiptera, Diptera
   2. Sexual viviparous insects giving birth to old larvae: Pupipara, *Glossina*

(From *Introduction to Entomology*. This simplified classification is used by permission of the Comstock Publishing Co., Inc.)

Discussion of Preceding Classifications.—The writer (Hagan, 1931) has already commented at length on the preceding classifications of viviparity. He said, in effect, that in Holmgren's and Comstock's classifications the primary consideration of viviparity is the presence or absence of fertilization of the egg. Manifestly, the act of fertilization or the self-sufficiency of parthenogenetic eggs is a situation which has arisen, and has been disposed of, before the embryo has initiated any part of its development. The two divisions, parthenogenetic and amphigonous, actually are types of egg production into which all insects may be grouped, regardless of their oviparous or viviparous production of offspring. It would thus appear that the assumption of the significance of these factors is entirely irrelevant.

As we review the events in the embryonic histories of some of the different viviparous forms listed by Holmgren and Comstock we will be impressed, not by the similarities among them in each class, but rather by the great diversity of wholly unrelated developmental specializations to be found there. All of this will be made clear when the details of development are presented.

We recognize in Comstock's groupings a distinct advance over that of Holmgren, for Comstock realized that not all embryogenies are of equal physiological significance. His discussion of the several viviparous examples in his list includes comments upon their degrees of complexity in structure and their various adjustments to the viviparous condition, especially on the part of the maternal organization. Thus we may accept his classification as, in fact, one quite superior to Holmgren's in this respect.

The Basis of Classification.—The proper approach to this problem appears to be the consideration of viviparity as a phenomenon whose various manifestations are justifiably separable into distinct classes. From this standpoint emphasis should be placed upon the nature of viviparity rather than upon extrinsic factors, no matter how important they may be in their other entomological applications. Such a classification obviously should be based on morphological and physiological modifications of mother and offspring, for in the proper elucidation of viviparous types, attention must be directed to these changes in both individuals. With this in mind, it is often necessary to separate individual species into their appropriate classes of viviparity without regard to taxonomic affinities. None of the preceding classifications satisfactorily groups the known viviparous species into classes with similar forms of modifications properly assorted.

The reasons why types of viviparity are based entirely upon adjustments to the viviparous condition, rather than on other criteria, are outlined in the following four paragraphs.

The preceding classifications, except Keilin's (1916) which applies only to Diptera, are founded upon a phenomenon occurring within the egg prior to embryological development; namely, the amphigonous or parthenogenetic initiation of the production of offspring. These conditions should not be the criterion upon which to segregate types of viviparity because they have nothing to do with embryonic processes, solicitude, nutrition, or birth. Something more pertinent to viviparity must be the basis of classification.

So far, all efforts to segregate oviparous embryonic development into clearly defined and limited numbers of types have failed. This is due, in part, to the uniformity with which embryos faithfully follow the major characteristics of development; and, in part, to the very frequent, but by no means similar, departures in detail from the expected appearance in individual embryonic histories. The embryonic development of insects in general has been traced very briefly in the preceding two chapters and its routine has been found to include a number of easily identified stages that regularly succeed one another in the production of offspring ready to hatch from the egg. Viviparous species as well as oviparous forms display these same changes in development. Thus, embryonic development alone has not proved to be a very satisfactory basis for classification of types, either in oviparous or in viviparous species.

In viviparous forms there has been added to the oviparous type of embryonic history a series of changes in certain organs. By virtue of these changes the embryo and the mother may enter into more intimate relations to assure the fulfillment of the viviparous condition. Sometimes the mother has insured only the retention of the young in her reproductive tract until they are to lead an independent existence; in other cases, both the mother and her developing offspring have contributed alterations which serve to distinguish one type of modification from another. These variations in the mode of providing security for the viviparous state include psychical and physiological as well as physical cenogenetic manifestations of adjustments that are readily identifiable. They vary not only in type but also very greatly in intensity of expression in different species.

Since all of the recognizable modifications provided by the mother or by the offspring are apparently concerned with promoting the viviparous condition, and since they are fundamental to the preservation of the developing young under the present circumstances, it would seem logical to use their divergencies in type for the separation of the kinds of viviparity known to us. Actually, they are the essential visible factors in the expression of the phenomenon known to us as viviparous reproduction.

The embryonic histories of some of the viviparous insects will be reviewed in succeeding chapters where it can be shown more clearly whether the following classification actually suffices to cover the kinds of viviparity that have been studied. If it does, it may also prove to be sufficiently elastic to add new types indefinitely, as they are discovered.

Hagan's Classification.—The author has proposed another classification of viviparity (Hagan, 1931). In it he included the insects normally able to produce living young in a stage subsequent to hatching. An attempt was made to subdivide the viviparous species into four general classes, based entirely upon modifications peculiarly suited to the manner of nourishing the young during their life in the mother.

Since this classification has been favorably received by embryologists both here and abroad, it forms the basis of the groupings adopted in these pages. Some critics have offered minor changes in it, for which the writer is greatly indebted. The majority of such alterations have been embodied in the present text.

TABLE 5

CLASSIFICATION OF VIVIPARITY (MODIFIED FROM HAGAN)

1. Ovoviviparity: The egg contains sufficient yolk to nourish the embryo until hatching and maternal deposition of offspring. No special nutritional structures are developed.
2. Adenotrophic (Intussuctio-) viviparity: The egg contains sufficient yolk to nourish the embryo until hatching. Specialized maternal organs nourish the larva in the uterus.
3. Haemocoelous (Exgenito-) viviparity: Embryonic development is in the haemocoele, not in genital ducts, and nutriment is acquired from maternal tissues by means of a trophamnion, trophserosa, or trophchorion.
4. Pseudoplacental viviparity: The embryo in the maternal genital tract obtains at least part of its nutriment by means of a pseudoplacenta.
    a) Attached embryo type: A pseudoplacenta, derived from maternal or embryonic tissue or from both sources, firmly unites parent and egg or embryo for a nutritional period of varying duration.
    b) Free embryo type: Pseudoplacenta wholly of embryonic origin. Contact of egg, pseudoplacenta, or embryo with maternal genital tract due only to pressure or proximity.

Two alterations from the original classification appear in the terminology, changing Intussuctio-viviparity and Exgenito-viviparity to Adenotrophic and Haemocoelous viviparity, respectively. The former was suggested by Professor W. M. Wheeler some time ago and Mr. R. E. Snodgrass proposed the latter. Johannsen and Butt (1941) shortened the descriptions of the types of viviparity and, following their suggestion, an effort has been made here to simplify them still further without loss of specificity.

In the original statement and definition of the types of viviparity one or two examples of insects characteristic of each class were cited. Johannsen and Butt have, however, added *Miastor* to the ovoviviparous class where, perhaps, it does not belong. This example, on the contrary, has been assigned to the group showing haemocoelous viviparity because Kahle (1908, p. 51) says, in effect, that the thickened serosa absorbs nutriment from the mother and makes it accessible to the embryo. And he states (p. 61) that the follicles generally migrate from the ovary to other parts of the maternal haemocoele during maturation, cleavage, or blastoderm formation. One cannot too clearly grasp exactly what is meant by the preceding statements or how prolonged or important serosal absorption is to the embryo. If it is essential to the survival of the embryo it would appear necessary to include the species in the class shown here. At all events, as the investigation now stands, this assignment should prevail until further data are obtained. As to the inclusion of the Chironomidae in Class 3, the case is less definite. Should later study of the embryology of the species concerned show no nutritional activity by the membranes then they should be transferred to the ovoviviparous type where Johannsen and Butt (1941, p. 136) have placed some species of *Tanytarsus*. Such a change would almost certainly require ovoviviparity be given two subclasses: (*a*) offspring extruded from the oviduct by the mother, and (*b*) offspring developing in the haemocoele and the hatched larvae emerging through the hypodermis of the mother. The Cecidomyidae and Chironomidae were placed in the same type of viviparity because their known development parallels *Miastor* in being haemocoelous. If Kahle's statements are correct, it is probable all these insects may show nutritive specializations.

Another valuable analysis of the original statement of the types of viviparity is evident in the recent discussion of Roonwal (1939). He divides pseudoplacental viviparity into two subtypes according to whether the embryo is attached to the mother by means of the pseudoplacenta or whether it is free in the genital tract. The first subtype is further subdivided into: (*a*) pseudoplacenta of exclusively maternal origin, (*b*) pseudoplacenta of both embryonic and maternal origin, and (c) pseudoplacenta of embryonic origin. Each of these subdivisions is supported by an example and there seems to be little doubt of the validity and discrimination shown in their segregation.

TABLE 6

ORDERS ARRANGED TO SHOW DISTRIBUTION OF MOST OF THE FAMILIES AND
GENERA SAID TO CONTAIN VIVIPAROUS SPECIES

ORDERS OF INSECTS	TYPES OF VIVIPARITY			
	1 OVOVIVIPARITY	2 ADENOTROPHIC	3 HAEMOCOELOUS	4 PSEUDOPLACENTAL
Dermaptera				Arixenia Hemimerus
Thysanoptera	Megathrips Pristothrips Bolothrips, etc.			
Blattodea	Blatta Blabera Eutegaster, etc.			Diploptera
Corrodentia	Hyperetes			Archipsocus
Anoplura	Pediculus			
Plectoptera	Chloëon			
Homoptera	Coccidae			Aphididae
Hemiptera				Polyctenidae
Lepidoptera	Tinea			
Diptera	Sarcophaga Tachinidae Anthomyidae Mesembrina Musca, etc.	Glossinidae Streblidae Nycteribiidae Hippoboscidae	Miastor Tanytarsus Oligarces	
Coleoptera	Micromalthus Corotoca Spirachtha Chrysomela Phytodecta			
Strepsiptera			Strepsiptera	
Hymenoptera	Paniscus			

There are two reasons why all of Johannsen and Butt's suggestions, and the subtypes suggested by Roonwal, are not included in their entirety here, although they may be necessary at a later date. One is that probably no two embryogenies are quite alike and there is the possibility that further analysis would quickly convert into a detailed and complicated taxonomic system what is intended to be a simple classification of the types of adjustments of insects to the viviparous condition. A second reason is that there is no known example to fit one of the ovoviviparous subtypes and too few cases to warrant extensive subdivision of pseudoplacental viviparity at this time. Roonwal has, nevertheless, called attention to the necessity for further work on the source of contributions to insect pseudoplacenta formation.

The embryonic phases of development of a great many viviparous species still are unknown. Where these insects may fall in the scheme of classification, herein adopted, remains for future investigation to reveal. Those whose viviparous condition has been reported are grouped in the accompanying table according to the available information concerning their embryogenies (Table 6 on preceding page).

Of the 23 orders generally recognized in entomological texts, 13 are said to contain viviparous species. On the other hand, several orders possess members which represent more than one type of viviparity in addition to their many oviparous species. Ovoviviparity, as a type, is most widely distributed among the orders showing viviparity, while adenotrophic viviparity is known only in the Diptera. In this case, however, it apparently includes all of the species in the families listed. One order, the Strepsiptera, is entirely haemocoelous for no other type has been found in it and Pierce (1909, 1911) states all species have the same embryogeny. This condition is the antithesis of about ten other orders which have, to date, shown only oviparity. Aside from Strepsiptera, the haemocoelous type has been very rarely encountered. Pseudoplacental viviparity involves the utilization of placenta-like structures to assist in the nutritional function and has appeared in several orders.

Attention is called to these observations here since the peculiarities of each type are to be given in greater detail when the embryonic histories of some of the species are described. A discussion of their significance among insects must also be deferred until the particulars of the embryogenies are presented.

LITERATURE CITED

Agassiz (1851), Champion and Chapman (1901), Comstock (1925), Dohrn (1870), Graber (1889), Guyénot (1913), Hagan (1931), Hansen (1894), Henneguy (1899), Holmgren (1904), Johannsen and Butt (1941), Kahle (1908), Keilin (1916), Lemoine (1893), Lowne (1895), Pierce (1909, 1911), Roonwal (1939), Roubaud (1909).

PART II

EMBRYOGENIES

Chapter 5

OVOVIVIPARITY—THYSANOPTERA, BLATTODEA, ANOPLURA, PLECTOPTERA, HOMOPTERA, LEPIDOPTERA, DIPTERA

The majority of the viviparous species of insects are included in this type, a most obvious situation since ovoviviparous insects depart least in their evolutionary deviations from the oviparous condition. While a large number of species have been cited as ovoviviparous, few writers have more than discussed the cases in very general terms or have even given the details of the female reproductive systems. This chapter devotes a disproportionate amount of space to historical material because the species mentioned have not been investigated adequately. Perhaps some of these insects actually possess other kinds of viviparity and would be classified elsewhere, were the facts known. In addition, new structures or, more likely, new uses for old ones may be revealed by the careful study of the embryogenies. One illustration may be given from the writer's own experience. Upon examining three species commonly known to be viviparous roaches on the island of Oahu, T.H., he found the most familiar one had the peculiar pleuropodia described in a later chapter.

Order Thysanoptera   Family Thripidae, etc.

Occasional viviparity has been reported in *Megathrips lativentris* Heeg. by John (1923), who obtained specimens of this species of thrips in Lachta, near Petrograd. From one female he dissected a young larva and nine eggs containing well-developed embryos. The larva had assumed its normal, straightened position and there was no evidence of the chorion, though it at once occurred to him that the latter had been accidentally ruptured through his manipulations. Another female was macerated in Eau de Javelle and subsequently washed for 24 hours in water. From it he obtained a larva and eight eggs. These ova also contained embryos in various stages of development.

Several females were isolated in small glass tubes which were frequently examined for the presence of eggs or hatched offspring. In some cases eggs only were deposited but all of them contained embryos in advanced stages of development. When these eggs eventually hatched the chorion of each egg could readily be detected. In other cases, young were found in the tubes but there were fewer egg choria than offspring, from which it was deduced that some of the young were the products of viviparous birth.

The female possesses eight ovarioles, yet from them 15 or 20 ova seem to mature and pass into the vitellaria and the paired oviducts. These eggs are fertilized in the ovariole where development starts within them. After the embryos have reached late stages in their embryogeny some of the eggs apparently hatch in the brood sac of the common oviduct while most of them are deposited a few hours prior to hatching. After the eggs and young are disposed of, the germaria liberate more ova which, in turn, experience ovarial fertilization and development. Nothing further is known of embryological significance.

Only recently Hood (1934, 1936, 1938, 1939) has described *Diceratothrips princeps, D. elegans, Zactinothrips elegans, Elaphrothrips zetetis, Zeuglothrips echinus, Pristothrips breviceps, P. peruviensis,* and *Bolothrips pratensis.* His observations strongly support John's contention that the Thysanoptera exhibit viviparity for he claims these species also produce living young. And Hathaway (1938) has reported viviparity as existing in a species of *Eupathithrips.*

Bagnell (1921) has reported the emergence of hatched larvae from the maternal genital tract of an adult female, *Dicaiothrips seychellensis,* which he was mounting. This information, in itself, would not be conclusive evidence since internal hatching could have occurred after the collection and killing of adults containing developing embryos. Combined with the foregoing observations it, however, strongly supports the possibility of viviparity in the order. It is quite evident the developmental history of these insects should be thoroughly investigated. It could then be determined whether the species mentioned are of the ovoviviparous type or belong in another classification.

LITERATURE CITED

Bagnell (1921), Hathaway (1938), Hood (1934, 1936, 1938, 1939), John (1923).

Order Blattodea   Family Blattidae

Several cockroaches have proved to be viviparous, yet none of their embryogenies have been studied. This is in part due to the fact such records were obtained from a few specimens, were observed by taxonomists or collected from observations of visitors in foreign lands. Most of the viviparous species are tropical and therefore not so readily available to embryologists. None of the ovoviviparous species has had its embryology presented, and it is hoped that this deficiency may be rectified. One species, possessing a pseudoplacental type of viviparity, is discussed in a later section as an original contribution.

As early as 1836, Robert reported the apparent viviparity of a cockroach from Senegal. Wood-Mason (1878) dissected fully developed offspring from the genital tract of *Panesthia javanica* which is distributed through the forested regions of southern Asia and in Australia. From the account one cannot be certain of viviparity in this species, for several oviparous species are known to retain offspring until shortly before hatching, then lay them as eggs. This may be such a case. Under "Entomological Notes," Anonymous (1890) an observation on viviparity was reported for *Panchlora nivea* Linne. Dr. C. V. Riley was of the opinion that the correct name of this specimen is *P. viridis*. Riley (1890, 1891a, 1891b) obtained records of viviparity in *P. viridis* which aroused considerable interest among his contemporaries. Davis (1930) seems to have confirmed Riley's report but his specimen is *P. cubensis*. He gives cogent reasons for believing that Riley's insects were also members of this species and not *P. viridis*. Holmgren (1904) announced viviparity in *Blabera* sp., *Eutegaster* and *Oxyhaloa* but the evidence is not entirely conclusive.

Zappe (1917, 1918) and Saupe (1929) have written about *Pycnoscelus surinamensis* (L). The former has not definitely committed himself as to viviparity in the species but the latter believes this is actually the usual condition. Zappe has recently stated, in a personal communication, that the insect is oviparous in Connecticut, while Williams (1931) says it is viviparous in the Hawaiian Islands. Saupe also described an oviparous species, *Blabera fusca* Brunner, in the paper quoted above. The eggs of this insect hatch very shortly after the deposition of the oötheca. Finally, Chopard (1938) cites viviparity in roaches, no doubt summarizing the literature available to him.

LITERATURE CITED

Anonymous (1890), Chopard (1938), Davis (1930), Holmgren (1904), Riley (1890, 1891a, 1891b), Robert (1836), Saupe (1929), Williams (1931), Wood-Mason (1878), Zappe (1917, 1918).

Order Anoplura   Family Pediculidae

A very doubtful case of viviparity has been reported by Weigl (1920) in his experimental studies of a louse, probably *Pediculus corporis* de Geer, which he calls the "Fleckfieberlaus." According to his article, partly developed embryos were apparently found in the eggs passing down the oviducts. This discovery was made in fixed material that had been sectioned and stained. Further, Weigl observed that young insects were to be found after four days in cages containing females, whereas it normally requires a period of six to eight days at body temperature before hatching occurs from eggs that have been deposited by this species. From these two facts, which are unquestionably true, he draws the inference that viviparity must take place, at least occasionally.

Hase (1921) has taken exception to Weigl's conclusions, pointing out his own earlier observations on similar phenomena. Thus, while he anticipated Weigl in noting the shortened postoviposition developmental period, he contends that only oviparity has been witnessed for neither he nor Weigl has seen the actual deposition of hatched offspring. He asserts that the essential difference between oviparity and viviparity lies in prenatal or postnatal hatching of the offspring.

LITERATURE CITED

Hase (1921), Weigl (1920).

Order Plectoptera   Family Ephemeridae

It seems most remarkable that any species of this order should veer toward the viviparous habit. In so many respects the group exhibits such conservative tendencies in its morphology that this accelerated evolution in reproductive methods is worth a most searching investigation to ascertain as fully as possible by comparative means just what particular divergences from the typical oviparous condition are manifest.

In a footnote, Von Siebold (1837) incidentally mentioned the discovery of viviparity in an undetermined species of this family of insects, but it was Calori (1848) who first devoted a paper to the subject, discussing *Chloëon dipterum* and its embryogeny.

The article contained descriptions of the egg and the developing embryos, and was accompanied by several illustrations of the latter as well as of the newly born offspring. Attention was called to the relatively long aerial life of this insect, which is in marked contrast to oviparous species. His contribution was later translated into French by Joly (1877), with a few additional remarks. These two authors supposed the subimago females had mated and the offspring had developed from fertilized ova but Eaton (1883–1888) contends that probably parthenogenetic development of the eggs takes place in this species.

A second species, *Notanatolica vivipara*, was collected by Wood-Mason (1890). Upon dropping a live female caddis fly into a glass of whiskey conveniently placed before him, he was surprised to see several hundred living nymphs emerging from the vulva of the insect. The gelatinous secretion serving to bind the ova into a common mass in other species was absent in this case. No comments were made regarding the presence of ruptured choria of the eggs, and hatching may have occurred as the expelled young came in contact with the liquid. We must recognize, too, the possibility of premature hatching of the offspring caused by the muscular contractions of the maternal insect.

Causard (1896) has published an account of *Chloëopsis diptera* (Latreille) which is probably the same species that Calori called *Cloë diptera* and is now known as *Chloëon dipterum*. The lower portion of the female reproductive system consists of two large but thin-walled sacs extending forward into the thorax and posteriorly to the last two abdominal segments. They were filled with eggs showing practically all stages of development within them. These brood pouches are probably the enlarged paired oviducts, for a septum containing tracheae separates the two; however, Causard did not definitely ascertain their anatomical relationship. The reproductive systems of both sexes remain paired during their lives but he frequently observed the rupture of the female openings posteriorly at deposition and the resultant formation of a large common opening in the maternal body wall to facilitate the expulsion of the offspring. He speaks of the viviparity of this species, yet has never found hatched nymphs in the reproductive system. On the contrary, he states definitely that even the most mature embryos still lie within the egg chorion. Bernard (1907) later cleared up this point and has shown the species to be oviparous; at least the specimens studied by him laid eggs.

Shortly after Causard's paper, Heymons (1897) briefly summarized the preceding literature on viviparity in the Ephemeridae and made the interesting statement that *Chloëon dipterum* is oviparous in Berlin. He suggests the possibility of seasonal viviparity for the species farther south. Giard (1905) used this species as an example of poecilogony but Bernard's (1907) studies would seem definitely to exclude the species from the poecilogonous series. In fact, Keilin (1916) clearly refuses to accept Heymons' and Giard's contention that facultative viviparity exists at all in the species. He expresses his belief in an error of anatomical interpretation, or in identification of the specimens collected to show poecilogony of *Chloëon dipterum*.

Since Calori proclaimed viviparity in this species, Bernard (1907) is the only author who has carefully studied the anatomy of the female reproductive tract in relation to the question of viviparity. He verified the mating of the two sexes and claimed that the species is normally and constantly viviparous. According to our present definition, the insect is oviparous since it deposits eggs with unimpaired choria. To support his statement Bernard cited the following facts: The eggs in the female are approximately in the same stage of embryonic development at any given time, contrary to Calori's statements on this subject. After copulation, the male dies while the female rests on a plant until the embryos are ready to be liberated, a matter of 10 to 14 days. Oviparous species, by comparison, deposit their eggs quickly after they are fertilized and the latter require a similar length of time, 10 to 14 days, for the embryonic history after oviposition. Oviparous species immediately deposit their ova when gently pressed by one's finger, while *C. dipterum* will not do so even when subjected to rougher manipulations. The eggs of this species, when prematurely removed from the mother and placed in water, at once absorb water, burst, and the embryo is destroyed; the unlaid eggs of other species, when thus treated, remain whole and, if fertilized, continue with their development. *C. dipterum* produces not more than 600 to 700 offspring while other species deposit no less than two or three times as many eggs. These figures are interesting when considered in connection with the number of ovarioles present in the female. The species under discussion has only one egg mature in each ovariole, therefore the number of eggs ultimately produced corresponds to the number of ovarioles present. Among other species, Bernard discovered several eggs of various ages in each ovariole. Moreover, in such cases the eggs are always enclosed by thick, dense choria while the eggs of *C. dipterum* possess exceedingly thin and delicate coverings.

Using these criteria as a working hypothesis, Bernard proceeded to examine eleven species of Ephemeridae to be found in the vicinity of Leipzig. Of these, only one, *Chloëon simile,* conformed to the characters denoting viviparity. To the two species, *C. dipterum* and *simile,* which he now thought to be viviparous in reproductive habits, he added *C. dimidiatum* as a third example, based entirely on Lubbock's (1865) description of the insect. Utilizing Palmén's (1884) data he expressed the belief that seven additional species will be found to be viviparous when their method of propagation is observed. One of his observations resulted in the discovery of five chromosomes in the species which, he adds, should be of interest to the student of chromosome behavior.

More recently the subject has appeared again in observations by Needham and Murphy (1924), Needham, Traver, and Hsu (1935), Berner (1940, 1941) and Edmundo (1945). Their contributions seem to show that oviparity rather than viviparity exists in the several species considered by them, which are: *Callibaetis vivipara, C. floridanus, C. pretiosus, C. montanus,* and an unidentified species in this genus.

Considerable space has been given to the literature treating viviparity in the Ephemeridae because the question as to whether or not the species concerned are at times, or in certain localities, truly viviparous has not definitely been settled. As has been shown, several writers have spoken of the viviparous condition of *C. dipterum* yet most of them have ascertained the presence of a chorion surrounding each egg as it is deposited. It might, indeed, be this fact which caused Heymons to state so positively that *C. dipterum* is oviparous near Berlin. The differences existing among the species in the number of eggs in each ovariole, in the relative thickness of the chorion, and the amount of embryonic development in the eggs prior to deposition may be freely accepted due to the careful observations made of these anatomical facts. Nevertheless, the production of hatched offspring has not yet been conclusively shown.

LITERATURE CITED

Bernard (1907), Berner (1940, 1941), Calori (1848), Causard (1896), Eaton (1883–1888), Edmundo (1945), Giard (1905), Heymons (1897), Joly (1877), Keilin (1916), Lubbock (1865), Needham and Murphy (1924), Needham,

Traver, and Hsu (1935), Palmén (1884), Von Siebold (1837), Wood-Mason (1890).

Order Homoptera   Family Coccidae (Scale insects)

On account of the comparatively close taxonomic relationship between aphids and coccids, one should expect some of the interest displayed in the parthenogeny and viviparity of the former group to extend to the scale insects. This assumption has not been fulfilled from the viewpoint of the embryologist since only a few investigations of coccid embryology have been made. The majority of these have considered oviparous species, so viviparous forms are scantily represented in the literature. Nevertheless, references to viviparous species are very numerous, due chiefly to the casual observations of taxonomists, to whom this subject is usually incidental.

As early as 1854 Leydig observed part of the development of *Lecanium* (*Coccus*) *hesperidum* by means of whole mounts of eggs taken from the reproductive tract. He gives, especially, the appearance of the ovary, the egg, and accompanying nurse cells whose functions were misunderstood by him, and asserts the species is viviparous. The last statement contradicts Burmeister's (1836) earlier description of oviposition in this species. Leuckart (1858) came to the conclusion that Burmeister and not Leydig was correct. The publication of Leuckart's opinion closed the matter until Signoret's (1868–1876) papers appeared containing a note on viviparity in *L. hesperidum*. Subsequent writers, including Teodoro (1916, 1921), Putnam (1880), Krassilstschik (1893), and many systematists insist that viviparity is the normal type of birth in the species. Dingler (1923) and Thomsen (1927), however, have confirmed Burmeister's and Leuckart's original observations on the oviparous condition of the insect. They have described the texture of the egg chorion and the ventral cavity beneath the mother in which the eggs hatch. The apparent contradictions among these writers can perhaps be explained away by simply assuming this might be another instance of the improper expansion of the term viviparous to include the deposition of eggs containing embryos.

Attention should be called to a paper by Thomsen (1927). The cytologists have not lagged in the study of the Coccidae, as have the embryologists. Thomsen's investigations cast serious doubts on the earlier report by Moniez (1887) who believed he had found the male of *L. hesperidum* permanently enclosed within the female reproductive system. Thomsen has furnished adequate cytological evidence to show the existence of two distinct races of this species: one a parthenogenetic race, the other a race in which both males and females are present but in which parthenogenesis may occur when fertilization is lacking. In justice to Teodoro (1916, p. 150) attention should be directed to his discussion of this subject and summary of the observations of others. He has never detected either the male of this species or spermatozoa in the female reproductive system. Schrader (1929) believes the same condition exists in *A. hederae,* a species which will be considered in the following paragraph. A paper by Poluszyński (1911) treating viviparous coccids should be included in our discussion but a copy of it could not be found in the United States.

A second species whose viviparous condition has repeatedly been cited is *Aspidiotus hederae* (*A. nerii* Bche). Metschnikoff (1866a, 1866b) described the germinal vesicle which had remained invisible to Claus (1864) in the latter's earlier study of the ovary and egg formation. He briefly outlined the formation of the blastoderm, the embryonic rudiment, the delicate amnion, the invagination of the germ band, the development of the limbs, and the origin and distribution of mycetoblasts. Of particular interest is his speculation whether a mid-intestine is present. The entire development was found to be similar to that of aphids. While raising no special point regarding the oviparity or viviparity of the insect, he seems to assign them to the former class (1866b, pp. 468, 473).

Brandt (1869) described the invaginated embryo, katatrepsis or rotation, and the rupture of the amnion. Krassilstschik (1893) considered the structure of the ovary, its contents, fertilization of the ovum, and the position of the developing embryo in the ovariole. Breest (1914) confined himself largely to the problem of the behavior of the symbionts and their migrations. Teodoro (1916, 1921) furnished a brief account of the formation of the early embryo up to the appearance of the mesoderm. Unfortunately for our purpose, the developmental histories of several oviparous species were combined with that of *A. hederae* and given in very general terms. He assures the reader, however, that variations in the different embryogenies would be only slight. With this reservation in mind, since no one has definitely shown *A. hederae* to be other than viviparous as claimed, a short outline of the available knowledge of its embryology will be given.

Female Reproductive System

No observer has supplied a satisfactory description of the reproductive system of *Aspidiotus hederae,* but Krassilstschik (1893) included a few remarks on the ovary and its connection with the paired oviduct.

The Ovary.—This organ consists of short pyriform or ovate ovarioles scattered over the haemocoelar surface of the paired oviduct. The upper portion of the ovariole is the germarium, lined with a single epithelial layer, which continues into the calyx stalk and joins a similar layer in the oviduct. The relative sizes of germarium and vitellarium (calyx) vary, the former being large when young ova are within its lumen but very reduced in dimensions and inconspicuous after the egg has passed into the lower portion of the ovariole. Likewise, the vitellaria differ in size depending upon the relative ages of the developing embryos within them, for, as in the aphids, embryogeny occurs in the ovariole and the ducts below serve mainly as conduction paths for the upward migration of spermatozoa and for the unhindered extrusion of the offspring.

Egg Formation.—The germarium is said to contain four large cells, the lower one being the young oöcyte while the superior three are, without doubt, large nurse cells. Their presence greatly distends the germarium and the ovariole thus becomes somewhat pyriform. The oöcyte obtains its nutriment largely, if not entirely, from the nurse cells for they are undergoing dissolution stages while the egg progresses toward maturity. It is probable that the epithelium also contributes yolk to the nurse cells, or directly to the oöcyte, for its cells become highly vacuolated. As the oöcyte enlarges it drops down to the calyx stalk where, surrounded except at the upper end by follicular epithelium, it becomes a mature ovum. When this state is attained the epithelium covers its anterior end as well and all communication with the germarium ceases. The fully developed ovum is eventually enclosed by a chorion secreted from the follicular epithelium. At this time it measures 150 microns in length and 60 microns in width.

Symbiont Invasion.—Some time before the chorion is laid down, symbiotic microorganisms find their way into the anterior end of the growing yolk mass. In fact, it is probable that they are carried in with the yolk as it accumulates (Fig. 10C). No definite mycetom is formed in *A. hederae,* the fat cells being, in part, converted into mycetocytes. These are scattered throughout the haemocoele wherever fat bodies form. It seems most likely that only a few symbionts are introduced into the young egg but they are believed to multiply as they become distributed in the embryonic body.

Development of the Embryo

It has already been stated that the embryological observations on *A. hederae* are meager and so generalized as to fit several species equally well. Several contributors also have called attention to the similarity of the coccid embryogeny to that of the aphids. For these reasons the following observations will be brief and will mainly call attention to certain known features which differ specifically from the aphid, whose history is presented in another chapter.

Fertilization.—Krassilstschik (1893) observed a clump of spermatozoa immediately below the lower end of the egg and its covering of follicular cells as the ovum approaches maturity. At least one spermatozoon penetrates to the ovum in such a case and fertilization takes place. The details of this process are lacking.

Cleavage and Blastoderm Formation.—Cleavage apparently occurs with considerable rapidity, for a blastoderm seems to form quickly. Cleavage nuclei are stellate and their cytoplasmic extensions are frequently seen to anastomose. Most of them migrate to the surface of the egg where they continue to multiply by tangential mitoses. From the first, each blastomere is sharply delimited and no syncytial condition exists in the blastodermic area. The remaining nuclei, left within the egg, function as vitellophags. The completed blastoderm extends as an uninterrupted sheet of cells over the egg immediately beneath the chorion. No signs of the blastopore, such as will be described for aphids, appear here.

Anatrepsis and Formation of the Ventral Plate.—The ventral blastodermic cells near the posterior pole of the egg become somewhat elongate and increase their numbers by mitoses. At the same time this area tends to flatten and invaginate into the yolk. This marks the initial step in ventral plate formation and is accompanied by anatrepsis as the developing embryonic rudiment becomes immersed in the yolk. The ventral plate grows in length, not only by invagination of the original blastodermal cells of this region but by active proliferation of new cells (Fig. 9). Anatrepsis, of course, results in the reversed orientation of the embryo experiencing this process, so here we find the anterior end of the ventral plate in a superficial position near the posterior pole

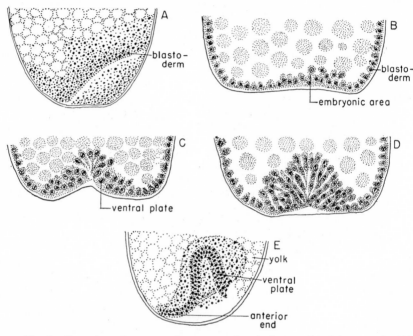

Fig. 9.—*Lecanium oleae,* an oviparous species similar to the viviparous *Aspidiotus hederae* in these stages. *A,* rudiment of ventral plate forming from thickened blastoderm at posterior pole of egg; beginning of invagination. *B, C, D, Pulvinaria vitis,* used similarly. Sections of margin, near center and at center of ventral plate rudiment. *E. Lecanium oleae,* ventral plate invaginating, blastoderm and early serosa omitted from first and last figures. (After Teodoro, Redia., **11**.)

while the more posterior portions are forming at the immersed end. Three sagittal views of different parts of the posterior end of the egg reveal the early conditions under which invagination begins. As the embryo continues elongating it assumes the typical hemipteran curvature but with less sharply defined angles. The cephalic portion is gently curved dorsally while the posterior end flexes ventrally (Fig. 10). Since the invagination resembles a cylindrical sheet of cells all portions of it are contiguous and the margins merge into the exterior blastoderm. The ventral

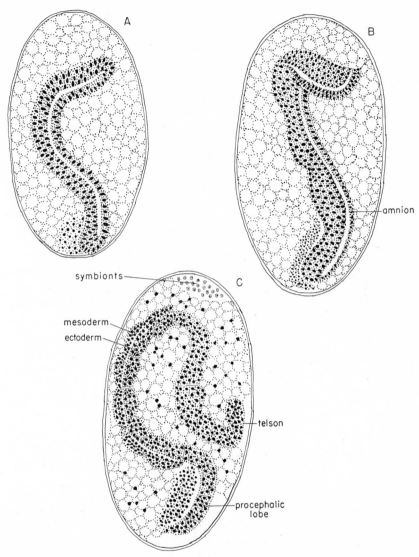

Fig. 10.—*Lecanium oleae.* Used to illustrate similar embryos of *Aspidiotus hederae.* *A,* invaginated germ band with amnion. *B,* characteristic curvature of germ band beginning, amnion thinning. *C,* anatrepsis complete. Procephalic lobes, mesoderm, and metameres largely formed; serosa omitted, as is also the amnion from the last figure. (After Teodoro, Redia., 11.)

plate arises as a narrow band along one side and the rest of the invaginated cells form the amnion. The blastoderm, still on the surface of the egg, becomes the serosa. The amnion thins out into a very delicate membrane, often difficult to see. The cells of the ventral plate behave differently. They become tall, columnar cells, with the nuclei disposed at different levels within them. Nothing definite can be given for the later stages of development.

It is unfortunate for our purposes that Teodoro (1916) employed no illustrations of *A. hederae*. Because he stresses the morphological similarity of all the specimens treated by him, his figures of certain stages of the oviparous species must suffice.

Order Homoptera   Family Coccidae (Mealybugs)

As was the case for the scale insects, the mealybugs, too, have frequently been reported as viviparous. These cases have not been recorded here, for no developmental data were found regarding them. As examples of the nature of some observations, however, attention may be directed to the more careful investigations of the entomological staff at the experiment station of the Hawaiian Sugar Planters' Association. Two species of mealybugs previously recorded elsewhere as being viviparous are *Trionymus sacchari* (Ckll) and *Pseudococcus brevipes* (Ckll). Williams (1931, pp. 112, 114) in speaking of them in the Hawaiian Islands, says they are oviparous but they hatch quickly, the eggs of the first species appearing at approximately 12-minute intervals and hatching 15 to 30 minutes after deposition. Of course, it is possible some insects are oviparous in one locality and viviparous in another but such conflicting records point out the need for further information on mealybugs.

Rau (1937) has reported viviparity in *Pseudococcus cuspidatae* Rau. Since this species can be reared readily or found in the field it may provide a convenient source of material for the embryological study of this group.

LITERATURE CITED

Brandt (1869), Breest (1914), Burmeister (1836), Claus (1864), Dingler (1923), Krassilstschik (1893), Leuckart (1858), Leydig (1854), Metschnikoff (1866a, 1866b), Moniez (1887), Poluszyński (1911), Putnam (1880), Rau (1937), Schrader (1929), Signoret (1868–1876), Teodoro (1916, 1921), Thomsen (1927), Williams (1931).

Order Lepidoptera   Families Tineidae, Pieridae

It is probable that several species of insects in this order reproduce viviparously, yet no one, apparently, has investigated their embryogeny. Scott (1863) captured a number of moths in New South Wales representing some undetermined species of the genus *Tinea*. When gently pressed between the fingers or upon being attached to corks the females immediately deposited larvae which actively sought food or shelter. Stainton (1863) exhibited Scott's specimens, using the name of *Tinea vivipara* given it by the latter, when reporting the discovery to the London Entomological Society. Nineteen years later, Müller (1882) collected a tineid moth in Brazil and forwarded it to the same Society, where Mr. R. Meldola described the circumstances under which it had proved to be larviparous. Müller's experience with it was similar to Scott's, and possibly both collected the same species of insect.

Still more recently Kusnezov (1908, 1910) first expressed his belief in the ultimate discovery of viviparity in species of the genus *Colias*, an opinion based upon anatomical evidence found in the adult females. He was more firmly convinced of this possibility, and so expressed himself, in his second paper. During the two-year interim between his papers he had carefully examined a very large number of Danaid Lepidoptera, in fact nearly all of the species inhabiting the palearctic region in which he resided. The female insects possess an enlarged common oviduct, even in the non-pregnant individuals, which corresponds to a brood sac or incubator pouch. Shortly after killing the specimens they were cleared in potassium hydroxide and stained in Congo red. Fully developed larvae bearing a complete cuticula and setae were found in the brood sac without any chorionic covering. Kusnezov states that the technique would not destroy the chorion usually present around eggs of this group of insects and that it is not probable that it could be absorbed by adjacent maternal tissues in the interval prior to their preparation for examination. Against this evidence for viviparity he frankly suggests the possibility of uterine development of the embryos after the mothers had been killed. Kusnezov maintains that this exhibition of viviparity is most likely produced by the influence of climate and is an expression of facultative viviparity by normally oviparous species. A list of the apparently viviparous species follows:

Colias palaeno L.

Colias nastes Boisd., subsp. werdandi
   Zett.

Colias nastes Boisd., subsp. melinos
   Eversm.

Colias phicomone Esp.

Colias erate Esp., subsp. polyogra-
phus Motsch.
Colias standingeri Alph.
Colias standingeri Alph., f. pamira Gr.
Gr.
Colias eogene Feld.
Colias eogene Feld., f. arida Alph.
Colias thisoa Mén.
Colias viluiensis Mén.
Colias hecla Lef.
Colias hyperboreus Gr. Gr.
Colias fieldi Mén.
Colias croceus Fourcr.
Colias aurora Esp., f. chloë Eversm.

Colias aurorinus Herr.-Schäff.
Colias aurorinus Herr.-Schäff., subsp.
heldreichi Stand.
Colias sagartius Led.
Colias wiskotti Stand., f. marcopopo
Gr. Gr.
Euchloë belemia Esp.
Euchloë belia Cram.
Euchloë belia Cram., f. ausonia Hübn.
Euchloë belia Cram., f. simplonia Frr.
Euchloë bieti Obth.
Euchloë tomyris Chr.
Euchloë grenuri Herr.-Schäff.
Zegris eupheme Esp.
Leptidia amurensis Mén.

The conclusions of Kusnezov regarding the viviparity of several Pieridae were quickly substantiated by Pierce (1911) but here, again, the viviparous condition is not proved beyond question. Pierce encountered a single fully developed larva in the brood sac of a female *Colias edusa*. It lay in the characteristic bent position, with the head and the tip of the abdomen touching, that was previously described by Kusnezov (1910). Two females of another species, *Parnassius apollo*, each contained a single larva in the brood sac, while two others showed only eggs within the same space. Klots (1935) has, in part, verified the probable viviparity of *Colias hecla*, a possibility suggested by Kusnezov, by reporting the discovery of a single larva in the enlarged oviduct of a female dissected by him.

LITERATURE CITED

Klots (1935), Kusnezov (1908, 1910), Müller (1882), Pierce (1911), Scott (1863), Stainton (1863).

Order Diptera   Families Sarcophagidae, Tachinidae, etc.

Ovoviviparity is a very common occurrence among the muscoid flies and is not unknown in other species of Diptera. Apparently the earliest accounts of larviparity are from Redi (1668) and Lister (1671) who observed the presence of larvae in the brood pouches (distended uteri) of dissected female flies, probably of the family Sarcophagidae. Lister suggested that Aldrovandi may have been aware of this condition also and predicted that other related species of flies may bear their young similarly.

Redi made numerous observations on the larviparous habits of coprophagous flies during the course of his classical experiments on spontaneous generation. He refers to the earlier observations on larviparity by Scaliger, whose experience was somewhat similar to that of Lister mentioned above. Since then various contributors have enlarged the list and, with more recent taxonomic facilities, have provided specific names in many instances. Of these observers we need mention a few, as Von Siebold (1837), Robineau-Desvoidy (1850, 1855), Lockwood (1873), Collinge (1906), Schmitz (1910), Townsend (1911b), Muir (1912), Awati (1918), and Uvarov (1928) who lists 46 species of Sarcophagidae and seven species of Tachinidae which appear to be larviparous.

It was not long before a more fundamental kind of investigation, the anatomical study of the female genital systems, was introduced to ascertain why eggs were retained by certain species while others promptly deposited their ova. Contributors to this field, in carrying on their studies, have often added materially to the list of viviparous Diptera. Among these workers Von Siebold (1838) was perhaps the first to discover that tachinids with long uteri were viviparous while those with shorter, saclike uteri were oviparous. Also, the writings of Dufour (1851) and Portchinski (1885, 1891, 1910) have been made even more valuable to us through the translations, comments, and comparative studies of Osten-Sacken (1887) and Townsend (1911a). In addition, there are the contributions of Marchand (1896), Holmgren (1904), Cholodkovsky (1907, 1908), Pantel (1910, 1913), Patton and Cragg (1913), Baer (1920), and Townsend (1908, 1911b, 1934a, 1934b). Portchinski, Pantel, and Townsend, especially, have continued the comparative study of the reproductive systems of Diptera.

Keilin (1916) reviewed the observations of several recent investigators of viviparity in Diptera, summarized the divergent views pertaining to the different types of viviparity and discussed the applicability of fundamental environmental influences which possibly govern this method of reproduction. Parker (1922) expressed the opinion that paedogenesis may occur in *Calliphora erythrocephala* Meigen, while Lowne (1895), Keilin (1916), Hall (1932), and Parker observed occasional viviparity in this species. Verhein (1921) has furnished a very detailed account of the cytology and ovogenesis of *Sarcophaga carnaria*.

Nevertheless, the whole field is unexplored, even though Cholodkovsky, Portchinski, Pantel, and Townsend have uncovered apparently fruitful sources of investigation for us and have shown the importance of seeking some knowledge of the embryogenies of these species. Prell (1915) and Townsend (1934) have called attention to the fact that one may find eggs representing all stages of embryological development in the uterus of a single gravid female of some species. Portchinski (1885) discovered that *Dasyphora pratorum* gives birth to single larvae instead of several together. Further, the larva reaches its third stage before birth and feeds outside the maternal body only a short time before pupation. Another species, apparently indistinguishable in external appearance from *Musca corvina*, since it was at first thus classified by Portchinski, has since been renamed *M. larvipara* by him. He also states it is the viviparous species and not *corvina*, with which Awati agrees (1920). Its larva is also born in the third stage of development while the second stage seems to be passed in the egg. Johnston and Bancroft (1920) cite *Musca australis* and *M. humilis* (*vetustissima*) as depositing second-stage larvae with intervals between each birth. Portchinski (1885), Pantel (1913), and Townsend (1934a, pp. 124, 144) express the opinion that at least some species of the genera *Dasyphora*, *Viviparomusca*, *Mesembrinella*, and *Eurychaeta*, secrete nutrients into the uterus from the accessory glands, or uterine cells, to further embryonic growth of their offspring. Such observations are rich in their suggested research potentialities and if some of these conditions are later proved true the insects involved must be transferred to other types of viviparity.

It has been found to be quite impossible to furnish a satisfactory list of the ovoviviparous Diptera, for so many citations were made without regard to the presence of an egg chorion, or whether the embryo really had hatched before birth. In many instances larviparity is claimed for a species whose offspring are distinguishable through the chorion yet not fully developed or ready to hatch before oviposition takes place. Such a species, of course, is not viviparous.

However, to assist those seeking further information on this subject the following limited number of citations of viviparous Diptera will be furnished: Portchinski (1885) lists *Mesembrina meridiana*, *M. mystacea*, and *Rhinoestrus purpureus*, while Cholodkovsky (1908) includes the genus *Sarcophaga*. Dufour (1851) cites the genus *Cephalemia* in the Oestridae and *Pycnosoma patorium*. Townsend (1934) gives many examples, including *Spilogaster divisa* and *Hylemyia strigosa*. Keilin (1916) reports that others have found viviparity in some Anthomyidae, *Hylem-*

yia variata and *Theria muscaria*. Aldrich (1932) described two new species, one a calliphorid named *Mesembrinella formosa,* the other an anthomyid called *Chortinus bequaerti*. Both were collected by Professor J. Bequaert who, in a personal communication, states they are viviparous. The most extensive listing is that of Pantel (1910) who includes many viviparous species of Tachinidae and Sarcophagidae in his Groups III, VII, VIII, and IX. Marchand (1896) lists *Echinomyia fera* as viviparous, and an interesting parasite of considerable economic importance, *Compsilura concinnata,* is said to be larviparous. Patton and Cragg (1913) discovered larviparity in *Musca bezzi* while the viviparity of *Oestrus ovis* is widely quoted. Mani (1934) observed a most unusual case, which he terms ovoviviparous, in a gall midge which, if possible, should be thoroughly investigated embryologically.

While citations of viviparity in Diptera are very numerous, and while it is undoubtedly true that many species do produce living young, it seems the embryological development of none has been studied. Perhaps two serious difficulties inherent in this task have deterred students who have turned, instead, to other problems. The two obstacles are: (1) the extreme rapidity with which dipteran embryos pass through their history in the egg, making it a formidable task to obtain a complete series of stages; (2) the very specialized and early development of the primordia of older tissues and organs in the young embryo or larva. Primordia not only appear chronologically long before they are functional but they also usually arise as inverted parts which must evert or unfold later in order to function. These conditions complicate the study of embryological details. Without doubt this fertile and difficult field of investigation will yield to the patient and careful efforts of students yet to come.

LITERATURE CITED

Aldrich (1932), Awati (1918, 1920), Baer (1920), Cholodkovsky (1907, 1908), Collinge (1906), Dufour (1851), Hall (1932), Holmgren (1904), Johnston and Bancroft (1920), Keilin (1916), Lister (1671), Lockwood (1873), Lowne (1895), Mani (1934), Marchand (1896), Muir (1912), Osten-Sacken (1887), Pantel (1910, 1913), Parker (1922), Patton and Cragg (1913), Portchinski (1885, 1891, 1910), Prell (1915), Redi (1668), Robineau-Desvoidy (1850, 1855), Schmitz (1910), Von Siebold (1837, 1838), Townsend (1908, 1911a, 1911b, 1934a, 1934b), Uvarov (1928), Verhein (1921).

Chapter 6

OVOVIVIPARITY—COLEOPTERA, HYMENOPTERA

Though Coleoptera are considered to be remarkably conservative in their methods of reproduction, three families may possess viviparity. The Micromalthidae show paedogenesis, larviparity, and cyclic alternations of reproductives. In these respects they resemble *Miastor*. A few species of Staphylinidae also appear to be viviparous, but nothing is known of the embryology of the species provisionally classed as ovoviviparous. Several species of Chrysomelidae are likewise ovoviviparous and some embryological data are available. Only a historical treatment of the single reported case of viviparity in Hymenoptera can be given at present.

Order Coleoptera   Family Micromalthidae

One species of this order, *Micromalthus debilis* Leconte, appears to have an embryonic history belonging to the ovoviviparous type. This species is the only known representative of the Micromalthidae and de Peyerimhoff (1913, 1933) has discussed and placed it in the first suborder, Archostemata, since, except for the Cupedidae, it appears to be one of the most primitive of the coleopterous families. Its method of reproduction has been outlined in part by Barber (1913a, 1913b) but none of the embryonic development has so far been published. The remarkable life history of the insect includes oviparous imaginal stages as well as paedogenetic oviparous and paedogenetic viviparous larvae.

In tracing the sequence of the various stages of the life history, as presented by Barber, we may most advantageously start with the paedogenetic larval form, in which it follows either one of two possible methods of reproduction. First, it develops within its body, and finally deposits a single, very large egg that hatches into a curculioid * first-stage larva which grows and molts

---

* Variations in the spelling of the following words appear in the literature: *amphiterotokous, arrhenotokous, caraboid, cerambicoid, curculioid, metrophagous, phytophagous, thelyotokous.*

to become a metrophagous larva. This larva transforms into a prepupal and later into a pupal stage. Upon emergence it is always an adult male individual. Second, the original paedogenetic larval form with which we started, or one apparently like it, may develop within its body several larval offspring which, upon emergence, appear as viviparous caraboid larvae. These larvae molt to become cerambicoid second- and, later, third-stage larvae. Some of these cerambicoid larvae develop into typical paedogenetic larval forms and are capable of repeating either of the two cycles. Others lose or do not have paedogenetic capacity, change to pupae, and eventually emerge as adult females. It is suspected by Barber that the imagoes mate and eggs are deposited which, in time, give rise to third-stage cerambicoid larvae, whose future possibilities of development along either of two lines have just been given in the two sentences immediately preceding. However, Barber had not yet obtained the sexual products of the adult females to prove this point at the time he reported these extraordinary series of cycles, though he had frequently observed copulation of the sexually mature adults.

Two more recent papers by Scott (1936, 1938) and one by Pringle (1938) have contributed further to the general knowledge of this insect, part of which knowledge is applicable here. In the first article by Scott, the essential fact established is the haploid condition of the male offspring of the paedogenetic, oviparous larva. The second paper describes very briefly the different forms, their reproductive organs, and the kind of offspring produced by each. These are imaginal males and females and, in addition, three paedogenetic larval reproductive forms.

The adult male was never observed in copulation although ample opportunity was thought to be furnished in order to obtain the bisexual products, if possible. The adult female was observed to possess large ovaries in the early pupal stage, but these organs suffered considerable degeneration of their anterior portions as the insect continued its metamorphosis. The mature female has two ovaries, each containing one or, occasionally, two immature ova with their accompanying nurse cells, oviducts, common oviduct, uterus, vagina, and spermatheca. It is believed this form is sterile.

The larval paedogenetic reproductives are indistinguishable in early stages but are easily recognized in the last or, often, in their penultimate instars. Of these the thelyotokous larva is considered the principal reproductive form. It produces from 4 to

20, or more, larvae of the female sex; these are born viviparously. Each embryo develops to the larval condition in a follicle, apparently in the vitellarium. The ovarioles are attached to "a common, short duct which leads to the outside. . . . There is no uterus, vagina, or spermatheca. The offspring devour their mother before changing to a phytophagous diet" (Scott, 1938). The arrhenotokous paedogenetic larva is normally oviparous, only one of the few relatively large ova being deposited with a more or less developed embryo within. The egg adheres to the parental body until hatching liberates the offspring, which is a male (haploid) larva. The latter attacks and entirely consumes the mother and the other ova in about a week. In case the offspring is lost the mother may subsequently produce thelyotokous larvae viviparously, thus becoming a paedogenetic larva of the next type to be presented. The haploid, parthenogenetic eggs are very much larger than those of the diploid, female-producing type, hence sexual dimorphism extends to this stage. Paired and common oviducts are present in the mother larva, but no spermatheca appears.

The amphiterotokous paedogenetic larva is a type segregated as distinct by Scott but one which Barber (1913) had earlier thought to be larvae perhaps incapable of reproduction. Large, male-producing ova mature but for some unknown cause are either not deposited or, if laid, have failed to hatch. At any rate, the development of a few smaller ova follows the maturing of the large ones, and from them larvae, apparently of the thelyotokous type, are born viviparously. This form likewise possesses paired and common oviducts. From Barber's description it is difficult to discriminate between this and the preceding type, especially since he stresses the effects of environmental influences upon the production of offspring. He suggests the necessity for an experimental approach to a fuller understanding of the life history of this species.

Scott's (1938) paper seems to show that reproduction in these insect forms follows a paedogenetic parthenogenesis in the larval mothers and that haploidy is the male condition. The eggs and larvae develop in large follicles within the vitellaria of the ovarioles and the products, large ova containing male embryos or the viviparously produced female larvae, are deposited through genital ducts opening outside the body. Apparently only one larval form is the source of male offspring, while all may produce female larval offspring. The evidence, however, seems to assign this species to the ovoviviparous type of development.

LITERATURE CITED

Barber (1913a, 1913b), de Peyerimhoff (1913, 1933), Pringle (1938), Scott (1936, 1938).

Order Coleoptera   Family Staphylinidae

Although the species in this family are very numerous, widespread, and in some cases quite specialized in certain habits, few of them have been reported as being ovoviviparous. Schiödte (1853) reported the presence of embryos in the eggs contained within one insect's reproductive system, and expressed the opinion that the termitophilous staphylinid species *Corotoca melantho, C. phylo,* and *Spirachtha eurymedusa* are viviparous. Dissections of adults were continued, and later, fully developed larvae were found in females of the first genus and several somewhat younger stages in the second (Schiödte, 1856). In these papers he is decidedly of the opinion that the three species are truly viviparous. His discovery remains to be confirmed by others and at present there are no data to indicate which type of viviparity might be involved. Until this information is available the species concerned have been tentatively included in the ovoviviparous group.

Lomechusa strumosa and *Atemeles pubicollis* var. *truncicoloides* are two species belonging to the myrmecophilous Staphylinidae which should be mentioned as possibly being ovoviviparous. Whether they truly are viviparous at all is open to serious doubt but since so much controversy has arisen concerning them a short historical account of the present status of the question seems justified. In 1888 Wasmann described in detail the supposed egg of *Lomechusa,* but two years later corrected his statements by admitting that he had formerly portrayed the appearance of a parthenogenetic ant egg. In 1895 the same thing happened, but this time the described egg was found to have been deposited by a worker ant. Nevertheless, Wasmann became convinced of the viviparous condition of the species and published his views on the matter, though references to these have been omitted here. Finally he summarized his data in two rather long papers (Wasmann, 1915a, 1915b) which, he insisted, were the result of constant and painstaking observations of the insects. *Lomechusa* must be definitely viviparous, he said, but *Atemeles* is either viviparous or lays eggs which hatch very quickly after deposition (Wasmann's ovoviviparity). The evidence presented by him is purely circumstantial, since he found no deposition of either eggs or larvae by these two species of insects and could not show how larvae constantly appeared in his formicarium.

For some reason, perhaps because of the lack of conclusive data to support him, Wasmann's earliest statements regarding viviparity in these insects at once divided a number of investigators into two groups with opposing viewpoints. Among those who unhesitatingly accepted his deductions was Donisthorpe (1909, 1916, 1926), who unfortunately seemed to have lost an excellent opportunity of witnessing the deposition of offspring and thus settling the question. Of the group who refused to accept Wasmann's contention we shall mention only Jordan (1913), who had somewhat the same experience as Donisthorpe. Jordan had actually observed deposition by a female in a secluded position and was personally convinced that an egg had been laid. In attempting to remove it from the formicarium for more careful scrutiny it was dropped and irretrievably lost. But he pursued his investigations further by carefully examining the uterine eggs. No embryos were found in them. Apparently Wasmann had not observed development in uterine eggs, for his illustrations include no sections of ovarian eggs with signs of embryos in them.

LITERATURE CITED

Donisthorpe (1909, 1916, 1926), Jordan (1913), Schiödte (1853, 1856), Wasmann (1915a, 1915b).

Order Coleoptera   Family Chrysomelidae

A few species of Chrysomelidae have caused conflicting statements in the literature regarding their method of reproduction, fortunately without the deplorable partisanship and contention displayed over *Lomechusa* and *Atemeles* among the Staphylinidae. It is quite possible that all of the observers of Chrysomelidae are correct in their statements for apparently actual hatching of the eggs often takes place just prior to deposition or immediately afterwards. Some observers have spoken of the viviparity of a certain species when the offspring have been deposited with the chorion still surrounding them; others have called this condition ovoviviparity, while a few have correctly designated it as oviparity. The eggs differ from those of other oviparous species only in the relative growth or development of their contents. They are still eggs and not the hatched product of eggs if the choria enclose them. The following historical chronological summary will reveal the differences in interpretation as far as the Coleoptera are concerned. The reader may note at once that the names of the species have been given in this discussion according to the usage employed by the various writers concerned. The synonymy is clarified in Table 7.

Perroud (1855) announced the probable existence of viviparity in *Oreina speciosa* and *O. superba* following his dissections of the adult insects and discovery of hatched larvae in the reproductive tract. This statement appeared between the two papers by Schiödte and ranks with the latter in being the earliest published records of viviparity in the Coleoptera. But in spite of his observations and published report on these dissected larvae, Perroud personally remained in doubt whether the species were truly viviparous or oviparous in nature.

The next writer introduces the confusion just referred to with regard to the use of the terms viviparity and oviparity. Rupertsberger (1870) described the production of offspring in *Chrysomela varians*. He states that this species lays no eggs but brings forth living young, and then adds the observation that a chorion or egg shell covers the offspring from which it frees itself in a very short time.

Bleuze (1874) published notes regarding ovoviviparity in *Chrysomela venusta* which were reprinted not only in France but also in Germany and England. Apparently his paper received wider attention than that of the original discoverer of viviparity in the family. Mayet (1874) tactfully commented upon Bleuze's paper and viviparity in other Coleoptera, at the same time calling attention to Perroud's original articles. Bleuze, however, was the first, apparently, to witness the actual deposition of living, hatched offspring for he says they laid no eggs but gave direct birth to larvae. His description of larviposition agrees closely with the subsequent accounts of oviposition in related species.

By watching the females of *Orina alpestris* var. *polymorpha*, Weise (1885) determined that a fully developed larva, enclosed in a chorion or egg shell, was deposited by them. He quite correctly viewed this product as equivalent to an egg, therefore the insect is oviparous, irrespective of the degree of maturity of the contents of the egg.

Hacker (1888) noticed some eggs that had been deposited by *Chrysomela varians,* but in inserting the leaf to which they adhered among fresh leaves they were crushed and failed to develop further. These were the only eggs he found from this species and all subsequent depositions consisted of free larvae, or true viviparity. It may well have been the case that the eggs recovered by him at first were sterile, or undeveloped fertile ones. This question Hacker did not answer, but he did express the thought that possibly the insect was sometimes oviparous and at other times viviparous. Thus he suggested facultative viviparity might be the rule for this species.

The following year Calloni (1889) collected a number of *Oreina speciosissima* adults and placed them in a small box. Upon his return home next day he discovered that ten larvae were also present in the container. Careful examination of the box revealed no evidence of the choria of eggs and it was assumed from this that uterine hatching must have occurred before birth of the offspring.

Chapman (1900) displayed a collection of *Orina* of various species at the meetings of the Entomological Society in London with the remark that some were oviparous while others were viviparous. In the same year Schenkling (1900) narrated some observations in the life history of *Chrysomela varians.* According to him, larviposition occurs on the plant leaf to which the offspring is at once firmly attached to assist in parturition. Larviposition seems to take place on two successive days, with none on the third day. Four larvae are born on each of the active days of deposition throughout the reproductive life of the mother insect until September and the estimated total number of offspring for the season is one hundred.

A most interesting account of larviposition was given by Champion and Chapman (1901) in discussing *Orina vittigera.* This event was observed several times and, invariably, free larvae were born. The results tend to confirm the records of viviparity in the species discussed by others and one must, in this case at least, be convinced that no mistake in the observations has been made. The additional comments regarding the production of offspring furnish undoubted proof of their accurate records, for Champion and Chapman remark that upon "one occasion the young larva seemed accompanied by a shred of membrane that attached it to the leaf. Another larva apparently had to free its legs from some membranous matter." Their further work will be referred to later but here we only make note of the first critical, thoroughly reliable, and detailed record of viviparity in the Chrysomelidae. Champion and Chapman also believe that *Orina cacaliae* and *O. gloriosa* are viviparous. This seems also to be true for *C. polymorpha* (Vetter, 1937).

Holmgren (1904) noted the apparent viviparity of *Chrysomela hyperici* which, he claimed, was a new addition to the list of viviparous insects. Later the identity of these specimens with *Chrysomela varians* Schaller was made (Rethfeldt, 1924). But in the meantime his student, Strindberg (1913), had contributed a valuable comparative study of the embryology of oviparous insects representing the orders Isoptera, Hymenoptera, and Coleoptera. The subject of the last order was *C. hyperici,* a name now considered to be a synonym of *C. varians* Schaller.

Further evidence of viviparity has come from Williams (1914), who watched the females of *Phytodecta viminalis* in larviposition. In addition to these observations he, like Perroud, dissected the reproductive organs from adult beetles and found hatched larvae in the oviduct. Williams then refers to a paper by Cornelius (1857) who had seen this same species oviposit. He, too, holds the view that *P. viminalis* may at different times be either oviparous or viviparous. According to Notman (1921), two related species, *P. affinis* and *P. pallidus* are oviparous in America, but the larvae may hatch within five minutes after oviposition. Notman surmises that these species also may be occasionally viviparous. Chapman (1903) believes both methods of reproduction are possible in *Orina tristis.*

Chrysomela varians again became an object of study, this time by Rethfeldt (1924) who found that the specimens he studied were oviparous, for a delicate chorion surrounded the larva at birth. Nevertheless he called them ovoviviparous. The paper is devoted to the embryogeny of this form and to theories of the evolution of viviparity in Chrysomelidae.

Barnes (1925) confined a female *Chrysocloa gloriosa* in a vial and found that within a few days she had deposited 12 living larvae. The beetle was 9.5 mm. in length but each of the offspring, due to air inflation, varied from 2 to 4 mm. Their total bulk was considerably greater than that of the parent. On the other hand, the mother's dry weight was 0.095 gram and the combined dry weight of the offspring was approximately half or 0.05 gram. Maneval (1938) claims *C. viridis* is also viviparous.

Henneberg (1927) wrote an article treating the oviparity of *Phytodecta rufipes*, whose offspring are enclosed in choria which rupture shortly after deposition. Most of his attention is centered upon the biological significance of the deposition of eggs containing fully developed larvae within them and the probable influences operating to bring about such a condition. His arguments and conclusions are very similar to those in an earlier paper prepared by Rethfeldt, though briefer. Presumably he had not seen Williams' (1914) paper for he predicts that *Phytodecta viminalis* L. will prove to be viviparous when it is examined carefully.

There are several possible explanations which would tend to harmonize the conflicting observations regarding viviparity or oviparity in these species; two of them seem to be worth mentioning. One is the probability that at least some of these species express a degree of facultative viviparity; that is, under certain environmental conditions the young are deposited slightly earlier and in the form of an egg with the chorion still intact around the contained larva. At other times, or under different circumstances, the eggs hatch within the maternal reproductive system and larvae are deposited. In many cases it seems to occur through a few minutes' delay in depositing the offspring by the mother.

The second possibility is that of confusion of species. The Chrysomelidae have always been a difficult group for the taxonomist, especially in earlier days, because of the different color phases of the members of some of the species. This was not recognized at first but, more recently, reliance is placed upon fundamental and stable characters. Table 7 lists the species as designated by the authors already mentioned, the present accepted name, and the name of the writer who declared each species to be viviparous or oviparous according to our definitions of these terms. The synonymy, except for the genus *Phytodecta*, was checked in the *Coleoptorum Catalogus* published by W. Junk, Berlin.

This brief survey does not exhaust the citations of viviparity that have occurred in the literature on Chrysomelidae but it does include most of the direct observations by various investigators and is sufficiently extensive to impress one with the great differences obtainable by the casual records of insects that possess

TABLE 7

SUMMARY OF THE LITERATURE REVIEWED SHOWING NAMES OF THE CHRYSOMELIDAE DISCUSSED, THEIR PRESENT NAMES AND THE NATURE OF THEIR BIRTH PRODUCTS ACCORDING TO VARIOUS AUTHORS

SPECIES NAMES AS CITED IN THE LITERATURE REVIEWED	PRESENT NAME OF SPECIES	OFFSPRING AT BIRTH ENCLOSED IN CHORION	OFFSPRING AT BIRTH NOT ENCLOSED IN CHORION
Orina alpestris Schumm.	Chrysochloa alpestris Schumm.	Weise (1885)	Champion and Chapman (1901)
Orina cacaliae Schrank	Chrysochloa cacaliae Schrank		Barnes (1925)
Chrysochloa gloriosa Fab.	Chrysochloa gloriosa Fab.		Bleuze (1874)
Chrysomela venusta (Suffr.?)	Chrysochloa gloriosa Fab.		Perroud (1855)
Oreina superba Olivier	Chrysochloa gloriosa Fab.		Champion and Chapman (1901)
Orina gloriosa Fab.	Chrysochloa gloriosa Fab.		Perroud (1855)
Oreina speciosa Panzer	Chrysochloa speciosa Fab.		Calloni (1889)
Oreina speciosissima Scop.	Chrysochloa speciosissima Scop.		Champion and Chapman (1901)
Orina vittigera Suffr.	Chrysochloa vittigera Suffr.		Maneval (1938)
Chrysochloa viridis Duft.	Chrysochloa viridis Duft.		
Chrysomela varians Fab.	Chrysomela varians Schaller	Rupertsberger (1870)	Hacker (facultative oviparity?)
Chrysomela varians Schaller	Chrysomela varians Schaller	Hacker (1888)	Rethfeldt. (viviparous when chorion is ruptured at parturition)
Chrysomela varians Schaller	Chrysomela varians Schaller	Rethfeldt (1924)	
Chrysomela varians Schaller	Chrysomela varians Schaller		Shenkling (1900)
Phytodecta affinis Gyll.	Phytodecta affinis	Notman (1921)	Notman (possibly facultative viviparity)
Phytodecta pallidus L.	Phytodecta pallidus	Notman (1921)	Notman (possibly facultative viviparity)
Phytodecta rufipes Fab.	Phytodecta rufipes	Henneberg (1927)	
Phytodecta (Gonioctena) viminalis L.	Phytodecta viminalis	Cornelius (1857)	Williams (1914) (facultative)

great color variations within the species and which may exhibit facultative viviparity or oviparity. In addition to this summary of literature on the production of offspring by the female, attention should now be directed to the literature relating to the embryogeny of these insects.

Champion and Chapman (1901) described the female reproductive system of *O. vittigera* as consisting of a pair of ovaries, each with 20 ovarioles serially arranged along the upper end of the paired oviducts. Fertilization takes place in the ovarian tubule where embryonic development also occurs so that the lowest eggs in the vitellarium are practically ready to hatch. The eggs pass down the paired oviducts into the common oviduct, the latter being somewhat enlarged and distensible to accommodate them. Growth of the larva continues in the egg after it leaves the ovarian tubule and hatching occurs at some undetermined time during its descent in the oviducts.

In addition to the detailed studies of Strindberg and Rethfeldt on *Chrysomela varians,* a species apparently exhibiting facultative viviparity, it seems appropriate to call attention to two valuable papers on related oviparous forms. The first is by Lécaillon (1898b) and the second by Paterson (1931, 1932). The latter, especially, will prove of interest because of its recent appearance and modern treatment.

Female Reproductive System

The Ovary.—The ovaries consist of from several to many ovarian tubules. For example, 20 are present in each ovary of *O. vittigera* (Champion and Chapman) but only 10 (Holmgren, 1904; Rethfeldt, 1924) are present in *Chrysomela varians.* Rethfeldt, however, thinks it probable that since 12 are present in the pupa two must become atrophied in the adult before it is sexually mature, since his count agrees with Holmgren's for the adult female.

Each tubule of the pregnant female is relatively very long and has been subdivided by Rethfeldt into several physiological areas (Fig. 11). The apical, or terminal, filament quickly unites with its fellows from the other ovarioles. Rethfeldt's drawings show cellular organization and nuclei in the central axis of the filament, which is different from the usual condition found in insects.

The terminal filament is followed by the germarium, which is filled with oögonia as well as darker and smaller nutrient

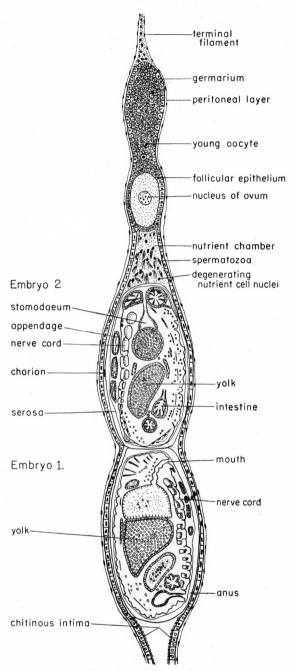

FIG. 11.—*Chrysomela varians*. Longitudinal section of an ovariole, two embryos, and large oöcyte. (Modified from Rethfeldt, Zool. Jahrb. Anat., **46, 2**.)

nuclei which have largely broken down and are enriching the oögonial cytoplasm by the addition of their products. The germarium opens into the vitellarium whose upper end in the gravid female contains one or two young ova, the lower one usually having acquired a follicular epithelium by this time. Below the last follicle lies a portion of the vitellarium that is filled with nutrient syncytial nuclei and clumps of spermatozoa. This area Rethfeldt terms the nutrient chamber. It seems to function for the retention of the spermatozoa which thrive on the disintegrating nutrient nuclei and their associated cytoplasm. The major portion of the vitellarium is filled with two large eggs containing embryos in different stages of development. Evidently these ova were fertilized as they passed downward through the nutrient chamber of the vitellarium. The wall of the ovarian tubule is typical, consisting of a single layer of epithelial cells and an outer tunica propria.

The Paired Oviducts.—The paired oviducts are very short and the walls have a somewhat tall or columnar epithelium within the tunica propria. They unite proximally to form a large egg calyx just before opening into the common oviduct. A peculiarity is the presence of a chitinous intima surrounding the lumen. Holmgren (1904) mentioned its appearance and Rethfeldt has confirmed the fact, and also pointed out that it extends up the ovarian tubule a very short distance to the lowest egg (Fig. 11). In the tubule and in the oviducts it hangs in downwardly directed folds. This remarkable condition is also described by several authors who have studied the reproductive system of *Melophagus,* where the apparently paired oviducts are lined with a chitinous cuticle. Perhaps one is justified in concluding that here, too, true mesodermal oviducts are lacking, their functions being taken over by diverticula from the common oviduct.

The Common Oviduct.—The wall of the common oviduct is normally much folded when not filled with eggs or larvae. The common oviduct and the paired oviducts possess longitudinal muscles outside the tunica propria. A peritoneal membrane covers the entire reproductive system. No seminal receptacles are present, and the unusual absence of these organs was, apparently, first noted by Holmgren (1904). Champion and Chapman (1901) remarked upon the necessity of ovarial pregnancy since the eggs began their development in the ovary. It was left for

Rethfeldt (1924) to ascribe the physiological function of a receptaculum to a definite area in each tubule.

Development of the Oögonia.—In a young adult female the nutrient nuclei and oögonial nuclei in the germarium are separated by no visible cellular boundaries. Later, after a period of active feeding and food storage in the fat bodies of the adult insect, the oögonia become readily distinguishable by virtue of the greater bulk of accumulated cytoplasm around each oögonial nucleus. Also, the oögonial nuclei are slightly larger and stain less intensively than the nutrient nuclei. At the lower end of the germarium, especially, the latter begin to disintegrate rapidly and become part of the cytoplasmic envelope around the nearest oögonia.

As the oögonial cytoplasm increases in bulk the immediately adjacent nutrient nuclei group themselves in several layers around it. The largest oögonium migrates a little way down the tubule in advance of the others, while at the same time its bulk enlarges rapidly, becomes invested by an egg membrane and the remaining nutrient nuclei gradually form a single-layered follicular epithelium. Simultaneously this oögonium, now a young oöcyte, presses down against the nutrient chamber, that section of the vitellarium which Rethfeldt has so designated, and eventually passes through and beyond it toward the lower end of the tubule. A second oögonium follows the same course and ultimately comes to lie between the first one and the nutrient chamber.

Rethfeldt's figures seem to show that all of the nuclei included in the germarium are enclosed in distinct cell membranes in the older females, but he mentions cellular organization, as distinct from the syncytial arrangement in the young adult, only for the partly matured ovum and the one-layered follicular epithelium, as has just been summarized. Neither Strindberg (1913) nor Rethfeldt describes the process by which the sperm enters the egg. This is, in itself, an intriguing problem, for the egg membrane forms early, no micropyle is evident, and the mature ovum is separated from the spermatozoa by a plug of cells in the vitellarium until the membrane appears (Fig. 11).

The Mature Ovum.—The egg is elongate oval in form and enclosed in a delicate, one-layered chorion. No micropyle has yet been discovered in the latter and Strindberg mentions the absence of sculpturing on its surface. The egg seems to have no distinguishable dorsal or ventral surface. Within the chorion is a superficial area of the egg which Strindberg speaks of as membrana vitellina and Rethfeldt calls a Keimhautblastem. It is a moderately developed area, so that one might assume that one author has observed a vitelline membrane and the other has called attention to the periplasm. Neither mentions both areas but they are clearly differentiated by Paterson (1931) in a related species studied by her. Within the membrane and periplasm is a thick granular layer interspersed with small spheres. The central portion of the egg consists largely of yolk spheres and fat droplets of larger size, and the plasma is relatively less abundant than in the cortical layer. The germinal vesicle is subcentrally situated. The color of the egg is orange red.

Development of the Embryo

Cleavage and the Formation of the Blastoderm.—After fertilization the zygotic nucleus divides and repeated mitoses occur in the syncytial daughter nuclei. Most of these migrate into the periplasm and become separated from each other by the formation of cell membranes. The superficial cells also divide and other nuclei, derived from the syncytial nuclei, continue to arrive at the periphery until the blastoderm completely covers the egg. The blastoderm cells are cuboidal or slightly columnar at first, but the cells later flatten out in the extraembryonic portion, leaving the embryonic blastoderm quite evident in the form of a circular plate of cells in a posterior ventral position of the egg. Rethfeldt has noticed that where two internally situated nuclei happen to lie close together within a common mass of cytoplasm, their subsequent mitosis is synchronous. The nuclei still within the interior become vitellophags, and the extraembryonal blastoderm, which takes no part in the formation of the embryonic rudiment, is transformed directly into the serosa. Strindberg homologizes blastoderm formation with the blastula stage of other Metazoa.

Many of the detailed activities of certain cells that are of importance to the fullest embryological treatment apparently have not been followed in this insect. Included in this list of omissions are such points as the migration of the cleavage nuclei, the presence or absence of the pole plasm, and the formation of the primordial germ cells which, in this group, usually are differentiated very early. Lécaillon (1898b) and especially Paterson (1931) supply stimulating accounts of several of these phases of development in related oviparous forms.

The Ventral Plate and Mesentoderm Formation.—The circular plate of cells that has just been distinguished as the embryonic blastoderm or embryonic rudiment is not sharply differentiated from the rest of the blastoderm at its margins. On the contrary, the taller cells of the more central portion only are clearly different while those closer to its edges gradually diminish in size until they show no characteristics that will serve to separate them definitely from the other blastodermic cells adjacent to them.

The embryonic rudiment, however, rapidly includes more cells that become columnar in shape, particularly anteriorly and posteriorly. This elongated mass of cells is the early ventral plate. At this stage it lies only along the ventral side of the egg and extends from the posterior end of the egg forward. As further elongation continues, the anterior end reaches the anterior pole of the egg and the posterior portion extends part way around the caudal pole, where it bends sharply and penetrates the yolk mass. Thus the end of the ventral plate lies in the yolk above the superficial portion of the posterior ventral part.

During this growth of the ventral plate the mesentoderm and the amniotic folds arise. Near the posterior end, and rapidly proceeding anteriorly, a band of cells along the median line invaginates dorsally toward the yolk, forming a narrow longitudinal groove which Strindberg maintains is a gastrulation process. The middle plate of invaginating cells preserves its attachment to the superficial lateral plates of cells of the ventral plate, thus causing the depressed middle plate to assume the shape of a troughlike groove. The lateral margins then advance toward one another and fuse along the median line, the result being that the invaginated middle plate is pinched off along the length of the ventral plate to form a mass of cells beneath it. This process is not so pronounced anteriorly, for the strip of median cells is narrower and they are covered over by the lateral plates while they still form only a shallow groove. It may also be noted that the number of cells in the middle plate is much greater posteriorly than in the anterior region of the body. By this means the embryonic ventral plate has changed to a two-layered condition, and the inner mass of cells along the median line is called the mesentoderm, for from it the mesoderm as well as the epithelium of the mid-intestine will trace its origin. With the acquirement of the inner mesentoderm the embryo is said to be in the germ band stage.

Amnion Formation.—The amnion appears during the formation of the germ band. To outline its complete development at this time seems to be desirable, although it will be necessary to consider with it the dorsal growth of the definitive embryonic body wall. The latter develops slowly along with the organs and other parts of the body. The most posterior portion of the ventral plate first produces the amnion. It consists of a wide fold that advances laterally somewhat more rapidly than in the middle, for the overgrowth of the sides as well as the posterior end of the embryo are involved. It is evident that the distance from the lateral margin of the germ band to a position over its median line is shorter than from the terminal end to the same point. Nevertheless, the central fusion of the amniotic folds from the right and left sides will lag slightly behind the forward median growth of the posterior margin.

Some time after the posterior portion of the germ band is covered by the amniotic folds the anterior end initiates the same process, but two separate folds start here, one on each side of the body. They soon fuse medianly, however, and continue their growth as a single fold. The caudal and cephalic folds finally unite where their lateral borders first touch as one advances anteriorly, and the other posteriorly, along the sides of the embryo. This meeting leaves a circular opening over the anterior third of the embryo for a very short time where the folds fuse last, but eventually this region, too, is covered by them. As soon as fusion has taken place over the mid-line of the germ band the upper and lower layers of the folds separate, one to retain its identity with the serosa while the other, the inner one, forms the amnion.

So far, the history of the amnion is not unusual except perhaps in the manner of relative overgrowth of the anterior and posterior portions, and the final closure of this envelope. Its further history is not so frequently met in viviparous insects. Extension of the amnion continues where it joins the embryonic body wall or ectoderm. The amnion begins to spread dorsally around the yolk by means of a fold that grows dorsally faster than does the embryonic body wall. At last it completely encompasses the yolk as the right and left folds meet and fuse dorsally. The outer layer of the amnion covers the embryo and the inner layer of amnion, but the inner extends only over the yolk from one margin of the body wall to the other (Fig. 12). The inner amniotic layer thus makes a provisional dorsal closure of the embryo. It is replaced in time as the embryo's definitive body

wall grows dorsally and fuses, first in the head, then in the posterior abdominal, and finally, in the thoracic and first abdominal
segments in the mid-dorsal line. As this occurs the inner amniotic
layer forming the provisional dorsal closure is pushed into the
interior of the embryo where it disintegrates. The outer amniotic
layer persists beneath the serosa as an independent, free, extraembryonal covering.

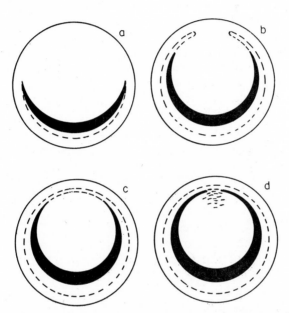

Fig. 12.—*Chrysomela varians*. Provisional dorsal closure and fate of the amnion
and serosa. Embryo solid black, outer line is serosa, amnion is broken line, yolk
in center. *a*, beginning growth of lateral body walls; *b*, amnion precedes overgrowth; *c*, fusion of amniotic folds and provisional dorsal closure; *d*, outer amnion
freed from embryo; inner amniotic portion, forming provisional closure, destroyed
and pushed into yolk area by overgrowth of lateral body walls in definitive closure.
(Modified from Strindberg, Zeitschr. wiss. Zool., **106**, 1, 2.)

Strindberg recognizes the fact that this description of the
formation of an independent and complete amniotic envelope
surrounding the embryo and lying beneath the serosa differs from
the condition recounted by Kowalevsky (1871) and Graber
(1888) and to these writers we might add Wheeler (1889),
Hirschler (1924), Lécaillon (1898a), and Paterson (1931), all of
whom have studied related oviparous forms. Rethfeldt (1924)
also does not agree entirely with Strindberg in his investigations
of this species, since the former regards the succession of events

in *C. varians* as following more closely those outlined by Lécaillon. Rethfeldt's impression is, that the outer amniotic envelope is ruptured, drawn dorsally, and ultimately forced into the embryonic body cavity with the definitive dorsal closure of the body walls, the entire process thus harmonizing with the descriptions of other observers.

When the developmental activities just outlined are completed, the embryo consists of two layers of tissues whose fate is essentially different. The more superficial one, formed now of the fused lateral plates of the former embryonic ventral plate, is the presumptive ectoderm. From it will arise the true body ectoderm and other ectodermal derivatives and organs, including the nervous system. The inner layer, made up at first of an irregular mass of cells, must undergo further differentiation in order to segregate certain portions which will enter into the formation of mesodermal structures, while a lesser number of the cells are to become wholly entodermal in nature. This description of events is quite in harmony with the gastrulation theory of Snodgrass (1935).

Another event occurs simultaneously with mesentoderm formation and the origin of the embryonic membranes. The germ band continues its anterior elongation so that it is finally somewhat longer than the egg. Its posterior portion is still directed dorsally around part of the posterior end of the egg but, because of a slight forward shifting of the germ band, the telson is no longer immersed in the yolk. Also, the line of differentiation between the embryonic and amniotic areas has been sharply defined by the relative size and shape of their constituent cells. The amnion now consists entirely of exceedingly flattened cells with small and widely spaced nuclei.

Blastokinesis.—With the posterior and dorsal growth into the yolk of the posterior end of the early ventral plate one might be able to recognize an abortive effort toward anatrepsis, although neither Rethfeldt nor Strindberg suggests it in his remarks regarding this phenomenon. Nevertheless this movement of part of the embryonic rudiment into the yolk causes the initiation of the amniotic fold, and this activity is homologous with amnion formation in numerous other insects. All hexapod embryos possessing an amnion acquire it at about this stage in their history. Strindberg does, however, call attention to the probability that katatrepsis occurs when the embryo elongates for it then seems to move slightly anteriorly and comes to rest even more superficially on the yolk than before, compressing the amniotic cavity. Korschelt and Heider (1899, p. 288) stated that the shifting corresponds exactly to katatrepsis.

Segmentation and Appearance of the Appendages.—The mesentoderm undergoes certain physical changes in shape shortly after it becomes definitely separated from the ectoderm. Most of the cells composing the tissue come to lie in two longitudinal, flattened strands on either side of the embryonic ventral mid-line, but a few, medianly placed, still join the two strands together. The mesoderm with its coelomic sacs will develop from the lateral strands, but the mid-intestinal epithelium, the entoderm, arises later from the thin layer of medianly placed cells. Strindberg's derivation of the mid-intestinal epithelium from these cells agrees with the observations of several others but this is a matter still unsettled, as one may realize from the discussions of Eastham (1930), Paterson (1932), and Snodgrass (1935).

Local accumulations of cellular material in definite areas of the germ band enable one to recognize the principal body regions. The broad cephalic lobes are followed by a narrower portion of the germ band, and the more slender abdominal section may be distinguished from the thoracic region. These areas are visible before the mesentoderm becomes separated into lateral strands. Narrow transverse bands soon arise in the three body regions after the lateral strands of mesoderm have arrived in their lateral positions. They delimit the boundaries of the various definitive body segments as they appear, and include the mesodermal tissue as well as the ectoderm. Strindberg is of the opinion that the median presumptive entoderm cell strand is not involved in segmentation.

Strindberg and Rethfeldt agree in reporting the presence of 18 segments in *C. varians*. Of these 6 are cephalic, 3 thoracic, and 9 abdominal in position. Ten abdominal segments were given for *Doryphora* by Wheeler (1889) and for *Lina* by Graber (1890). Paterson (1932) records 20 segments in *Euryope* and Hirschler (1924) found the same number in *Donacia*. Eleven of these are abdominal.

The appendages appear simultaneously with the segmentation of the embryo. They are formed as outlined in the chapter on the general embryology of insects. No mention is made of the presence of transitory swellings on the intercalary segment such as have subsequently been observed by Paterson in *Euryope*, and it must be presumed that they have not been present in the specimens studied. Likewise, there is no information available regarding the presence of evanescent abdominal appendages. While they are very frequently encountered in insects, including the Coleoptera, Wheeler (1889) found none in *Doryphora* nor did Paterson (1932) in *Euryope*.

With the acquirement of limb buds, the embryo begins to shorten in length and becomes wider as the ectodermal body walls start to extend dorsally. In this proliferation the mesoderm takes an active part within the overlying ectoderm and follows the latter in the circumscription of the yolk. Finally, the embryo lies in a straight line extending from the anterior to the posterior end of the egg. The yolk meanwhile undergoes a secondary cleavage into large polygonal masses, each containing one or more vitellophags, and the several organ systems arise and differentiate. These will be briefly treated.

The Nervous System.—Two rows consisting of a few ectodermal cells on either side of the ventral mid-line of the embryo become multilaminate by transverse divisions, the inner cells elongate, enlarge, and take histological stains less deeply than adjacent cells. As these cells below the surface layer enlarge, they form swellings which at first project internally toward the mesoderm. The two strands soon appear in ventral view as swellings of the ectoderm because their size and number tend to press this tissue outward as swellings known as the neural ridges. The ridges rapidly extend posteriorly to the most posterior abdominal segments. In the cephalic region, the neural ridges are deflected slightly laterally in order to pass anteriorly beyond the stomodaeal invagination. Here, too, each ridge is considerably wider than elsewhere along the body. Their elevation leaves a deep depression in the median line, called the neural groove, which becomes shallower as the neural ridges widen and press against each other. Cells derived from neural groove ectoderm form the intrasegmental commissures for the right and left members of each ganglionic pair, beginning with the tritocerebrum. The superficial ectodermal cells of the neural groove are later forced out by internal tissues and restore the smooth, even contour of the ventral body wall.

Some of the cells beneath the ectoderm of the neural ridges align themselves in longitudinal rows and vertical columns, enlarge greatly, as previously mentioned, and may then be distinguished as neuroblasts. Since no mitotic figures could be detected, Strindberg is of the opinion they may multiply by amitotic divisions. The derivatives of the neuroblasts form the longitudinal nerves and the intrasegmental ganglia.

The brain is composed of the fused ganglionic masses of the protocerebrum, the deutocerebrum, and the tritocerebrum. The first is divided rather early into the protocerebral lobes and the optic lobes. The tritocerebrum arises laterally to the stomodaeal invagination while the others originate anteriorly to it (Strindberg). During katatrepsis, the brain is drawn to its definitive position over the oesophagus. The suboesophageal ganglion is also formed by the fusion of three pairs of ganglia; the mandibular and the two maxillary ganglia. The three pairs of thoracic ganglia are closely aggregated but not fused, while there is a distinct pair of ganglia in each of the first eight abdominal segments (Strindberg, Rethfeldt). Paterson (1932) has found 10 abdominal ganglia in her work and others have observed either 10 or 11 in various species. She is probably correct in surmising that more are present in young embryos of *C. varians*. Both of the preceding authorities refer to figures of old embryos for this abdominal ganglionic number. These and other very interesting details are given by Strindberg, to whom the reader must be referred.

The stomatogastric or sympathetic nervous system consists of the frontal and oesophageal ganglia, both of which arise in the usual manner as invaginations of the dorsal wall of the stomodaeum. The former is situated over the oesophagus anterior to the brain but the latter migrates to a position behind the brain and dorsal to the alimentary tract. The two are connected by the recurrent nerve. From the oesophageal ganglion a posteriorly directed, unpaired nerve continues over the digestive system. From Strindberg's description it appears probable that the ganglion oesophagi referred to is the hypocerebral ganglion described by Imms (1925).

Tracheae and Oenocytes.—The first signs of tracheal invaginations occur as slitlike stigmatic openings close to the anterior margins of the meso- and metathoracic segments and the first eight abdominal segments. The mesothoracic stigmatic openings are the largest while the metathoracic pair later disappears entirely so that only nine pairs are to be found. The invaginations are short, directed inward, and develop into tracheae in the usual manner. Oenocytes are situated beneath the ectoderm of the first eight abdominal segments near the blind ends of the primary tracheal invaginations.

The Maxillary Gland.—Labial glands seem to be absent in *C. varians.* The maxillary glands, however, are long and prominent. They originate at the outer base of the first maxilla, pass medianly and posteriorly where they end blindly near the stomodaeum.

The Alimentary Tract.—The stomodaeal and proctodaeal invaginations are visible some time before the extremities and the labrum make their appearance. The stomodaeum invaginates first, extending dorsally toward the yolk but later projecting posteriorly. As it lengthens, the blind, distal end carries with it the entodermal layer which always intervenes between it and the yolk. Paterson (1932) does not believe entoderm is represented here at all. Some of the mesoderm cells also remain constantly in contact with the inner wall to form the stomodaeal musculature.

The stomodaeum differentiates relatively late in embryonic life into the pharynx, oesophagus, crop, and proventriculus, the last represented only by the cardiac valve. Six longitudinal folds of ectoderm protrude into the lumen of the oesophagus, causing it to assume a stellate shape in cross section. The crop is a pyriform dilation behind the oesophagus whose ectodermal cells project as villi into its lumen. The walls of the posterior part of the crop fold sharply in and constrict the size of the lumen but do not entirely close it because the central portion remains open. This fold might be compared to a diaphragm since it is made up of the infolded ectoderm which covers its anterior and posterior surfaces. Between these ectodermal surfaces is a layer of mesoderm that was drawn in with the infolding. Strindberg aptly calls this diaphragm-like arrangement the ring fold. It will later project slightly into the larger lumen of the mid-intestine as the cardiac valve. The blind end of the fore-intestine remains closed till very late in embryonic life.

The proctodaeal invagination is much longer than the stomodaeal and is coiled or thrown into loops during its anterior growth. As invagination proceeds the proctodaeal wall near the blind, inner end gives off three pairs of slender, finger-like evaginations which are the rudiments of the Malpighian tubules. These ramify through the haemocoele and fat body, extending forward to the metathorax. The entodermal layer is carried forward by the advancing end of the proctodaeum and covers it, as already explained in the case of the stomodaeum.

The entoderm gives rise to the mid-intestinal epithelium some time after katatrepsis. It is formed in bipolar fashion from proliferations extending posteriorly from the entoderm cells in the vicinity of the stomodaeum and anteriorly from similar but more voluminous cellular aggregations at the blind end of the proctodaeum. As these layers grow toward each other ventrolaterally and ultimately fuse upon meeting, they also spread medianly along the ventral mid-line but more slowly dorsally over the yolk. It does not fully close above until after the definitive overgrowth of the body walls is complete and the inner amniotic layer is pushed in against the yolk.

Strindberg gives the impression that the longitudinal strands of entoderm lying ventrolaterally also participate in the formation of the mid-intestinal epithelium although he does not definitely make such a statement. Paterson (1932) has found this to be true for *Euryope*. Finally, a large intestinal sac, the mid-intestine, encloses the yolk and the inner amnion within it. Mesodermal cells from the inner or splanchnic layer accompany the extension of the entoderm to produce the musculature which surrounds the mid-intestinal epithelium.

The blind ends of the stomodaeum and proctodaeum fuse with the mid-intestine anteriorly and posteriorly respectively, but they remain closed. Shortly before hatching, the stomodaeal end wall breaks down and its lumen becomes continuous with that of the mid-intestine. At this time the diaphragm-like cardiac valve projects posteriorly into the lumen of the mid-intestine. The proctodaeal opening appears only subsequent to hatching.

The Coelomic Sacs.—The origin of the mesentoderm layer, its separation into mesodermal and entodermal units, and the segmentation of the mesodermic portion have already been considered. The laterally placed segmented masses of mesoderm occupy positions above most of the ectodermal segments. The cells of each segmental mesodermal mass so rearrange themselves that a hollow space appears in the interior. These cavities are the coelomic sacs and are formed in all but the proto- and tritocerebral and last abdominal segments. As the lateral ectodermal walls of the embryo grow dorsally around the yolk after katatrepsis, the coelomic cavities elongate. The outer wall of coelomic mesoderm becomes the somatic layer and the inner is the splanchnic mesoderm. Cardioblasts, which are at first rounded, appear in the dorsal portion of the somatic layer but they later become stretched and quite attenuated. They push upward with the mesoderm and in uniting in the dorsal mid-line become the dorsal vessel or heart. The aorta is formed from the coelomic wall of the deutocerebrum and extends from the brain backward until it joins the heart.

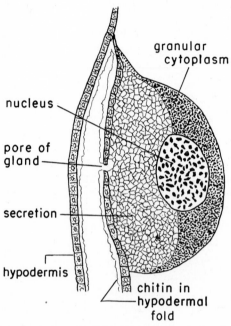

granular
cytoplasm

nucleus

pore of
gland

secretion

hypodermis

chitin in
hypodermal
fold

Fig. 13.—*Chrysomela varians*. Anal hypodermal gland of embryo. (After Reth-feldt, Zool. Jahrb. Anat., **46**, 2.)

Glands.—Rethfeldt (1924) mentions the presence of hypo-dermal trichogen cells and other unicellular glands in the older embryos equipped with chitin and setae. A pair of anal glands (Fig. 13) are of peculiar interest because of their remarkable size and function. Each measures 72 microns in depth and 105 microns in breadth, with an oval nucleus 50 microns long and with a diameter of 35 microns. In his illustration, the cytoplasm of the cell is clearly divided into an outer foamy portion and a basal dark, granular part. These two glands secrete a sticky fluid that, Rethfeldt believes, causes the newly born larva or the freshly laid egg to adhere firmly in an upright position to the substratum on which it is found. The upright posture and the tenacity with which the products of parturition remain fixed in place have been frequently the subject of remark by observers of Chrysomelidae.

LITERATURE CITED

Barnes (1925), Bleuze (1874), Calloni (1889), Champion and Chapman (1901), Chapman (1900, 1903), Cornelius (1857), Eastham (1930), Graber (1888, 1890), Hacker (1888), Henneberg (1927), Hirschler (1924), Holmgren (1904), Imms (1925), Korschelt and Heider (1899), Kowalevsky (1871), Lécaillon (1898a, 1898b), Maneval (1938), Mayet (1874), Notman (1921), Paterson (1931, 1932), Perroud (1855), Rethfeldt (1924), Rupertsberger (1870), Schenkling (1900), Snodgrass (1935), Strindberg (1913), Vetter (1937), Weise (1885), Wheeler (1889), Williams (1914).

Order Hymenoptera   Family Ichneumonidae

Shevyrev (1912) has published a paper, in Russian, which seems to indicate that viviparity may occasionally occur in the genus *Paniscus*. In pages 85 to 93 of his paper appears a résumé of observations on two specimens caged in the laboratory. After some two weeks of captivity one female died and the other was killed by Shevyrev. Both were dissected. During their confinement they had been supplied with hosts upon which to deposit eggs. These hosts were ignored, one female depositing a few ova at random in the cage.

Upon examining the females he found their reproductive systems quite typical, with 12 ovarioles of the polytrophic type grouped at the upper end of each paired oviduct. The ova in the oviducts contained well-developed embryos, the oldest ready to hatch or already open at one end with the heads of the larvae protruding beyond the choria of the eggs. In fact, the maternal oviduct had been perforated by their feeding at the time of dissection.

He then examined pinned and dried specimens of *P. opaculus* Thoms., *P. testaceus* Grav., and *P. gracilipes* Thoms. All of them revealed some fully developed and, at times, partially hatched larvae. Attention also was drawn to the rapidity with which eggs of *Paniscus* hatched when deposited on hosts, emergence usually following deposition by a very few hours, or, more rarely, 24 to 48 hours.

From these statements Shevyrev concluded the same conditions prevail in these species that obtain in certain ovoviviparous flies; while oviposition often occurs, delayed deposition results in viviparity. It must be confessed these conclusions, in themselves, are not very convincing since captive specimens, or pinned specimens, may possibly retain viable eggs longer than would be the case under normal environments.

Additional light has recently become available which substantiates the observations of Shevyrev. Kerrich (1936) in his studies on *Polyblastus* has discovered that complete embryonic development precedes deposition of the egg in members of this genus. In seeking hosts for her offspring, the female has the habit of extruding the larva-containing egg and carrying it about with her by means of the egg pedicel which is clasped by the valves at the tip of the ovipositor. From one to several such ova may be extruded before a host is discovered. In this case, the oldest eggs may hatch to the extent that the anterior end of the larva protrudes from a slit in the chorion. Therefore, if a host is promptly found, the intact egg is attached to it; if delay occurs a partially ruptured egg allows the larva to escape immediately and attack the host.

While ovoviviparity may occasionally take place in these insects, these data scarcely establish the fact. It would be very interesting to have further light thrown upon the problem of reproduction in these species for, if they are facultatively viviparous, this would be the first of the Hymenoptera to be so recorded.

LITERATURE CITED

Kerrich (1936), Shevyrev (1912).

Chapter 7

ADENOTROPHIC VIVIPARITY—DIPTERA
(GLOSSINIDAE)

The embryonic histories treated under this heading all show specific modifications whereby the embryo, as a hatched larva, makes nutritional use of the products secreted by the maternal accessory glands of the reproductive system. The insects to be considered are the Pupipara and, apparently, all Glossinidae. All are ectoparasites of the higher vertebrates and most of them are of great economic importance.

Order Diptera   Family Glossinidae

Viviparity in the tsetse flies was discovered by Bruce (1897) in his investigations on nagana in Zululand in 1895–1896. Some time later, Minchin (1905) and Stuhlmann (1907) gave detailed descriptions of the reproductive system and observations on the older larvae, which proved to be similar to the organization possessed by the Pupipara. Several writers contributed to a knowledge of larval anatomy, among whom Austen (1904), Roubaud (1909a), and Newstead (1918) have been widely quoted. Roubaud (1908, 1909a, 1909b, 1919, etc.) has provided a large amount of information concerning the nutritional and physiological relations of the female and the uterine larva.

In spite of the fact that the literature on the tsetse fly is enormous, no details of the development of the embryo within the egg seem to have been published, although certain phases of the larval uterine life have been treated. This information, together with a summary of the reproductive system of the female insect, is all that can be furnished from other sources. Additional notes on the structure of the ovariole, the oöcytes, and fragmentary data on the development of the embryo of *Glossina tachinoides* are contributions by the author, rendered possible through the courtesy of Dr. T. A. M. Nash who reared the material in Africa.

111

Female Reproductive System

The reproductive system of *Glossina* shows a very high degree of specialization. The ovarioles are greatly reduced in number, a distensible common oviduct harbors the offspring until full growth is attained, and the accessory glands supply the pabulum for the larva.

The Ovary.—The paired ovaries are elongate, tapering organs, each composed of only a single ovariole. The latter usually contains four or five follicles at a time and the right ovariole alternates with the left in the production of ripe ova. In a gravid female they are asymmetrical in size because, like the Pupipara, only one egg matures at a time. Their apices extend laterally in the haemocoele while their basal portions approach each other in order to join the oviduct in the median line. The structure of the ovary, otherwise, offers little to differentiate it from the same organ in the Pupipara.

The entire upper portion of the reproductive system, to the uterus, is surrounded by a thick supporting tissue composed of a rich network of tracheae ramifying through layers of both large and small cells, the latter possessing very small nuclei. The distal free portions of the system consisting of the ovaries and their ducts, together with this investment, lie securely embedded between the cells of the fat body.

The ovariole is divisible into two general portions, the germarium and the vitellarium. The elongate terminal filament, common to most insects, is lacking. The outer wall of the germarium is composed of an exceedingly thin, tough, fibrous tissue, the tunica propria. The lumen is filled with oögonia, which are closely compacted, large cells with little cytoplasm and no visible cell membranes. Their nuclei are relatively enormous, taking up nearly all the space within the cells they occupy. Each contains two or three large clumps of chromatin but no visible linin (Fig. 14). Near the junction of the germarium with the vitellarium small clusters of these cells appear to be separated from one another by the infiltration of delicate partitions of epithelial cells from the vitellarium. The abundance of this tissue in the lower part of the germarium has been somewhat exaggerated in the figure because the ovariole bends just beyond the margin of the drawing.

The vitellarium is the relatively longer and wider proximal portion of the ovariole. One's views regarding the presence or absence of paired oviducts must determine one's concept of the length of the vitellarium and the location of its lower termination. This question will be explained briefly when considering the paired oviducts. Outside of the fibrous tunica of the vitellarium a light musculature appears which continually increases in amount with oblique, longitudinal, and circular muscles present

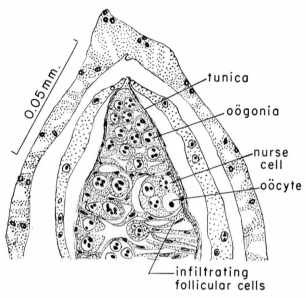

Fig. 14.—*Glossina tachinoides.* Longitudinal section of the adult germarium. A mesodermal investment serves to support the organ, the tunica propria is thin and extensions from the follicular epithelium infiltrate between individual clumps of nurse cells and oöcytes.

as it extends down over the common oviduct and uterus. The lumen of the upper end of the vitellarium is lined with a thin, flattened, or cuboidal layer of follicular epithelium, extensions of which seem to project into the lower end of the germarium as previously mentioned. Lower down, this tissue is thicker as the cells become columnar and begin functioning as nutrient organs in the follicles.

The Paired Oviducts.—Minchin (1905) is of the opinion that the ovaries unite directly with the common oviduct and Newstead, Evans, and Potts (1924) agree with this view. On the other hand, Roubaud (1909) and Stuhlmann (1907) believe that paired oviducts are present at the point of junction, an anatomical relation which will be encountered in the discussion of the reproductive system in *Melophagus*.

The Common Oviduct.—The unpaired portion of the reproductive system lies medially and extends posteriorly as a rather large organ divided topographically into the oviduct, uterus, vagina, and vulva (Fig. 15). The oviduct is comparatively short and wider at its base where it expands to join the uterus. The

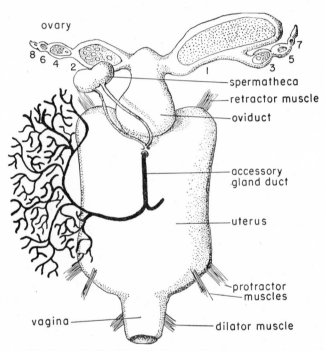

Fig. 15.—*Glossina palpalis*. Dorsal view of female reproductive system with right accessory gland omitted. Numerals represent the order of succession of ova from the ovarioles. Diagrammatic. (Modified from Roubaud, La Glossina palpalis.)

latter is relatively large and thick walled, but considerably thinner when distended during gestation. Tracheae are abundant over its outer surface but have been omitted in the accompanying figure. The uterus is abruptly constricted at its base and opens into a short tube, the vagina, which intervenes between the uterus and the vulva. Exteriorly, the uterus and vagina are provided with circular, oblique, and longitudinal muscles already mentioned and, in addition, several large muscle bands, inserted in the maternal hypodermis, are attached to them. The latter serve, with the tracheae, to support these organs firmly and to retain them in position, but are most essential in parturition when they, with the others, act primarily in ejecting the larva. Internally, they are lined with a layer of ectodermal cells which secrete a chitinous intima that extends also into the oviduct (Fig. 16).

The Accessory Organs.—The accessory organs consist of a pair of seminal receptacles and the paired milk glands. The former are two small, orange-yellow spheres that are firmly united by a transparent tunica propria which invests them. The spermathecae are composed of a single layer of large vacuolated cells. From each a long, slender, slightly convoluted tube with a narrow lumen passes to the basal, dorsal portion of the oviduct at its junction with the uterus. The cavities of the receptacula, as well as the lumens of their ducts, are lined with an intima and the characteristic color of these organs is due to the latter's hue. The intima of the ducts is reinforced with spiral thickenings, the epithelial cells are not vacuolated, and longitudinal muscles invest them. Circular muscles around their base form a true sphincter muscle, which may serve to close the openings of these ducts at times.

The milk glands arise on the dorsal wall of the uterus just behind the ducts of the seminal receptacles. The common excretory duct of the glands soon branches distally into two. Each branch continues posteriorly over the uterus where it, in turn, divides into four main collecting tubules. The tubules rapidly split into very numerous tubular glands which ramify throughout the haemocoele and end, according to Roubaud (1909a), in tiny caeca. The glandular portion penetrates the fat body where the outer wall of each tubule is furnished with tracheoles and lies in intimate contact with the fat cells. The lumen of the tubules is lined with chitin equipped with spines, so that the morphological arrangement is quite similar to the milk glands of the Pupipara.

Between gestations the ramifying portions of the glands are rather small and comparatively inconspicuous, but their period of enlargement and activity corresponds to that of gestation. Their product is a milky-white granular secretion containing a small proportion of fatty droplets. The major portion of it is probably albuminoid in nature. Both the ducts of the seminal receptacles and the milk glands open near each other in the uterus, at the end of an elongate papilla which projects into the lumen (Fig. 16).

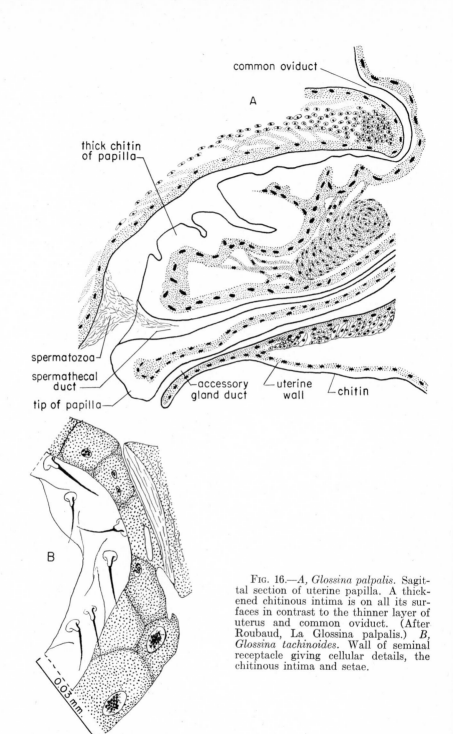

common oviduct

A

thick chitin
of papilla

spermatozoa

spermathecal
duct

tip of papilla

accessory
gland duct

uterine
wall

chitin

B

0.03 mm.

FIG. 16.—*A, Glossina palpalis.* Sagittal section of uterine papilla. A thickened chitinous intima is on all its surfaces in contrast to the thinner layer of uterus and common oviduct. (After Roubaud, La Glossina palpalis.) *B, Glossina tachinoides.* Wall of seminal receptacle giving cellular details, the chitinous intima and setae.

If the preceding account is compared with the description of the Hippoboscidae in Chapter 8, it will become strikingly evident that the general topography of the reproductive systems of the Glossinidae and the Pupipara are essentially alike. The three principal points of divergence are relatively minor. One of these differences is the number of ovarioles possessed by the species in each group. All Glossinidae, apparently, have a single ovariole in each ovary while the Pupipara have two. This disparity is counterbalanced, however, as will be shown later, by the presence of a few more follicles in the ovarioles of the Glossinidae. Thus, since the reproductive requirements in the frequency and number of ovulations are approximately the same in the two groups, these needs have been adequately provided for in a slightly different fashion.

Another dissimilarity is found in the seminal receptacles of the two groups. In Glossinidae these organs are two in number, while three are almost constantly present in their closest relatives, the Muscidae. In function and in conformation they are typical muscoid organs. On the other hand, in the Pupipara they often vary in shape, size, number, and function. This might indicate either of two things: they are degenerating or altering their function. Examples of these changes may be given from the comparative studies recently made by Hardenberg (1929); they are three in number in *Crataerrhina* and *Stenopteryx* but only two in *Cyclopodia, Nycterobosca,* and *Ascodipteron* and further they function in these genera as spermathecae; they are two in number in *Melophagus, Lipoptena,* and *Hippobosca,* where they fail to function in the capacity of seminal receptacles. They are strongly branched in *Hippobosca* but remain unbranched in the other genera as in Muscidae in general. Hence we find that the discrepancies between Pupipara and Glossinidae in the accessory glands may be considered to be of little significance in our comparisons of species since the first group, itself, shows considerable variation within its genera, even in the genera of one of its families (Hippoboscidae). However, the consideration of their evolution, ultimate fate, and the problem of their efficiency in connection with viviparity and fertilization is highly pertinent.

A third alteration is one of topography. In the Glossinidae a distal portion of the common oviduct is definitely smaller than the uterine part and in this regard they resemble Hippoboscidae. However, the Nycteribiidae and Streblidae both lack the constricted section, usually designated as the oviduct, and the ovaries are united directly with a uniformly large uterus. Aside from these points one finds a remarkable example of convergence in the reproductive systems of these four families of Diptera, the Glossinidae, Hippoboscidae, Nycteribiidae, and Streblidae, to meet the maternal functional demands of adenotrophic viviparity. The number and structural arrangement of the ovarioles and their follicles, the enlarged uterus and the milk glands are strikingly similar in these families. While it is logical to assume that these characteristics may have developed prior to the morphological differentiation of the Pupipara into the present family groups, it appears necessary to explain the similarities of this group with Glossinidae as a matter of convergence on the part of the latter.

Development of the Embryo

The Egg.—The oöcytes are liberated from the germarium at the apex of the polytrophic ovariole and pass into the vitellarium, where they are invested by the follicular epithelium. As the follicle and its contents move down the vitellarium new follicles are formed above the first. Since ova mature and are released alternately from the two ovaries, it follows that the oöcytes must alternate in age, i.e., the oldest being in one ovary, the next in the other ovary, and so on. A short strand of follicle cells connects successive follicles in the tubule. At these points the vitellarium, having little within, is contracted, while around the follicle it bulges more or less, depending on the bulk of the contents. Four follicles are usually present in each ovary, hence Glossinidae have eight oöcytes in various stages of development just as does *Melophagus* in the Pupipara. In both, then, the follicles are equal in number even though there are twice as many ovarioles in *Melophagus,* a condition referred to earlier.

Actually, transverse extensions of the follicular epithelium seem to separate the new follicle from the germarium, an observation noted also in the description of the terminal chamber. Presumably each young follicle should enclose a single oögonium. Four successive mitoses of this cell and its descendants produce a total of 16 cells, the lowest of which is invariably the oöcyte. The remaining 15 become nutrient cells. This series of events was not followed completely but the process seems to conform to the same pattern which Verhein (1921) has fully described for the Muscidae. At any rate, at the close of this activity and the cessation of further mitoses the follicle is definitely established with two classes of cells within. The upper portion of the follicle contains 15 nurse cells, the lower end contains an oöcyte. With these general observations and orientation in mind it is now possible to inquire into the details of the behavior of the follicular epithelium and the nurse cells, and trace the development of the ovum.

The follicle cells are apparently all alike at first. They increase in number when forming a follicle but remain constant thereafter. Their early shape is cuboidal, cell boundaries are visible, the nuclei are large, ovate, and centrally situated. Their cytoplasm soon begins to show distinct polarity due to stored inclusions. With the changes in them, to be described, it is quite probable they contribute materially to the growth of the nurse cells and indirectly to the oöcyte. It would be difficult, otherwise, to account for the great size of the mature egg which is several times larger than the early oöcyte plus all its accompanying nurse cells. The bases of the cells, adjacent to the wall of the tubule, are already granular and deeply staining; their paler free ends projecting toward the contents of the follicle, are filled with small vacuoles indicating the accumulation of substances whose composition remains undetermined. From this point the follicular epithelium around the nurse cells and over the oöcyte behaves differently according to its location. That portion enclosing the nutrient cells will be given first attention.

The follicular epithelial cells surrounding the nutrient cells maintain their cuboidal shape throughout the period the nurse cells are obtaining a supply of nutriment from them. Near the end of their secretory activity, however, they become stretched laterally as a thin squamous tissue, greatly extended to encompass unbroken their portion of the follicle. As this alteration of shape occurs, it is probable their role of acquiring nutriment for transport to the nurse cells within is nearing its close. They are being depleted of their remaining nutriment, losing their nutrient function and are acquiring the passive role of a limiting membrane (Fig. 18).

Follicle cells also circumscribe the young oöcyte. They do not long remain cuboidal but elongate into tall columnar cells. They possess large subglobular nuclei with prominent nucleoli. The ends projecting inward against the oöcyte contain numerous fine vacuoles that are empty in routine preparations. Nevertheless, their presence indicates that these follicular cells, too, have acquired a surplus of some substance, presumably fatty in nature. A nutrient function for them is denied by Verhein (1921) who has made a very detailed study of the oöcytes and egg formation with similar conditions in oviparous *Calliphora*. He claims the well-defined, free ends of the follicular cells preclude the transfer of nutriment. It is quite true, as he remarks, that follicular cells in other species of insects, where nutriment is apparently supplied by them, possess very indistinct, or no discernible, outer margins. The follicle cells around the oöcyte are very tall even when those enclosing the nurse cells have become squamous.

Some time after the nurse cells start transferring nutrients to the oöcyte, the zone of demarcation between these follicular cells around the oöcyte and the anterior squamous cells surrounding the nurse cells is abruptly and sharply defined. There is no transitional length of cell between them. At their junction with the squamous type above the partly enlarged oöcyte, an invagination of the columnar follicle cells takes place. Since this invasion occurs all around the upper end of the oöcyte, the infiltrating cells evenly constrict the opening between the oöcyte and its nurse cells and eventually assist in cutting off almost entirely the remnants of the depleted nurse cell mass. This is accomplished about the time the oöcyte reaches maturity.

The nurse cells, 15 in number, are at first indistinguishable morphologically from the oöcyte, since all 16 were derived from the same source by four mitoses. In Muscidae, according to Verhein (1921), the nurse cell nuclei, in the mitoses which produce them, suffer a chromatin reduction escaped by the oöcyte cell. This, no doubt, is the factor limiting their capacity to that of nurse cells alone. They at once start acquiring a large amount of material from the surrounding cuboidal follicular epithelium, a portion of which is promptly passed to the oöcyte. Thus all 16 cells grow rapidly and about equally at first until the nurse cells assume their final size and the follicle cells are greatly distended as described. At this time nurse cell nuclei are centrally placed in the cells, possess a thick membrane and a coarse reticulum on which are distributed large chromioles, either singly or irregularly clumped.

The nurse cells now acquire no more nutriment from the follicular epithelium but give up their own stored reserve to the oöcyte. In doing so, the nurse cells more distal to the oöcyte are first to show the effects of this drain upon them. During later stages the cells next the oöcyte continue to enlarge, apparently at the expense of those more anterior. Finally, the nuclear membranes break down and chromatin is continually being cast into the cytoplasm where it is added to the nutriment conveyed to the oöcyte. The life and function of the nurse cells are almost over (Fig. 19).

The early oöcyte cell probably retains its full complement of chromatin while nurse cells seem to lose part of theirs. But the oöcyte is also a positional cell and seems to be invariably the lowest of the 16 within the follicle. It very early possesses a finely granular, homogeneous cytoplasm but this soon gives way to a differentiated peripheral cytoplasm. The latter encloses a large number of fine vacuoles that cause this portion to stain more faintly than the internal cytoplasm. As its bulk increases through the further acquirement of nutriment, the cytoplasm seems to become almost entirely peripheral, thick, finely granular, and highly vacuolated. The more central portion of the oöcyte fills with yolk spheres.

As oöcyte enlargement continues the peripheral cytoplasm does not increase in amount but is expanded into a more delicate periplasm. The inflow of nutriment seems to occur all along the surface contiguous to the nurse cells; the minute circular pores, described in *Calliphora* by Verhein (1921), were not distinguishable. A partly filled oöcyte shows zones within varying from freshly acquired granular nutriment to the denser mass of yolk spheres more deeply situated. This is clearly seen in sagittal sections.

Polar granules appear in the polar cap at the posterior end of the oöcyte, when it becomes about half its final size. All later stages and the mature ovum show the polar cap which consists of a slightly thickened peripheral plasm. In it lie two layers of small, darkly staining granules that cover most of the polar area (Fig. 19). It is possible one of the granular layers is derived from the other, for sections show that each granule in the inner layer lies closely beneath another more superficially situated. This appearance, however, may be due simply to their close approximation, rather compacted condition, and regular distribution. The cap represents the area wherein the future primordial germ cells of the embryo will first segregate from the somatic cells.

When the oöcyte is almost completely supplied with yolk, the follicular cells surround it with the exception of a restricted area directly over the future micropylar area. Abutting against the cytoplasm of the maturing oöcyte at this opening appears an inverted mushroom-shaped clump of nucleated cytoplasm. As one follows it upward in serial sections it contracts continually in diameter until, near the center of the nurse cell mass, it becomes very narrow. In some cross sections of the middle and upper portions it is greatly compressed but more often it shows an open lumen; the lower portion is always a solid mass of tissue. At the upper end it appears to be united to the wall of the ovariole, or vitellarium, just below the undeveloped mass of young oöcytes adjacent to the germarium. Verhein (1921) has found the same structure, at the identical developmental stage of the oöcyte in

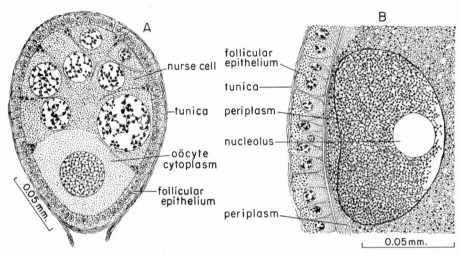

Fig. 17.—*Glossina tachinoides. A,* follicle with oöcyte sectioned slightly diagonally, not all nurse cells sectioned medianly. Slight invasion of follicle cells between central cells. *B,* portion of follicular wall and oöcyte to show position of nucleus before fertilization and thinning of adjacent periplasm. Slightly younger than Fig. 18*B.*

Sarcophaga, and claims this strand of cells extends down to the oöcyte in order to form the micropyle. The sunken, completed micropyle possesses a superficial plug similar to that described for related Muscidae. The manner of downward growth, or projection, of this mass of tissue in the Diptera should be carefully studied in order to ascertain its origin, the time of its earliest appearance, and its functional relationship to adjacent structures (Fig. 18*B*).

The oöcyte nucleus is invariably situated just beneath the peripheral cytoplasm almost at the anterior (micropylar) end of the egg. It is characterized by a thick limiting membrane, a clear nucleoplasm, and a very evenly distributed, faintly staining, fine reticulation set with minute chromioles. One large nucleolus, three or four smaller ones, or none may be present; but if they are visible they stain intensely with eosin. The large ones seem to contain a number of vacuoles. In closing the discussion of these tissues it seems desirable to compare their nuclear sizes before passing to a consideration of the ovum. The oöcyte nucleus may be approximately half the size of the nucleus of a mature nurse cell and the latter fills almost two thirds of the cell it occupies. The nucleus of a follicular cell is only one fifth the length of an

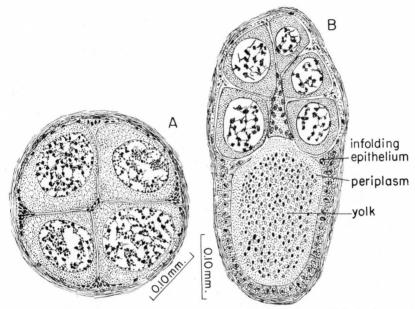

Fig. 18.—*Glossina tachinoides.* A, upper portion of nurse cell body in cross section showing muscular tunica, squamous epithelium of follicle, 4 nurse cells and trace of central cytoplasmic cone at their inner, common junction. B, slightly diagonal section of follicle showing infiltration of columnar follicular epithelium between nurse cell body and the oöcyte. Follicular epithelium squamous around nurse cells and columnar over oöcyte. Syncytial nuclei forming mushroom-shaped mass in center of nurse cell body. Stage a little older than shown in Fig. 17B.

oöcyte nucleus. An idea of their relative dimensions may be obtained from the accompanying figures where these cells appear (Figs. 17, 18, 19).

As the oldest oöcyte enlarges it greatly distends the portion of the follicle in which it lies. One side of the ovariole, apparently, bulges considerably more than the rest of the ovary so the other follicles of the ovariole no longer are situated directly behind the first one, but folded over in a row beside it (Fig. 15).

The ovum possesses a completely rearranged cytoplasmic content which distinguishes it from an oöcyte. The rather coarse vitelline membrane remains unchanged within the chorion. The granules and yolk spheres are uniformly distributed throughout, even the cortical region being richly supplied. A coarse granular meshwork fills the egg and within its spaces lie vacuoles. Some of these are large and clear because their contents have dissolved in the reagents. They are spaced rather well apart. Others are

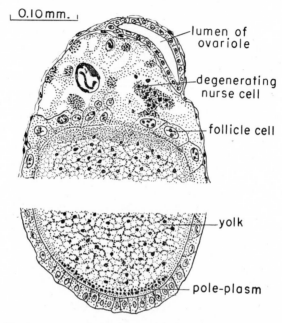

Fig. 19.—*Glossina tachinoides*. Anterior and posterior ends of nearly mature oöcyte in sagittal section with pole plasm (granules), degenerating nurse cell mass and infiltrating follicular cells almost encircling the egg. Central part of oöcyte omitted.

round, pink in color, and perhaps only one third the size of the first. They are considerably more numerous. In addition, an exceedingly large number of very much smaller vacuoles, or granules, each distinctly discernible, almost fills the remaining space. Finely granular cytoplasm forms another, more delicate, reticulum and condenses somewhat around the larger types of vacuoles.

The mature egg is subcylindrical with rounded ends, the anterior tapering slightly and ending in the papillate micropylar cap. In lateral view one sees a shallow concave upper surface rising gently toward the poles, while the ventral outline is somewhat more curved but in a convex plane, especially anteriorly since this pole tapers considerably. The delicate chorion retains the reticulations marking the limits of the follicular cells that secreted it. Stuhlmann (1907) describes it as consisting of a thicker outer lamella with the inner one much thinner, a fact the writer has been able to confirm. The trabeculae, uniting the two, flare out at their junctions with the outer and inner layers of the chorion.

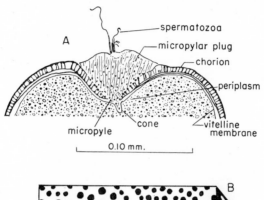

Fig. 20.—*Glossina tachinoides*. *A*, sagittal section of micropyle, posterior end of egg and chorion showing spermatozoa penetrating micropylar plug. *B*, free-hand stereogram of chorion consisting of thin endochorion and thicker exochorion joined by trabeculae whose outer ends are often visible on the surface of insect eggs. Trabeculae are not secreted opposite lateral cellular membranes, hence the polygonal appearance.

That they are laid down in a roughly polygonal pattern is shown in surface view (Fig. 20). The micropylar area is filled with a clear substance which forms a cap in this depression. After passing into the uterus this mass may be filled with filaments which, perhaps, are spermatozoa that have been cut in various planes in the accompanying illustration. The orientation of the egg in the oviduct and in the uterus is typical of insects.

Blastoderm Formation.—Since early cleavage did not appear in the slides nothing can be said regarding this process or as to the probable origin of yolk cells. All of the slides of cleavage contained central cells of two kinds, distinguishable only by their nuclei. The nucleus of one was similar in size and chromatin distribution to blastoderm nuclei and presumably was derived

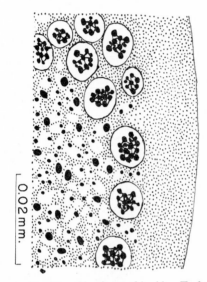

Fig. 21.—*Glossina tachinoides.* Early stage of blastoderm formation; cleavage nuclei migrating through yolk to periplasm.

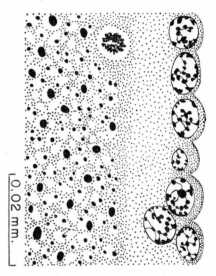

Fig. 22.—*Glossina tachinoides.* Intermediate stage in blastoderm formation with nuclei in superficial part of periplasm which is beginning to cut in between them. One nucleus in yolk in mitosis; periplasm separating into layers.

from the latter by immigration into the yolk, or by never having reached the surface of the egg. The second type of nucleus was considerably smaller and almost filled with dense chromatin. At all times after early blastoderm formation they were rather centrally distributed with a slightly larger number near the two poles. Their significance was discussed in the consideration of the general embryology of insects.

Nuclear migration to the periplasm, which had become rather dense, granular, and a little thicker than the diameter of the nuclei, resulted at first in a rather scanty distribution of isolated nuclei, or in small nests of them consisting of two to ten nuclei in each. Where several occurred together, only a few lay against the periplasmic layer, the others being behind and deeper in the yolk (Fig. 21). While in this rather scattered arrangement a few individual nuclei were observed to have already penetrated the periplasm and were situated close to the periphery of the egg. All of them eventually penetrated the periplasm and spaced themselves in a very superficial, uniform layer. Since the whole surface at last bore them in such even distribution many must have divided prior to entering the periplasm, for which there seemed to be some evidence as prophase may be seen in Figure 22. This, too, may account for the nests of nuclei so frequently encountered. From this description it is evident that not all nuclei reach the periplasm simultaneously. These observations agree with those of Weismann (1863), Kowalevsky (1886), and Graber (1889) on oviparous Muscidae, and with Pratt (1900) and Hardenberg (1929) in their studies of Pupipara. On the contrary, Blochmann (1887), Voeltzkow (1889), and Noack (1901) noted thin isochronal migration in the oviparous muscine species investigated by them.

One can see by the description of the ovum and this account of early blastoderm formation that the egg of *Glossina* is intermediate between the typical muscine ovum with its thick periplasm and the very thin peripheral cytoplasmic layer of *Melophagus*, as described by Pratt (1900). But, quite like the sheep tick's history, a thicker periplasm ultimately is acquired before the blastoderm is completed. The migration of the nuclei to their subperiplasmic location also is more typical of the Pupipara than of the Muscidae and coincides closely with Pratt in his study of *Melophagus*.

After the nuclei reach their definite positions the periplasm is found to be more densely granular in their immediate vicinity, especially between the nuclei and the vitelline membrane. Beneath the nuclei it is less granular for some distance, perhaps a little more than the diameter of one of the nuclei. Just below this area, granules again are accumulating to form an inner periplasm (Fig. 23). It is not typical for muscine eggs since they possess a layer of yolk between the two layers, which this egg seems to lack. Perhaps this deepened area is simply an extension of the peripheral layer, in which case no inner periplasm is formed. The intervening stratum of yolk between the outer and inner periplasmic layers of muscine eggs is generally thin and interrupted so that it consists largely of isolated sheets of substance, always rather small in amount. *Glossina* eggs, lacking such yolk islands, more closely approach the condition in *Melophagus* ova which,

Hardenberg (1929) says, possess no yolk between the cortical layers.

Because the periplasm is already slightly thicker than the diameter of the invading nuclei, they take their positions as do the nuclei of other Muscidae. According to Pratt, *Melophagus* nuclei pass into a much thinner cytoplasmic zone and, to accommodate them, the cytoplasm accumulates beneath individual nuclei, thus causing the inner surface of this layer to be highly irregular in outline.

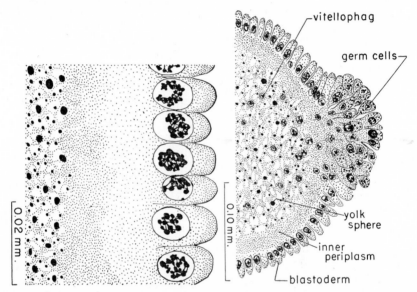

FIG. 23.—*Glossina tachinoides.* Late blastoderm formation with nuclei retreating deeper into periplasm and lateral membranes penetrating between them. Periplasm definitely three layered with no evident yolk in it.

FIG. 24.—*Glossina tachinoides.* Sagittal section of end of egg showing primordial germ cells (pole cells) projecting beyond adjacent blastoderm.

The first evidence of cell formation consists of depressions, or furrows, on the surface of the egg which press in between the nuclei, thus separating them from one another (Figs. 22, 23). With continued and deeper furrowing, the quantity of cytoplasm above the nuclei is materially increased, no doubt due to the retreat of the nuclei from the surface. The nuclei alter their shape at the same time, or else rotate about 90° and change their polarity as well, for their long axes no longer parallel the surface of the egg but lie perpendicular to it. The furrows deepen until they have penetrated the outer periplasm. To the present the

cytoplasm has been continuous over the egg along the lower sides
and bases of the cells below the line of cleavage furrows. When
cell membranes are established down to the inner border of the
outer periplasm, the lateral furrows cease their inward growth.
Apparently a horizontal separation of the inner margin of the
periplasm from the layers below takes place practically simultaneously over most of the egg, leaving only the anterior, micropylar area and the posterior pole still continuous with the underlying part of the egg. The fact that the periplasm is considerably
thicker posteriorly may partially account for its failure to
separate with the rest. Polar cell formation, to be mentioned
later, may be another factor. However, the cells forming over the
rest of the egg quickly acquire basal cell membranes which
separate them from the inner egg mass. They constitute the
blastoderm. The cells, individually, are rather tall columnar with
the nuclei a little below their centers (Fig. 24). Below the cells
another periplasmic layer, denser along its inner border, continues
to isolate them from direct contact with the yolk.

Let us now summarize our discussion of periplasmic behavior.
The mature oöcyte contained only a relatively thin periplasm.
This layer, however, thickens materially before the nuclei of the
future blastoderm reach it. During nuclear penetration it constantly increases in thickness. Its outer border beneath the vitelline membrane is smooth and even in contour but next to the yolk
it is very irregular and remains so until cleavage is complete. This
irregularity below is due to extensions into the yolk where the
latter, of course, is constantly supplying nutriment to the living
cytoplasm. When the inner periplasm forms, this layer is not
involved in early blastoderm formation. Between the two layers
of periplasm eggs of related Diptera show a narrow, intervening
layer of yolk but this was not visible in the present sections of
Glossina.

After the blastoderm cells are completely formed they no
longer leave the surface beneath the vitelline membrane smooth
and even. Instead, each cell possesses a rounded free end projecting toward the membrane. Since the cells vary in width and
height, the surface appears quite irregular in sections (Fig. 24).
Although several nuclei are present in the posterior pole plasm,
the blastoderm is interrupted by the presence of pole cells over
that area.

Pole cells are the primordial germ cells of the insect, presumably being derived from one of the early cleavage nuclei which

had migrated to the posterior cytoplasm. Several authors have described them in various insects, and have discussed their origin and significance. Noack (1901) treats them in considerable detail for the higher Diptera, and *Glossina* apparently conforms with his account in all essential details.

In relating the structural appearance of the oöcyte, attention was called to the polar plasm at the posterior pole with its polar granules forming a disc, or cap, over the posterior end of the egg. The cytoplasm is slightly thicker there, too, during blastoderm formation. While nuclei are migrating into the superficial periplasm to give rise to the cells of the blastoderm, some nuclei invade the posterior pole plasm. If earlier observations on other insects are true here, it is probable these nuclei arise from a single cleavage nucleus, or strictly limited number of nuclei. The cap of granular cytoplasm around each nucleus was not distinguished in *Glossina,* which may have been due to the age of the particular sections observed or to faulty staining. From these first polar nuclei about 40, or possibly 50, nuclei are finally derived by several mitoses. While located at the posterior pole they are rather eccentrically placed, extending farther toward the dorsal side of the egg than to the ventral. Each definitive cell arises in a manner quite similar to the blastoderm proper, but is a very much taller columnar cell, protruding well above the general level of the blastoderm (Fig. 24). Thus, these cells are at once distinguishable by their location and their greater length. Nevertheless, the true blastoderm cells immediately surrounding them are also higher than those a little distance away, so the latter distinction is not quite so marked as in most insects. Even so, however, their elevation above the surface exceeds that of several related Diptera whose polar cells have been previously described.

When the blastoderm is complete its cells, in general, are slightly more than twice as tall as their width. The layer, while only roughly of uniform height superficially, has a very smooth and even basal outline where the cells rest upon the deeper cytoplasm. The nuclei, also, are distributed in an even plane throughout. This condition is not long maintained, for the blastoderm cells begin to crowd one another, probably due to further divisions within the blastoderm, though mitosis was not observed there, and the uniformity of the nuclei is somewhat disturbed as some are forced to lower elevations by mutual pressure. Longitudinal sections of the blastoderm stage show the inner periplasm to be almost continuous beneath the cells except at the poles, where yolk masses make it appear quite irregular in thickness. There is no evidence of anterior or posterior proliferations such as Hardenberg (1929) described in the egg of Pupipara.

The Ventral Plate.—An area along the ventral side of the blastoderm, embracing several rows of cells on either side of the mid-line, becomes taller than the rest of the blastoderm cells. The latter, in fact, now gradually diminish in height, as they assume new functions. This area extends from the anterior pole posteriorly to the polar cap of germ cells, which has, meanwhile, moved still more dorsally on the egg. With continued growth the plate encompasses both poles and extends dorsally over the yolk for the muscine embryo at first is longer than the egg. Its two distal portions, therefore, are recurved near its extremities so that the anterior portion is directed back over the top while the posterior end now points anteriorly. The posterior embryonic rudiment, thus established, grows faster than the future cephalic portion and it extends for a greater distance over the dorsal yolk. It seems clear that the lengthening of the ventral plate is accomplished by the continuous inclusion of more blastoderm cells within the plate area, rather than by any mitotic increase of ventral plate cells. Indeed, this acquisition of adjacent cells both anteriorly and posteriorly may, in part, account for the gradually diminished height and squamous character slowly assumed by the remaining blastoderm cells at this time, and a little later.

Superficially Visible Grooves and Bands.—At about this stage, or slightly earlier, eggs of Muscidae possess two transverse superficial grooves. One is approximately one fourth the length of the egg from the anterior pole, the other, one sixth the length from the posterior end. The former extends almost around the egg, the latter somewhat less. Both grooves are deep constrictions ventrally but gradually become shallower until they fade out entirely toward the dorsal side. The egg and the ventral plate are thus marked off into three general areas, of which the intermediate section is much longer than the combined length of the polar portions. The anterior portion of the egg possesses another groove which lies slightly in advance of the anterior transverse fold and runs diagonally upward and forward about two thirds the way dorsally. This is the anterior converging fold. If an egg is cleared, mounted, and viewed by transmitted light the middle section may be found to possess several bright, transverse bands crossing the ventral side and running a little dorsally. They are five in number, serially arranged, so that this section is divisible into six areas, each of approximately equal length. The bands are not grooves but later do invaginate slightly. Their visibility at present is said to be due to shortened blastoderm cells at these places. They are usually indistinguishable in serial sections.

Weismann (1863) described and named these grooves and bands and subsequent authors have usually referred to them. Since no whole mounts of *Glossina* embryos of this stage were available, these structures, in general, were not seen but sections bore some evidence of the anterior converging and transverse folds. These, however, appeared far shallower than those drawn of *Musca* by Weismann (1863) and Voeltzkow (1889), or than in the illustrations of *Calliphora* shown in publications by Graber (1889) and Noack (1901).

Formation of the Germ Band in Muscidae.—The converging, anterior and posterior folds are particularly serviceable external characters by which further embryonic growth may be readily identified. For one thing, they clearly indicate that longitudinal growth takes place within the ventral plate, and later in the germ band, because the boundary of the posterior furrow is shifted polewards with continued development. Further, the spaces elongate between the five bands of the middle section of the embryo. No such movement of these folds or bands occurs dorsally, however, showing that growth within the egg is limited definitely to its embryonic portions. It does not include the dorsal or lateral blastoderm which covers the rest of the egg. The anterior and posterior transverse grooves also delimit the yolk. The larger central mass of yolk lies internally between these two boundaries but lesser amounts of yolk project beyond them. One mass is crowded into the anterior, or head region; the other, rather narrowly limited in circumference, extends into the caudal end.

The inner layer of Muscidae is of the invaginate type, already described in the chapter on general embryonic development. Its formation in this family will be briefly presented. Presently, two new folds arise. These are directed longitudinally along the sides of the ventral plate near the upper end of the five transverse bands which subdivide the middle section of the embryo; that is, slightly less than halfway from the ventral mid-line of the egg toward the dorsal side. The median portion of the ventral plate may now be termed the middle plate and the portions of the ventral plate to the sides of the longitudinal folds are the lateral plates. The anterior and posterior margins of the lateral plates are, at least at first, bounded by the transverse folds. The middle plate, consisting of tall columnar cells, sinks in toward the yolk along the ventral mid-line, and, simultaneously, the lateral folds grow downward over the area formerly covered by the ventral plate. Overgrowth proceeds more rapidly nearer the transverse folds, more slowly in the center of the egg. Since the lateral plates are still attached to the middle plate along the inner margins of the lateral, or longitudinal, grooves, the edges of the latter are drawn medianly at the same time. At last the margins of the lateral plates meet and fuse along the ventral line of the embryo, at the same time drawing in the edges of the middle plate beneath their union. Thus the submerged middle plate is rolled into the form of a long, cylindrical tube lying between the confluent lateral plates and the central yolk mass. As soon as it is freed from the overlying ectodermal portion of the embryo, as the united lateral plates may now be called, it spreads out laterally over the internal surface of the embryo. The embryonic ectoderm in this region is, consequently, continually separated from the yolk by this mesodermal rudiment.

To this point various authors seem to agree in all essential points in the development of the mesoderm of the Muscidae. It is now necessary to present some of the steps involved in the continuation of this invagination into the two distal portions of the germ band, and to give a few examples of the theoretical interpretations placed upon the observations that have been made. This, of course, involves entoderm formation.

A little earlier, attention was called to the migration of the posterior transverse fold toward its pole as the embryo elongates. Voeltzkow (1889) figures the germ band at its greatest length in *Musca* as extending from the ventral anterior end of the egg, along the ventral surface, around the posterior pole and forward dorsally almost to the margin of the anterior transverse fold. He finds no movement of the latter, therefore, because the anterior end of the embryo does not migrate over the anterior pole. The depth of the furrow is strongly emphasized by him and the stomodaeum is said to arise in it where it meets the anterior end of the fusing lateral plates as the mesoderm invaginates. The posterior transverse fold is not significant in the formation of the mesoderm posteriorly.

Graber (1889), in his observations of *Lucilia* and *Calliphora*, found the anterior end of the germ band just covered the anterior pole, while the stomodaeum was anteroventral or ventral in origin. The length of the embryo and its position in the egg agree closely with Voeltzkow. The posterior transverse furrow had in this stage already migrated to the dorsal side of the egg where its direction would no longer be transverse but horizontal because of its shift. The furrow, in this position, was seen by Graber who thought it to be accessory to a continuation of the earlier appearing longitudinal folds which produced the mesoderm ventrally, an error to which Wheeler (1891) called attention. However, he found the inner layer consists of two kinds of cells with respect to their fate; one is ectodermal in nature, although invaginated, and is now formative hind-intestinal, the other presumptive mid-intestinal tissue.

Noack (1901) came to widely different conclusions in his studies of *Calliphora.* He agreed with Graber regarding the length of the embryo and its position in the egg. These points may therefore be accepted as being verified by common agreement; since Voeltzkow certainly erred in identifying the anterior end of the ventral plate in the earlier stages, his conclusions may be disregarded. They will later be referred to in connection with conditions in *Glossina.* The chief point of departure refers to the developmental origin of the mid-intestinal anlage.

Before doing so, however, it must be pointed out that chronological sequence has been ignored in order to present the involved conditions in detail without describing the migration of the furrow or the presence of pole cells. The proctodaeum of Muscidae develops prior to the appearance of the stomodaeum. Noack has found the anterior extension of the middle plate invagination to be interrupted by the anterior transverse furrow, which does not shift in position. After some delay it passed around this obstacle and continued forward to the converging fold. The depressed area at the junction of the fused lateral plates and the converging fold continued to press inward toward the yolk, thus forming the stomodaeum of ectodermal tissue. But before doing this the area of ectodermal cells embraced within the arms of the converging fold had already sunk below the general level of the ectoderm. Remaining attached posteriorly to the wall of the forming stomodaeum, it was carried into the embryo by the elongating end of the fore-intestine. The anterior end of the enteron is formed from these submerged ectodermal cells whose origin, therefore, is ectodermal rather than from the end of the inner layer.

The posterior end of the germ band, in its dorsal and anterior growth over the upper surface of the yolk, had pushed the pole cells and the posterior transverse fold with it until the latter lay entirely dorsally. Its folds, then, ran longitudinally on the upper side of the embryo and into the dorsal blastoderm. This was the position assumed by them when Graber (1889) had misjudged their significance. An area here, including the pole cells, behaved as related for the stomodaeum so that here, too, a rudiment of the enteron, derived from ectoderm, is carried in by the developing hind-intestine. In this instance it is the posterior part of the enteron and within its folds lie the pole cells.

It will at once be apparent that, according to Noack, the mid-intestinal anlagen are purely ectodermal in origin while in most other insects these rudiments are said to come either from portions of the inner layer—which is often referred to as the mesentoderm to indicate that relationship—or they are derived from the inner ends of the stomodaeum and proctodaeum. Further, these two rudiments lie beyond the proctodaeal and stomodaeal invaginations and are thus wholly independent of the invagination creating the mesoderm. Again, the withdrawal of the mid-intestinal areas from the general ectoderm leaves two gaps in these locations which must be replaced by overgrowth of adjacent cells of the superficial layer. Finally, the authors generally agree that the invaginating middle plate gives rise only to mesoderm throughout its length. A conflict of opinion arises only as to the actual location of the end of the invagination and as to whether or not the enteron rudiments are parts of it.

This summary of the formation of the inner primary layers in the Muscidae reveals the nature of problems involved in these developmental stages. Noack's careful and critical study shows the meticulous efforts taken to record events faithfully, and he has had the benefit of earlier, experienced investigators on the same subject. Therefore, his recorded account of these stages must be considered the most recent and accurate available. The situation in *Glossina* may be similar or may present several modifications of detail when such stages can be subjected to scrutiny. Some comments are offered on the latest phase of this developmental stage of the embryo. Actual invagination of the middle plate to form a tube was not seen.

The Germ Band of Glossina.—The fully extended germ band of this species is relatively longer than those of the Muscidae so far described. Its disposition in the egg is such that the future cephalic portion is wholly dorsal (Fig. 25), and the space intervening between the two extremities of the germ band is not only relatively short but is also situated almost over the center of the egg. No doubt the caudal portion extended even farther forward than shown in the accompanying sketch before the invagination of the proctodaeum occurred. This figure is a composite one forced upon us because of the lack of exact orientation when cutting sections; the proctodaeal region appearing in some sections, the stomodaeal in others.

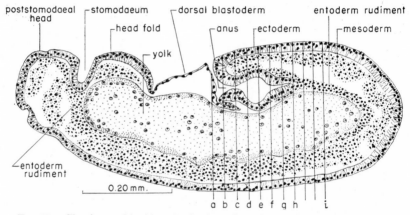

Fig. 25.—*Glossina tachinoides.* Sagittal section of germ band with stomodaeal and proctodaeal invaginations. Reconstructed from two sections on same slide. Anterior end to left, dorsal side up. For explanation of letters *a–i* see Fig. 26.

The Proctodaeum.—The rudiment of the hind-intestine appears earlier than the stomodaeal invagination, and the process is more complicated. Immediately within the external opening the lumen is a narrow transverse slit which continues only a short distance before it suddenly opens into a taller chamber. The roof of this enlarged portion possesses two diverticula which are, presumably, the rudiments of the Malpighian tubules (Fig. 25). The innermost portion is again narrow and ends blindly. The cells forming the walls are quite like those of the embryonic ectoderm, from which, of course, they have been derived. Beneath the anal opening the ectoderm joins the dorsal blastoderm, this junction being obscured by the somewhat intricate folding of what is, for the present, surplus tissue.

If one examines carefully the position of the terminal portion some further details preceding or accompanying proctodaeal invagination become evident. The posterior end of the germ band originally was lying flat upon the dorsal yolk. When the formation of the rudiment of the hind-intestine begins, the embryo, perhaps responding to the factors governing many insects, starts to sink tail-first into the yolk. This movement is never carried to the stage of completion shown by hexapod embryos with wholly immersed germ bands, for only its very tip subsides into the yolk, then stops. At the same time the proctodaeum invaginates to the point represented by the illustration (Fig. 25). An important feature to note is that the proctodaeal invagination does not involve the very end of the germ band but occurs a little anterior to it as in other insects. For this reason the extreme end of the germ band is a little deeper in the yolk and the proctodaeal opening lies directly above it. This immersion of the tip of the germ band draws down also a portion of the dorsal blastoderm, as previously mentioned. If these observations are correct the dorsal blastoderm does not bound the posterior margin of the proctodaeum at all but is only passively drawn into the yolk by the migrating tail end of the embryo.

Selected serial cross sections of the proctodaeal region are shown in Figure 26. This embryo was approximately the same age as the one represented by Figure 25 in sagittal section. By comparing the two figures the proctodaeal invagination may be clearly understood. Despite the variability in both height and width, all the sections were drawn by camera lucida with the same magnification and projection distance. The sections are each 8 microns in thickness and total 136 in number for the entire embryo. From these were selected sections 79, 82, 85, 88, 91, 94, 97, 100, and 109 which are mounted in order from left to right in each row of the drawing. It might be well to recall the fact that the dorsal side of the end of the embryo will lie on the dorsal yolk while its ventral surface is above, just beneath the chorion.

Section (a) shows no part of the embryo. Only the dorsal blastoderm covers the yolk anterior to the tip of the abdomen, a few cell tips of which appear in section 80 on the slide. Section (b) cuts through the tip of the embryonic abdomen which overhangs the dorsal blastoderm. The latter is depressed downward into the egg where it joins the embryo. Section (c) cuts across the posterior narrowed part of the proctodaeum in the anal region. Below the proctodaeum the folded dorsal blastoderm and the embryonic ventral ectoderm of the anal region are united. The sides of the embryo join directly to the margins of the dorsal blastoderm. In section (*d*) the embryonic abdomen lies directly over the yolk, having replaced the dorsal blastoderm. The latter is present only laterally. Section (*e*) contains the proximal end of the enlarged chamber of the hind-intestine. The evaginating

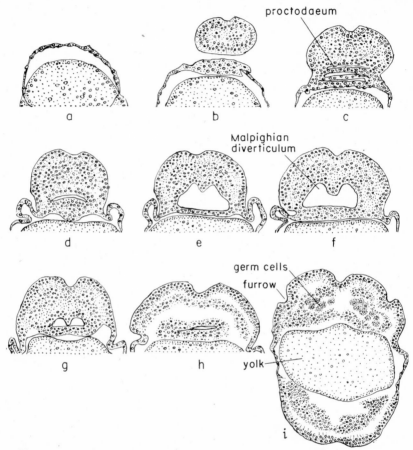

Fig. 26.—*Glossina tachinoides.* Cross sections of proctodaeal region of a germ band very slightly older than shown in Fig. 25 where sections *a–i* are indicated as closely as possible by vertical lines. Only the posterior, dorsal portion of the embryo, above the yolk, is shown in all but the last drawing. Same magnification in both figures.

Malpighian tubules push out, papilliform, toward the ventral abdominal side of the embryo (dorsally in relation to the egg surfaces). These diverticula are really represented only in one plane in these sections. By noting their presence in the next sections figured, one may ascertain their length as covering at least six or seven sections. Section (*g*) is through the internal third of the intestine, where it again is a wide but much depressed cleft extending horizontally in the abdomen. Other features of these illustrations will be mentioned later.

One might here conclude with the comment that the embryo in succeeding sections is quite evidently becoming broader as our views cover the more anterior portions of the germ band. Section (*g*) is narrower, a fact which might be due to the section coinciding with the inner margins of one of the pairs of transverse bands that have become depressed grooves by this time. In this expansion, the embryo has continually settled more definitely down onto the yolk and its ventral surface is flatter.

The Stomodaeum.—The fore-intestine arises from a position over the dorsal surface in a manner similar to that of *Melophagus* rather than anteroventrally as in muscids. The invaginating ectoderm forms a rather large, rounded depression which deepens into a finger-like tube with an unconstricted external opening. The point of indentation starts, not near the end of the germ band as it does in the case of the proctodaeum, but rather in the center of the dorsally lying, anterior end of it. Penetration interiorly is nearly at right angles to the surface. The bottom of the tube is evenly and bluntly rounded. The lumen is of uniform diameter and the cells are purely ectodermal in appearance. Anteriorly and laterally to the stomodaeum the germ band ectoderm is thickened slightly. This area composes most of the head region of the larva.

Voeltzkow (1889) and his predecessors have recognized the variability in length of embryos of the same developmental age. In addition to this fact, which likewise holds true for *Glossina,* the embryos of the tsetse fly exhibit some differences in their relative advance over the dorsal yolk, especially in a consideration of the location of their fore- and hind-intestinal invaginations. This fluctuation may be correlated with the amount and shape of the yolk mass surrounded by the original periplasm, but it is of interest.

It was noticed in making cross sections of a number of embryos of an age represented by Figures 25, 26 that the number of sections obtained fluctuated around an apparent average of 140 for each embryo. That did not include the chorion, or other extraembryonic material, only embryonic tissue. This number of sections, or some approximate number, is a measure of the greatest length of the embryo in any one plane. By assuming that all

the embryos appeared in exactly 140 sections, the positions of the
stomodaeal and proctodaeal invaginations were then fixed by simple proportion. Of course, embryos with different numbers of
sections had the appropriate correction made to bring all to the
same scale. A few examples will serve to illustrate the results
obtained, all based on 140 sections.

Embryo 1, stomodaeum at section 14, proctodaeum at section 97.
Embryo 2, stomodaeum at section 15, proctodaeum at section 93.
Embryo 3, stomodaeum at section 22, proctodaeum at section 91.
Embryo 4, stomodaeum at section 28, proctodaeum at section 82.

The embryos were too few in number to afford any statistical
treatment, had that been necessary. A simple examination of the
measurements, however, will serve to bring out the point that the
exact positions of the stomodaeum and proctodaeum are not fixed
in relation to one another nor to the greatest length of the embryo.
No doubt, embryos 1 and 2 may be contracting in anatrepsis. The
relative positions of these two points of measurement varied by
one section for the stomodaeal measurement and four sections for
the proctodaeum. The latter has about four times as far to
migrate to return to its pole as the distance to be traversed by the
stomodaeum. These two, then, are comparatively uniform, but
they fail to show a similar association in their measurements with
the remaining two. The last embryo has the longest germ band,
for its two extremities are closest together, yet its divergence
from embryo 3 is the reverse of the measurements between embryos 1 and 2; that is, its stomodaeal position is six sections back
of embryo 3 while its proctodaeum is nine sections ahead.

The Mesoderm.—When the fore- and hind-intestinal invaginations are present, the mesodermal strand has spread out laterally and flattened in the germ band. In fact, for a time the space
in the ventral mid-line is almost entirely free from mesoderm. It
occupies most of the space under the cephalic lobes, although the
stomodaeum and a narrow ventral extension of the yolk are found
medianly. In a sagittal section (Fig. 25) the mesoderm may be
seen against the ectoderm with some indication of segmentation,
presaging events soon to follow.

With the completion of the mid-intestine one finds the major
portion of the interior of the embryonic body filled with this organ
and its contained nutriment (Fig. 28). The space between the
enteron and the ectoderm is at first almost entirely taken up by
undifferentiated mesodermal elements although the germ cells,
the fore- and hind-intestines, neuroblasts, developing tracheae

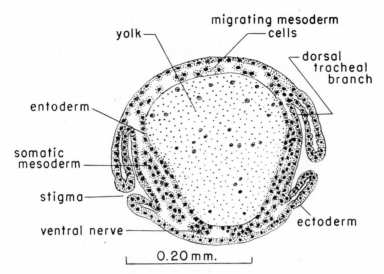

Fig. 27.—*Glossina tachinoides*. Young larva in cross section with forming ectoderm, partially developed mid-intestine and tracheal invaginations possessing
dorsal and ventral branch rudiments.

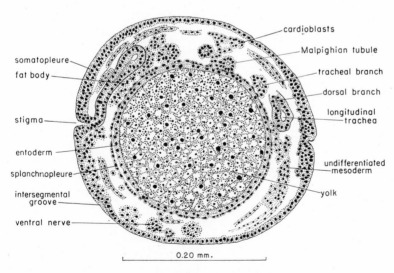

Fig. 28.—*Glossina tachinoides*. Embryo with mid-intestine completely surrounding the yolk.

and the cardioblasts occupy lesser portions of it. This profusion of formative mesoderm is not evident in the slightly later stage represented by the figure to which attention has just been called, the reason for which will shortly be explained.

Groups of mesoderm cells begin to arrange themselves into strands in which the individual cells are aligned in a linear series with their centrally placed nuclei rather widely spaced. These strands are first noticeable immediately beneath the ectoderm,

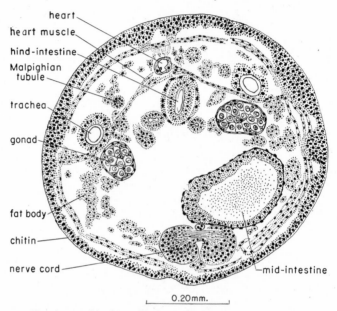

Fig. 29.—*Glossina tachinoides*. Early cuticular stage embryo in cross section before hatching. Semidiagrammatic.

particularly along the dorsolateral and ventrolateral parts of the body. They vary from about three to five in number in these locations. From them the dorsoventral segmental muscles are derived. A longitudinal section makes it clear that the same process, involving dorsal and ventral mesodermic cells, is likewise forming the anteroposterior muscle strands. The muscles, so formed, seem to be typically muscine in distribution though not so numerous as in the more active larvae of the latter group.

From the inner mesoderm an exceedingly thin layer of squamous-like cells invests the elements of the digestive tract. These cells give rise to a very weak splanchnic musculature which appears to be largely supportive in nature since little, if any, contractility is required of it (Figs. 28, 29).

The heart muscles also are formed from this tissue (Fig. 29). These extend from the lower lateral sides of the dorsal vessel as two narrow bands which run beneath the fat body and longitudinal tracheae and seem to be inserted at, or near, the ectodermal layer. Each muscle consists, apparently, of three muscle fibers which expand at their cardiac attachment into the broad digitate winglike envelope. In an embryo of late cuticular stage, prior to hatching, these muscles become extremely delicate and lie firmly adherent to the inner border of the fat body and terminate there. Also two shorter muscles, one on each side, extend from the upper lateral margins of the dorsal vessel to the dorsal hypodermis.

The remaining mesodermal cells, not yet otherwise differentiated, are transformed into two irregular sheets of fat body cells which are suspended in a general dorsoventral direction and run anteroposteriorly in the cavity. The utilization of the mesoderm in the formation of these various organs and investments greatly reduces their total bulk so that there is left a generous haemocoelar space within the embryo.

The Entodermal Rudiments.—At the inner end of each of the two intestinal primordia is an elongate mass of cells whose origin was not observed. These cells will form the mid-intestine. The posterior one seemed to bear evidence of arising as described by Noack (1901) in Muscidae. Their proximal ends are in contact with the fore- or hind-intestinal invaginations, and from these each extends toward its respective pole around the end of the yolk. The mid-intestinal rudiments press in ventrally between the mesoderm and the yolk as each elongates to span the space between their tips. At first they are each several cell layers in thickness but they soon thin out as their cells migrate laterally and upward to encompass the yolk as a one-layered epithelium (Figs. 27, 28). In the Pupipara (*Melophagus*) such thick long groups of cells do not occur as entodermal rudiments. Instead, a thin sheet of cells preceded by a number of somewhat isolated, independently migrating cells, covers the dorsal side of the yolk first and extends downward to the ventral surface. In this method of forming the mid-intestine, *Glossina* closely follows the Muscidae rather than the Hippoboscidae.

The Gonads.—Whether the pole cells had any association with the entodermal cells is unknown. Cells that are quite distinguishable in this stage are found lying in two lateral, somewhat dispersed masses in the mesodermal region of sections 109 to about 114 in the embryo in Figure 26, section (*i*). These cells are larger, each is independent of its neighbors, and the cytoplasm is more granular and more deeply stained. These are thought to be surviving cells from the original pole cell mass which have attained their present positions.

In a longitudinal section of an embryo which has just completed the formation of the mid-intestine, the germ cells, or pole cells as they have previously been called, come to lie in two

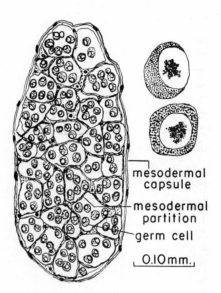

mesodermal
capsule

mesodermal
partition

germ cell

0.10mm.

Fig. 30.—*Glossina tachinoides*. Gonad of first stage larva in longitudinal section with two greatly enlarged primary germ cells beside it in freehand drawing to show clear, vesicular nucleus, clumped chromatin and densely granular cytoplasm.

irregular, loose masses posteriorly. They extend from the anal margin of the penultimate segment forward over the last third of the yolk. In a half-grown embryo these masses are slightly drawn anteriorly until they are situated entirely over the posterior midintestine. They have also become more compactly grouped into cylindrical aggregations of shorter length and are surrounded by mesodermal cells. Some of the latter come to envelop them closely in order to form a thin, cellular, gonadal membrane about them. In a very late embryonal stage, or the early larval stage, sheets of tissue, one cell in thickness, infiltrate between groups of germ cells, thus partitioning the gonad into several chambers

(Fig. 30). In the accompanying figure just referred to, two of the germ cells have been greatly enlarged. The nucleus is large, clear, and contains a dense mass of chromatin near its center. It is invariably eccentrically placed in the cell and the left-hand drawing is typical of this condition; in the one to the right the nucleus lies against the upper cell membrane. The gonads are not functional until the adult stage is attained but they lie laterally in the embryo between somites 9–11.

The Amnion and the Neural Groove.—When the germ band is formed the remainder of the blastoderm covering the yolk may properly be termed the dorsal blastoderm, to distinguish its cells from those entering into germ band formation. The amnion is formed over the germ band of many insects by an evaginating fold along the margins between these areas. Pratt (1900) and Hardenberg (1929) speak of the merest rudiment of an amnion in the embryology of *Melophagus*, while several authors recognize the same suggestion of an amnion in the Muscidae. No trace of such an organ could be detected in *Glossina* embryos of the age represented in Figures 25, 26. Perhaps this stage was already too old, for the amnionic rudiment is transitory in muscids.

Voeltzkow (1889) and Noack (1901) refer to the dorsal blastoderm, or to portions of it, as the amnion since both believed a part of the proctodaeal invagination to be bounded by extra-embryonic tissue on one side and by the ectoderm of the embryo on the other. Graber (1889) thought all of the dorsal blastoderm became either amnion or serosa, depending upon its particular location. In the first place, the amnion covers the ventral surface of the embryo or encloses the entire embryo and the yolk in some instances; it never covers only the dorsal yolk alone as assumed, for instance, by Voeltzkow. Again, both amnion and serosa, when formed, become accessory embryonic structures, taking no part in the ultimate formation of the embryo. Since the dorsal blastoderm seems to have the function of forming part of the dorsal ectoderm in *Glossina*, the term employed for it herein seems to be more satisfactory than designating it either as amnion or serosa.

In the ventral mid-line of the ectoderm a second depression appears and is represented in Figure 26. This occurs along the line of fusion of the original lateral plates when the middle plate was pushed to the interior to form the inner layer. It is the neural groove. The cells involved become very tall and some along the margins of the groove are forced into the interior, or arise there by transverse division of the columnar ectodermal cells. It was not determined which method of furnishing these inner cells was utilized, though delamination appears more probable. The nerve cords are formed only in a late germ band stage, about the time the embryo begins to shorten. They arise from the two strands of cells which lie internally on either side of the neural groove whose origin was just described. From the first they are connected at intervals by other neural cells which arose from the median portion of the groove. Such fused masses will become the intrasegmental ganglia, while the two separate cords will comprise the intersegmental connectives of the main ventral nervous system.

The Yolk.—Noack (1901) emphasized the appearance of a condensed peripheral border around the yolk of muscids, with yolk cells within and a membranous outer margin. Such a condition cannot be described for *Glossina,* yet the denser outer border is present. A membrane also exists but this, no doubt, is simply a surface tension membrane, not a structure. The presence of a few nuclei meets one's expectations because the yolk is constantly being compressed as well as being consumed by the growing embryo. Its sharp outlines appear to be due simply to these factors. The yolk shown in Figure 25 is only that portion to be enclosed by the mid-intestine when the latter develops. Lesser amounts, both anterior and posterior to the main yolk mass, are separated from the latter and utilized directly by the adjacent embryonic tissues.

Blastokinesis.—Anatrepsis, or the migration of the young germ band away from its original position on the yolk, is not clearly shown in *Glossina* or in *Musca.* Perhaps the nearest approach to it is the dorsal overgrowth of the yolk by the extremities of the germ band and the partial submergence of the tip of the abdomen as described. Many other insect embryos perform a very distinct movement or inversion—unusual migrations being that of *Tenodera* (Hagan, 1917) and of *Calopteryx* (Brandt, 1869).

Just as the embryo has grown into an elongate germ band with the structures outlined in the preceding paragraphs, it finds it necessary to alter its length and position in the egg so that, in part at least, new structural modifications may appear. One reason why this change is necessary seems to be that it affords more ample space in which to develop the dorsal ectoderm untrammelled by too great constriction of this region. The lateral walls,

containing both the thickened ectoderm and the underlying mesoderm, have also continued their lateral growth upward toward the
dorsal side and require more room for adequate growth. This contraction in length and retreat of the germ band to the ventral and
lateral sides of the egg may be called katatrepsis, for it is entirely
comparable to this movement in insects with shorter germ bands.
Whatever the motivating forces may be, the embryonic extremities are found to be drawing away from each other toward their
respective poles. Eventually the anterior end stops its movement
when the cephalic portion, including the enlarged areas embraced
within the cephalic lobes, has reached the anterior pole with the
stomodaeal opening directed upward. The caudal end, having
farther to travel, ultimately assumes a like position. It is drawn
backward and down until the anal end of the intestine is directed
posteriorly in the egg. As the definitive larval shape is gradually
attained the true terminal segment is pulled down over the
apparent end with its anal opening. This new alignment brings
the anus to its final ventral position, where it appears on the posterior margin of the twelfth segment. There are 13 somites altogether, according to Roubaud (1908).

During this shift some changes in tissues and organs have
occurred which must be mentioned. The dorsal blastoderm no
longer lies in folds, either laterally or beneath the end of the
proctodaeum. Instead, it is greatly stretched in order to cover the
exposed extraembryonic area now present. This, too, perhaps
further explains the squamous appearance of its constituent cells,
the first stretching having been accounted for early in the description of the ventral plate.

The intestinal rudiments have grown rather rapidly too, and
have succeeded in maintaining their connections with the internal
entodermal primordia. As the oral end of the stomodaeum is
carried forward the course of the latter no longer is directed
ventrally but runs from the foremost point of the body almost
exactly horizontally inward to the upper portion of the anterior
enteron cells opposite the yolk. The elongation of the fore-
intestine is accompanied by its differentiation, as follows. The
lumen of the first part is much constricted in diameter, compared
with the original invagination, but is still circular in cross section.
This future pharyngeal portion is short. The longer portion following the pharynx internally to the enteron has a very narrow
slitlike lumen whose sides are greatly compressed. The inner end
is closed.

Originally, the proctodaeal invagination was directed posteriorly over the yolk toward the end of the egg. This, of course, means that it extended toward the more anterior portion of the abdominal region, since this part of the body was reversed over the dorsal side of the egg. To explain what happens most clearly we must remember that the hind-intestine increases materially in length over the rudiment shown in Figure 25. This is actually the case, as in other embryos, although not previously mentioned here. If the inner two fifths of the intestine should remain approximately undisturbed in position while the anal three fifths are pulled backwards in the egg to the caudal pole, a bend in the intestine would occur between these two lengths. Moreover, because of the bend, the entire intestine would resemble a hairpin, with one leg slightly shorter and lying beneath the longer.

Nothing has been given regarding the segmentation of the body because the sections show little concerning this feature. Whole mounts of young embryos are necessary to explain structures that appear most clearly externally. However, Figure 25 shows some aggregations of the mesodermal tissue and the sections through the periphery of this embryo showed that segmental grooves had already appeared in the ectoderm as well. Presumably these developed from the transverse bands as suggested by Noack (1901). The embryo at the time katatrepsis occurs is definitely segmented. It shows in longitudinal and cross sections of the ectoderm, the mesoderm, and the developing nerve trunk.

Tracheae.—The earliest rudiments of the tracheal invaginations appear with the commencement of katatrepsis. These consist of paired ectodermal invaginations, all but one arising laterally. The posterior pair open, not laterally, but close together near the upper margin of the end of the body. Pratt (1900) reports eleven pairs in the Melophagus embryo, the last three of which appear together on the anal segment. Glossina embryos, of the developmental age shown in Figure 27, also possess eleven pairs but ten of these occur in serial order as lateral tracheal invaginations on the future thoracic and abdominal segments. The last segment bears a single pair. This distribution is typical of the muscine insects.

A lateral trachea starts as a short solid strand of cells pushing in from the ectoderm at right angles to the surface of the body. All arise simultaneously. A lumen appears in the strand and ends internally in a very slight enlargement. The cells covering this ampulla now give off two branches, one directed dorsally, the other ventrally (Fig. 27). Extensions of the lumen invade the bifurcations readily so they are hollow practically as fast as they elongate. Later on, the dorsally directed branch bends at a sharp angle and continues forward to fuse with the corresponding member of the next anterior pair of tracheae at the latter's point of similar deflection.

With this union of the dorsal diverticula on each side of the body, the two main tracheal trunks are established, with the exception of the anal pair. The posterior trachea seems to arise as a more bulbous invagination for the lumen, from the first, is large, oval, and open. The development of this pair was not closely followed but apparently a single strand continues forward and ventrally, with a number of bends, until it joins the dorsal branch of the most posterior lateral trachea on its side of the body.

The fate of the ventrally growing branches of the lateral tracheae was not followed. It is possible that each gives rise to the ventral segmental tracheal branches. They certainly form no part of the longitudinal trunks. As they grow downward, they bend like the dorsal branches, only these flex in a posterior direction. They do not, however, extend far enough to unite into a trunk. On the contrary, after the main dorsolateral longitudinal trunks extend throughout most of the segments of the body, the ventral branch seems to lose its connection with the ampulla of the primary invagination. The ampulla subsides and only the dorsal branch persists as a long slender tube connecting the longitudinal trunk with the ectodermal opening to the exterior (Fig. 28). The lumen of this tube is eventually occluded and the anal openings become the functional spiracles of the larva.

As soon as the embryo acquires a cuticula, this investment likewise lines the longitudinal tracheal trunks. It is even visible within the lumen of the primary invaginations and within their dorsal branches. These branches remain attached to the longitudinal trunks, despite the fact that, with the great development of the anal connectives, the lateral tracheal invaginations are practically closed.

Shortly after the longitudinal trunks are established and the yolk is completely surrounded by the mid-intestine, dorsal roots commence to grow from the longitudinal trunks. These dorsal extensions arise between the junctions of the lateral tracheal branches with the longitudinal trunk. Growing dorsally into the mesoderm, whose cells are just beginning to assemble into the somatic musculature, fat body, etc., they then turn anteriorly and end blindly within approximately 20 microns in an embryo just prior to hatching from the uterine egg (Fig. 29). These tracheal branches, when formed, serve to secure the normal supply of air circulation throughout the body. Six such branches were found in the abdominal portion of the young embryo presented in Figure 28. Another series of branches, derived from tracheal connectives between stigmata and longitudinal trunks, passes straight in toward the mid-intestine.

The Hatched Larva.—The egg hatches within a day or so after it reaches the uterus (Newstead *et al.*, 1924) and since it is fertilized just prior to lodgment there, development must be very rapid. An account of the larva in the maternal uterus, including its molts and descriptions of some of the internal organs, has been provided by Austen (1904), Stuhlmann (1907), Roubaud (1909), and others. Roubaud, especially, has contributed to the information pertaining to this stage.

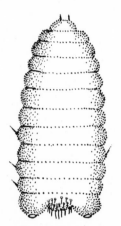

FIG. 31.—*Glossina palpalis.* First instar larva, dorsal view, anterior end up. (After Newstead, Evans, and Potts, 1924.)

Hatching of the young larva occurs in the typical muscoid manner by escape from a longitudinal opening in the chorion. Contrary to the conditions surrounding the first larval stage in *Melophagus,* this larva is very closely in contact with the uterine walls at all times. Furthermore, it is provided with sufficient musculature to enable it to move the anterior segments and slightly constrict portions of its body. This latter function is particularly advantageous later during birth and in forcing its way into the soil in which it pupates.

The larva molts twice while it is in the uterus, the first time shortly after emergence from the egg and again when it has practically completed its growth. The discarded cuticula is dislodged from the buccal region last of all and may be found, together with the chorion, lying in the anterior end of the uterus beneath the larva.

First Instar Larva.—The newly hatched larva is whitish in color and cylindrical in shape but tapers anteriorly (Fig. 31).

Viewed from the side, the anterior end of the body appears sub-triangular in outline. The mouth is situated anterodorsally and on either side project the small antennae and maxillary palpi, the two structures fused basally into a single organ. A few long, slender setae, with dilated distal portions, are scattered over the body. The posterior segment is larger than any of the others and here the respiratory apparatus is represented exteriorly by a pair of abdominal stigmata which are rather widely separated by a slight ridge between them. The hypodermis in the stigmatal region is relatively thicker than upon other parts of the body. The length is about 1.5 mm. according to Newstead *et al.* (1924).

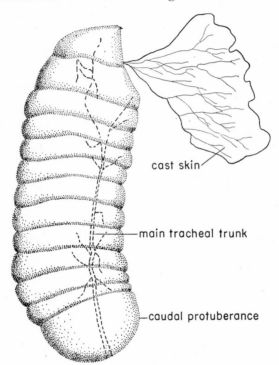

cast skin

main tracheal trunk

caudal protuberance

FIG. 32.—*Glossina palpalis.* First instar larva completing first molt, lateral view. (After Roubaud, La Glossina palpalis.)

Second Instar Larva.—After the first molt the larva appears approximately as before but larger (Fig. 32). Also, the spiracular region at the posterior end of the abdomen is somewhat more prominent. The first suggestions of respiratory lobes are distinguishable by the increased lengthening of the postanal segment and also by the slight swelling and rounding of the lateral halves of the segment. The depression between these two lobes is very shallow and extends dorsoventrally along the posterior surface between the two abdominal stigmata. This furrow deepens with further growth on the part of the larva, and the lobes become larger. Short stout setae are now present over the body surface and are more numerous than were the setae of the first instar.

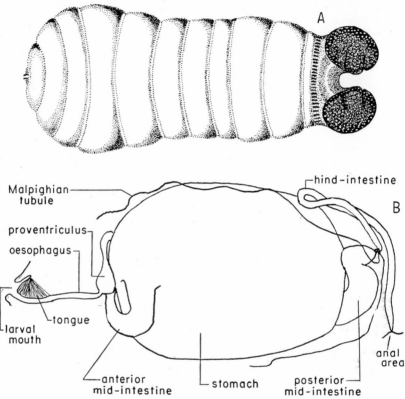

Fig. 33.—*Glossina palpalis*. *A*, third instar larva, dorsal view. A large inter-protuberal cavity now apparent due to the extreme expansion of the caudal pro-tuberances. *B*, lateral view of digestive system at time of birth. (Modified from Roubaud, La Glossina palpalis.)

Third Instar Larva.—The third stadium, shortly before pupation, shows a strong recession of the cephalic region, so that the larva is more nearly cylindrical anteriorly with a rounded contour when viewed from the dorsal surface (Fig. 33). At the posterior end the respiratory, or caudal, lobes have suddenly become very prominent through the rather abrupt deepening of the furrow which separates them. These lobes are now heavily cuticularized and black in color; in fact, the entire postanal segment is strikingly prominent because of its darkened appearance which sharply contrasts with the creamy white of the rest of the body, as well as its peculiar shape. Each lobe is subglobular, being slightly compressed on the inner, or median, surface where one of the stigmata is situated. Two shallow furrows on the posterior and inner surfaces separate the lobe into three divisions, one

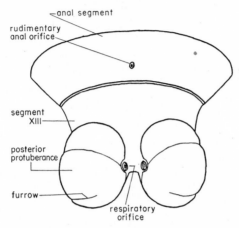

Fig. 34.—*Glossina tachinoides.* Greatly enlarged posterior segments XII and XIII of young, 4.5 mm. larva, ventral aspect. (After Roubaud, La Glossina palpalis.)

dorsal, one median, and one ventral. The surface of the postanal segment is rugose and near its anterior margin some of these rugae are arranged in rows to form a definite pattern. The respiratory lobes are covered with hundreds of small papillae, each of which, in all but the oldest larvae, is a functional minute stigmatic opening leading into the posterior chamber of the longitudinal tracheal system.

Thirteen body segments are present, including the cephalic and the postanal segments. Roubaud (1909) states that the anal opening occurs on the ventral surface of the twelfth segment and that the postanal segment is the thirteenth (Fig. 34). Newstead et al. (1924), however, maintain that the anal segment is the thirteenth which has been displaced ventrally.

Larval Respiratory System.—Each anal lobe contains a large branching tracheal trunk with which the hundreds of minute stigmatal openings are connected. A large thin-walled air sac or chamber is situated near the center of the lobe, and on either side of the sac is a branch of the main tracheal trunk that passes in from the abdominal stigma. Roubaud (1909) has shown that three such trunks exist, only one of which contains an open lumen and it is this one that is united with the stigma. All of this respiratory apparatus is in direct functional communication with the paired abdominal stigmata and their open tracheal trunks but the details have not been presented. From each respiratory lobe the main longitudinal tracheal trunk runs anteriorly in the dorso-lateral portion of the larval body with branching, finer tracheae extending to various parts of the body.

The excellent investigations of Roubaud (1909) show that the three branches of the main tracheal trunk in each respiratory lobe lead to the paired abdominal stigmata and to two, no longer functional, which are located in the shallow furrows extending across its lateral and posterior surfaces. Newstead (1918) has recognized the polypneustic condition of the larval respiratory apparatus and has homologized it with that of the Pupipara.

Larval Digestive System.—The provisional larval mouth opens directly opposite the papilla which hangs from the dorsal anterior wall of the maternal uterus through which the ducts leading from the spermathecae and the nutrient glands pass to discharge their contents. A cibarium-like cavity lies immediately behind the mouth and from its dorsal wall the sucking tongue (labrum) is suspended. In general, the structure and function of the tongue correspond to the same organ described for the *Melophagus* larva (Fig. 42*B*), and its rhythmic, rapid titillations may be clearly observed through the transparent body walls of the living insect. The pharynx is rather large in diameter in the region surrounding the tongue but back of the tongue it narrows somewhat to unite with the larval oesophagus (Fig. 33).

The oesophagus is rather large at its junction with the pharynx but rapidly decreases in size as it passes backward horizontally. Its posterior end is sharply bent in a vertical direction where it empties into the larger lumen of a tube, termed the proventriculus by Roubaud, through a valve. The epithelial layer of cells appears to be embryonal in nature with indistinct cell boundaries and the numerous small nuclei disposed at several levels within them, especially in certain portions of the organ where the cells are narrow and very elongate. The outer musculature surrounding the organ is poorly developed and difficult to observe.

The proventriculus is a pyriform organ which has its long axis projected dorsally in the haemocoele. The proventricular valve, through which the lumen of the oesophagus communicates with it, extends well into its interior at the dilated base. The proventriculus constricts to a comparatively small diameter dorsally, where it joins the anterior end of the mid-intestine. The cells in the walls of the basal portion are columnar with unvacuolated cytoplasm and their internally directed ends are covered by a plate, possibly chitinous in nature. Exteriorly the cells possess a poorly developed layer of circular and longitudinal muscles. The thickness of the proventricular cells rapidly diminishes dorsally until these cells merge insensibly into those of the mid-intestine. Here the thickened revetment is no longer visible and the cuboidal cells are highly vacuolated. The vacuoles themselves are few in number in each cell, but they are large.

The anterior end of the mid-intestine enlarges slightly as it continues the dorsal direction taken by the proventriculus but also it inclines a little to the left in its upward progression. Suddenly it forms a loop by bending to the right and ventrally, extending a short distance below the horizontal level of the oesophagus. At this point it bends to the left and gradually enlarges to approximately twice its former diameter as it turns dorsally once more and opens into the main portion of the mid-intestine at the left anterior margin. This section of the mid-intestine is capable of great distention and rapidly fills most of the haemocoelar space of the growing larva. Roubaud (1909) states that in a larva 3 mm. in length this portion of the mid-intestine measures 1 mm. in length and 1.3 mm. in diameter. It has received various names, referring mainly to its capacity as a storage reservoir; for convenience, it will be termed the stomach in these pages, with the mental reservation that such a designation is employed only for ready reference to a particular part of the mid-intestine.

At the lower right end of the stomach the mid-intestine continues as a large tube but it is much smaller than the former, approximating in size the anterior portion of the mid-intestine where it joined the stomach, as previously described. The posterior portion of the mid-intestine turns dorsally and gradually narrows. When it reaches to about the center of the haemocoelar cavity it bends abruptly in a posterior direction and constricts sharply to unite with the hind-intestine. This junction is marked by the presence of two pairs of Malpighian tubules.

The outer wall of the mid-intestine is composed of a very thin layer of muscles that appear to be weakly developed. The cells lining the lumen of the anterior portion of this organ are cuboidal but are slightly taller than wide. A few large vacuoles appear in each, the nuclei are situated basally, their cell membranes are indistinguishable, and their free ends are prolonged into the lumen as pseudopods. Evidently they are actively absorbing quantities of the nutrient solution for larval growth.

The cells of the stomach are very flat and are stretched by the great distention of this region of the mid-intestine. Indeed, the walls of the stomach are quite laminate, with only slight swellings to indicate the presence of the nuclei within the cells. The cellular cytoplasm between the nuclei is also vacuolated, indicating that digestive and absorptive processes are in operation here, too, although this activity may be considerably less than in the less flattened cells of the anterior portion of the mid-intestine. Roubaud's critical examination of the stored nutriment has convinced him that only the most superficial portion of it has been altered by the cells of the stomach.

The cellular structure of the posterior section of the mid-intestine is similar to that of the anterior portion. The cells, which are irregularly cuboidal, contain large vacuoles and the nuclei occupy a somewhat more central position. At the point of junction with the hind-intestine the lumen of the mid-intestine is entirely closed, so that there is no possibility of the contents passing farther down the digestive tract. At this place, also, the outer muscular layer is better developed and thicker than elsewhere, yet its elements retain an embryonic appearance rather than that of active, strongly functional muscle cells.

The hind-intestine is directed at first dorsally to the upper surface of the stomach where it bends posteriorly and ventrally in a loop and then proceeds to the anus on the ventral side of the larva. Its diameter is a little larger than the oesophagus but is distinctly smaller than the posterior portion of the mid-intestine. The lumen is closed at its point of attachment to the mid-intestine and is similarly obscured at the anal junction. Therefore, the hind-intestine has no actual outlet at either end. The epithelial cells of the wall are undifferentiated and are surrounded exteriorly by a thin musculature. Interiorly, they secrete a chitinous intima which lines the lumen of the tube.

The Malpighian tubules branch from the upper end of the hind-intestine as paired tubes, one on each side. Shortly after leaving the intestinal connection, each tube divides to form a pair of functional Malpighian tubules. One tubule of each pair passes dorsally and anteriorly over the whole of the length of the stomach, while the other goes ventrally and anteriorly along the latter's posterior half. The ducts open freely into the lumen of the hind-intestine and this organ undoubtedly serves as a storage reservoir for waste products.

The processes of digestion and absorption are assumed entirely by the epithelial cells of the intestinal tract, for there are no salivary glands or gastric caeca present in the larva. The alimentary tract of this group is thus as devoid of specialized digestive glands as it is in the larvae of the Pupipara. This condition is not surprising in view of the fact that the nutriment ingested by the larva has been already subjected to the processes of alimentation before being dissolved in the maternal haemolymph. The milk glands have only extracted some of this nutriment that is already in assimilable form for the maternal body cells and have passed it on to the offspring in the uterus. However, it is not maintained that this transference of nutriment is a simple one, for no physiological or histochemical examination of the sequence of events has yet been made.

Several writers have called attention to the close larval contact with the uterine papilla through whose tip both spermathecal and lactiferous ducts discharge. There seems to be no doubt that the relation here is more intimate than it is for the same parts in the Pupipara. Apparently, from the accounts before us, the larvae of the latter group merely ingest the secretions lying before the mouth in the uterus, and pass them down their alimentary tract by the aid of the sucking tongue. The larvae of Glossinidae, however, with their mouths in closer association with the glandular opening, are said to engage in a true sucking operation. At present we may accept the relationship as analogous to that obtaining in Mammalia, yet it remains to be proved whether the larvae actually exert a suction within the duct of the gland.

The great surplus of pabulum that is finally stored in the larva remains largely untouched by it during uterine life. It is probable that its utility here is the same as will be discussed for the young *Melophagus*. Roubaud (1909a) has, however, discovered that the peripheral portion of it, in direct contact with the walls of the stomach, is apparently undergoing some change since it appears to be slightly more granular. One difference between the nutriment in the stomach of Glossinidae and the Pupipara exists and may be recognized. The stored material in the former family does not tend to aggregate into small muricate balls as it does in the latter group.

LITERATURE CITED

Austen (1904), Blochmann (1887), Brandt (1869), Bruce (1897), Graber (1889), Hagan (1917), Hardenberg (1929), Kowalevsky (1886), Minchin (1905), Newstead (1918), Newstead, Evans, and Potts (1924), Noack (1901), Pratt (1900), Roubaud (1908, 1909a, 1909b, 1919), Stuhlmann (1907), Verhein (1921), Voeltzkow (1889), Weismann (1863), Wheeler (1891).

Chapter 8

ADENOTROPHIC VIVIPARITY—DIPTERA
(PUPIPARA)

The embryogenies of the Pupipara are apparently remarkably alike, though only the development of the members of the Hipboscidae has been examined in any detail. They also show a surprising similarity to the Glossinidae and for this reason the known embryogenies have been given quite fully in order to emphasize this fact as well as to afford comparative comments on the groups concerned. The Braulidae are mentioned here on account of their early inclusion in the Pupipara and because their method of reproduction has not hitherto been given historical treatment.

Order Diptera　　　　Family Hippoboscidae

The Pupipara include the families Hippoboscidae, Nycteribiidae, Streblidae and among older authors, at least, the Braulidae. Practically all of the embryological investigations on the Pupipara have been concentrated primarily, or exclusively, upon the sheep tick, *Melophagus ovinus* L.

The first discussion of this peculiar type of viviparity was given by the celebrated Réaumur (1742) in his *Mémoires*. He realized that no eggs were laid by the species he examined but that, on the contrary, hatched offspring were born. He thought the young were nymphs and, because of this, called the group of insects involved *Nymphiparea*. The ovaries were found to be quite atypical in number and fused by enveloping tissues. He dissected out embryos in late larval stadia and found the outer cuticula, two elongated tubes which he decided were tracheae, and an enormous internal whitish mass of homogeneous substance that entirely filled the body cavity. De Geer (1776) also devoted considerable space to these insects in his *Mémoires*. Bonnet (1779) confirmed some of Réaumur's observations but took exception to the latter's concept of the internal homogeneity of the unborn offspring, claiming that there is actually an organiza-

159

tion of parts within the unidentified mass that was the embryo. He observed the movements of the hatched young which, to him, were like pupae. Therefore, he was inclined to conceive of the group as giving rise to pupae. Latreille (1805) claimed that the embryo developed from an egg and passed its larval life within the mother's body. He adhered to Bonnet's belief that the birth product is a pupa and coined the term *Pupipara* to designate these insects, a term now recognized as being wholly inaccurate. In this connection it may be interesting to cite Root's (1921) observation that *Melophagus* is pupiparous but all the rest are apparently larviparous, while Drake and Jones (1930) describe the mature larva at birth as "enclosed in an obovoid capsule and pupal case. . . ."

However, it was not until Dufour (1825, 1845, 1851) took up the work that any further progress was made toward the embryological study of these insects. His rather extensive publications and numerous illustrations are evidence of his industry in seeking confirmation of his views on the reproductive activity of the Pupipara. His first paper treats of the adult female, the ovaries, the special glands of the oviduct, the copulatory organ and, finally, the product of parturition. Dufour's later publications are principally devoted to an amplification of the earlier conclusions. The second paper, especially, is fully illustrated and the subject matter is well presented in detail. The accuracy with which he described the female genital tract has won the approval of Massonnat (1909), a more recent student of the Pupipara.

Unfortunately, perhaps, we remember Dufour largely for one serious error in his observations and conclusions, often forgetting that there was no histological technique in his day. From an historical viewpoint his principal erroneous contention should be mentioned. He insisted with ever increasing assurance in succeeding papers that the mother insect contained no true egg or larva in its reproductive system but a fetus which is attached to the ovary by an umbilical cord. He affirmed Réaumur's view of the homogeneity of the offspring with its consequent lack of differentiated organs.

An excellent, short critique of the preceding literature was furnished by Blanchard (1846a, 1846b) who had made observations upon *Ornithomyia* and other genera. He maintained that eggs were truly present from which larvae developed. In the latter he discovered the ventral nerve cord and longitudinal tracheae.

Leuckart (1854, 1858) turned his attention to the problem with, at first, the production of a short paper on his investigations of larval anatomy. Perhaps he was the original discoverer of the posteriorly closed mesenteron. The second publication contains a carefully prepared series of illustrations, and his characteristically critical analysis of the sequence of development brought out many points previously obscure or unknown. For instance, he discovered very early stages of the egg prior to development and showed the great similarity between the larvae and pupae of this insect and equivalent stages of the Muscidae. He ascertained that the late embryo was a larva which changed to a pupa shortly after birth. In spite of this no serious attempt, apparently, was made to drop the name Pupipara and succeeding writers have continued to use it, largely for purposes of convenience (Osten-Sacken, 1881).

No further work was undertaken on the embryology of the group for 35 years. Then Pratt (1893, 1897, 1899, 1900) was encouraged by his teacher, Leuckart, to take up the problem. His earliest investigations treated the anatomy of the *Melophagus* larva in the maternal uterus. Upon returning to America he continued his studies at Haverford College and Harvard University and published three more articles on the subject. The third paper dealt with certain details of the female genital tract in relation to the viviparous condition. The second and fourth contributions consider especially the imaginal discs in the embryo and the larva. The embryological development of the insect is only too briefly given in the last paper. Lassmann (1936) has added considerably to the early history of the egg and the formation of germ cells and gonads.

Quite recently, Hardenberg (1929) added to our knowledge of the reproductive systems and the early embryogenies of the Pupipara in a comparative study of the group. He asserts that each ovary contains two ovarioles in the species included in this group which corrects Dufour's earlier statement that *Hippobosca* and *Ornithomyia* ovaries had but one.

The embryogeny of *Melophagus ovinus,* the sheep tick, has been carefully investigated, so that its developmental history is almost as well known as that of any viviparous insect. The principal contributions on this insect are those of Dufour, Leuckart, Pratt, and Hardenberg, whose names are given in chronological order. Anyone who is particularly interested in this species and its development should also consult Berlese's (1899) account of the later changes occurring in the insect and Lassmann (1936) on germ cell formation. The embryonic development of other species of the Pupipara has been studied very little, or not at all. Hardenberg (1929) contributed toward such knowledge but not enough to enable us to present a summary of another insect at this time.

Female Reproductive System

The reproductive system is large and occupies considerable space in the haemocoele. The genital organs consist of paired ovaries, each with two ovarioles, and short paired oviducts, the common oviduct, the uterus with two pairs of accessory glands opening dorsally into it and the vagina. Since these various portions of the reproductive tract have been studied in some detail and have been found to be curiously modified in places, it will be necessary to discuss them separately. These peculiarities are due to the necessity of retaining the egg until hatching and of feeding the larva until it is ready to pupate.

Each ovary is surrounded by a very thick peritoneal covering that binds the two ovarioles into one elongate-oval mass. This covering is composed largely of enveloping mesodermal tissue, which Pratt (1899) calls connective tissue, with a relatively small amount of muscle fibers. It continues proximally as a covering over the oviducts and vagina with an increasing preponderance of muscular tissue until practically only the latter occurs around the vaginal portion. The musculature of the paired oviducts is rather definitely arranged with circular muscles within and longitudinal strands ectally. In addition to the circular and longitudinal muscles that cover the vagina, there are a number of strong muscle bands which extend from it to the exoskeleton. The vaginal portion is the only one thus firmly held in position mainly by muscles, the remaining parts being supported by tracheae and nerves. The muscles strengthen the walls of the reproductive tract, assist in passing the ova down the oviducts, and are especially necessary in the expulsion of the fully grown larva at parturition.

The Ovary.—The ovary is cylindrical to oval in shape, depending upon the state of maturity of the oldest egg follicle in it. Within the outer peritoneal covering, which has just been mentioned, there is a second, thinner peritoneal sheath which invests each of the two ovarioles individually, except for a common wall between the two. It unites with the outer covering only at its point of origin, the apical end of the outer peritoneal covering and extends down over the ovarioles with its lower end open. It terminates abruptly before it reaches the oviduct. The ovariole consists of: (1) a very short conical anterior extension which lies embedded apically in the stroma of the inner peritoneal sheath and which Pratt (1899) believes is a part of the germarium; (2) a germarium containing a mass of undifferentiated cells; and (3) a vitellarium that always contains two egg follicles, unless possibly only one is present for a short time just after the liberation of a mature ovum from it. An outer tunica propria covers the ovariole beneath the inner peritoneal sheath and is usually prolonged beyond the second follicle. When the lower egg follicle is very large the tunica extends around it and is closed at the lower end, otherwise it is open. The ovariole is attached only at its tip to the peritoneal covering and unites proximally with one of the paired oviducts.

The germarium contains a number of small nuclei which lie in cytoplasm that shows no cellular boundaries. These nuclei appear to be alike and, because of their subsequent history, it is probable that they are primary germ cells although none of the writers has committed himself on this point. With a slight constriction the germarium passes over into the vitellarium.

The vitellarium in each of the four ovarioles of a pregnant female insect normally contains two egg follicles of quite different ages. Also, the follicles in any one ovariole are either younger or older than those in the other ovarioles with which either may be compared. Thus, a mature ovum is liberated from each ovary in alternation, and within the individual ovary the ovarioles likewise discharge ova in reciprocal sequence. Only one egg descends at a time and the remainder are held until the product of the first, the mature larva, is ready to be born. Then a second ovum passes down the reproductive tract. The usual manner of indicating the order of ovulation is to designate the ovarioles of the right ovary as R_1 and R_2, while those in the left are labeled L_1 and L_2. Ovulation will occur in the sequence R_1, L_1, R_2, L_2, the cycle being repeated as the upper follicles move down in the ovarioles.

The Paired Oviducts.—These are connected with the ovarioles by means of the outer peritoneal layer of muscles and connective tissue, the inner peritoneal sheath and the tunica propria of each ovariole terminating before reaching them. The oviducts are very short. They fuse proximally to form a large subspherical median chamber, the fundus, according to Leuckart (1858) and Pratt (1899), or the atrium of Massonnat's (1909) and Hardenberg's (1929) terminology. Besides the outer peritoneal covering, each oviduct is composed of a single layer of epithelial cells and an inner cuticula surrounding the lumen. At their junction with

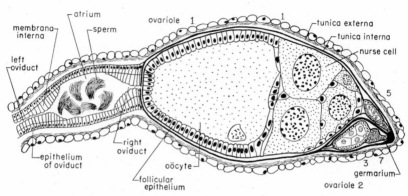

Fig. 35.—*Melophagus ovinus*. Longitudinal section of ovariole in right ovary, paired oviducts and cross section of the atrium. Left ovary omitted. Numerals 1, 3, 5, 7 are placed beside the follicles in their developmental sequence, 3 and 7 belonging to ovariole No. 2 of this ovary. (Modified from Pratt, Zeitschr. wiss. Zool., 66, 1.)

the atrium the chitinous lining is thrown into backwardly projecting folds (Leuckart, 1858; Pratt, 1899) or into individual cellular chitinous plates (Berlese 1899, 1909; Hardenberg 1929) which prevent the migration of spermatozoa toward the ovaries.

The suggestion of these investigators that the paired oviducts are lined internally with a cuticular membrane is rather surprising and leads to an unusual conclusion regarding the origin of this part of the reproductive system. Since an inner membrane is present it would follow that these paired oviducts are ectodermal in nature. Wheeler (1889) and others have traced the development of the paired oviducts from mesodermal tissues in other insects and consequently they should contain no cuticula. It may well be that no one has attempted to distinguish the lower limits of the true paired oviduct from the upper extension of the atrium of *Melophagus*. The passage is very short and lacks differential characteristics, except, perhaps, the presence or absence of the cuticula along the lumen. Hardenberg speaks more definitely of the chitin being in the atrium in the vicinity of the openings of the paired oviducts, but omits any discussion of the lining of the paired oviducts themselves.

Berlese (1899, 1909) as well as Pratt (1899) has provided figures showing the details of the connection between the atrium and the ovaries (Figs. 35, 36). If one should accept the cuticularized portions of these ducts as merely lateral extensions of the atrial chamber the presence of the cuticula could be readily un-

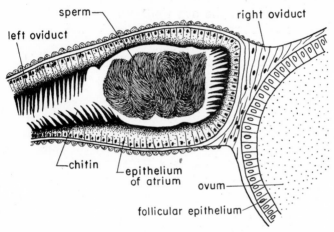

FIG. 36.—*Melophagus ovinus*. Longitudinal section of left oviduct and part of follicle No. 1; cross section of atrium and unsectioned right oviduct. (After Berlese, Gli Insetti.)

derstood. In this case the true paired oviducts must be assumed to be either wanting or reduced to a very small circlet of cells immediately adjacent to the ovaries. Such a rudimentary condition is found at the lower ends of the ovaries of *Miastor* where cells fail to develop into true oviducts, and in the Strepsiptera where, in the adult insect, the oviducts become greatly diminished in size and functionless. Indeed, Metcalfe (1933) has recently insisted that in some other species these parts are replaced in part by ectodermal extensions from the common oviduct.

These conclusions do no violence to our concept of the extent of development in the oviducts of insects, for it is generally accepted that most of the paired oviducts have suffered drastic reduction from the original segmental distribution of the ovarioles along the extensive paired oviducts of the primitive condition. The oviducts in the Pupipara may be considered as exceedingly abbreviated structures whose function has been almost entirely taken over by lateral extensions of the atrium, or they may be quite absent and the ovarioles may be thought of as uniting directly with the common oviduct, as is the case in the Glossinidae. With this interpretation in mind we will, for convenience, continue to designate these portions by the terms usually employed for them.

The lumen of the atrium is larger than that of the paired oviducts and serves two purposes. First, it unites the paired oviducts with the common oviduct, and, second, it stores the sperm for the fertilization of the ova that pass through it, thus functioning as a seminal receptacle. Its lining of epithelium is thinner than that of the paired oviducts yet its cells are still columnar in shape. Its cuticular intima is very delicate.

The Common Oviduct.—The common, or median, oviduct also is short and the lumen within it is narrow. Near one end it forms the atrium; proximally it opens abruptly into the dorsal side of the large uterus. The cuticular lining is quite thin and the epithelial layer is composed of cells that are only slightly elongate. Interspersed between them are a few cells having the appearance of being glandular in nature. This species is not unusual in possessing a uterus and a vagina as secondary invaginations following the common oviduct. The latter are not parts of the oviduct despite their occasional inclusion with it in the literature. Figures 15 and 99 may make this clear and the labeling follows the more modern ideas of homologies.

The Uterus and Vagina.—The lower end of the genital tract is distinctly divisible into two parts: the anterior uterus and the proximally situated vaginal region. The uterus is enormous. The egg hatches within the uterus and the young larva is nourished there until it is ready to pupate. The anterior end of the uterus projects slightly beyond the junction of the common oviduct and its dorsal wall. This bluntly conical projecting tip was overlooked by Von Siebold (1837) and Dufour (1851) but was later described by Leuckart (1858) as the bursa copulatrix, although he remarked that he had never found spermatozoa in it. Von Siebold already had found spermatozoa in the atrium and regarded the latter as the functional seminal receptacle, a view with which subsequent writers have agreed, except for Dufour, who referred this function to the anterior milk glands. It might be observed in this connection that Hardenberg (1929) has found what he believes to be the reduced, and perhaps functionless, rudiment of a bursa copulatrix in the ventral wall of the vulva. Such an organ is usually absent in the Diptera (Comstock, 1925).

In the case of the virgin female the uterus is depressed, but in the gravid female it varies in shape and size according to the degree of development attained by the larva within it. A full-grown larva causes great distention of this organ, which may reach almost to the thoracic segments. While thus enlarged, the maternal organs are pushed laterally or dorsally and the yellowish white offspring can be seen through the ventral abdominal body wall of the mother. The uterine walls are highly muscular, as previously observed. These circular and longitudinal muscles not only fortify the uterine walls, but, in conjunction with the strong muscle bands extending from the uterus to the maternal cuticula, assist in parturition. The cuticular intima becomes increasingly thicker toward the vagina. The ventral wall contains areas of glandular cells, which were first described in *Hippobosca camelina* by Massonnat (1909), and whose inner ends are highly vacuolated. A similar condition obtains also in the extreme anterior, conical portion of the uterus. The secretory products evidently are discharged into the lumen of the uterus (Hardenberg, 1929).

The vagina is the posterior portion of the reproductive tract. The dorsal wall is normally flat except for three externally visible folds, two lateral and one median, that extend anteroposteriorly the length of the vagina. During the passage of a larva through this region the dorsal wall, of course, is elevated and the borders of these folds provide amply for the required expansion of the lumen. Posteriorly the vagina opens to the outside of the body through the vulva.

The reproductive system in the virgin female is not prolonged in a straight line within the haemocoele. The vagina and uterus lie flat, one before the other, but the common oviduct stands vertically in the body at approximately 90° from the direction of the main uterine axis. From the atrium the right and left paired oviducts branch off horizontally toward the lateral body walls. The ovaries project beyond the paired oviducts and in the same direction.

The common oviduct makes an acute angle with the uterus in an old or pregnant female. When the uterus contains a full-grown larva it may be so distended, especially in its long axis, that the common oviduct is completely prolapsed and lies back against the uterine dorsal wall.

Accessory Organs.—Two pairs of glands originate on the dorsal wall of the uterus and discharge their contents into the latter through a common excretory duct. Both pairs are usually spoken of as the milk glands. The first or anterior pair consists of two short, thick, unbranched tubes. Since their cellular differentiation departs from that of the second pair in no essential respect, it will not be given here. The secretion from this pair of glands, however, is quite distinct in physical properties. It is dense and mucilaginous and accumulates in each cell as a single large vacuole that lies close to the lumen into which it empties.

This pair of glands was supposed by Dufour (1845) to be the seminal receptacle. Leuckart (1858) and Pratt (1899) sought elsewhere for such a structure, as has been mentioned, for no spermatozoa could be discovered in the lumen of the gland. Zacharias (1928), however, has frequently encountered them here in his preparations. Hardenberg (1929) believes, with Pratt, that the function of a seminal receptacle has been assumed by the atrium in *Melophagus*. Yet he also is of the opinion that this anterior pair of glands is a true seminal receptacle and when it functions as such in the Pupipara the atrium is absent. He has observed spermatozoa in the anterior glands of *Stenopteryx*, *Craterrhina*, the Streblidae and Nycteribiidae. Thus, he homologizes the first pair of glands with similarly placed structures in the Muscidae. They are no longer referred to by him as the anterior milk glands but as the seminal receptacle.

The second or posterior pair of milk glands are simply called the milk glands. In contrast to the first pair, just discussed, they are very long, dichotomously branching glands ramifying throughout a large proportion of the haemocoelar space. Directly above the common opening into the uterus they branch off from the anterior pair by means of a single duct. As this duct is traced away from the uterus it emerges from the musculature and connective tissue stroma that surround it basally and divides into the paired condition. Shortly thereafter the glandular portion is encountered whose structural details will be briefly enumerated. The lumen is lined with a thick chitinous cuticula strengthened by a spiral thickening that causes it to resemble the intima of a trachea (Hardenberg, 1929). Pratt (1899) describes the reinforcement as serrated lines formed by the inwardly projecting adjacent cells, while Zacharias (1928) speaks of the intima as being scalloped. Numerous pores perforate the membrane to permit the ready entrance of the glandular secretion into the lumen.

A thin epithelial layer lies outside of the cuticula, to which the latter owes its origin. Next to the epithelial layer appear the relatively large gland cells which also are regularly arranged in a single layer. These vary greatly in size and appearance at different times, for they exhibit periodicities of activity and quiescence which coincide with the state of pregnancy. When a larva is present in the uterus these glands secrete profusely. Active cells are much larger than they are in the resting period, their nuclei are large and the cytoplasm is coarsely granular with many small or large vacuoles. Their outer margins are circumscribed by an external limiting membrane (Pratt, 1899).

Development of the Embryo

The Egg and Its Formation.—The follicle in a young ovary originates as a compact mass of similar cells derived from the germarium. Later rearrangement separates the posterior half of these cells into a single layer of smaller, peripheral follicular cells while the remainder form an inner mass of slightly larger ones. The cells in the internal cell mass, about eight in number, increase rapidly in size. The extreme posterior one enlarges slightly faster than the others and is at once to be recognized as the oöcyte. Its nucleus is somewhat different from the others in appearance, containing fewer chromatin granules and a nucleolus. Immediately above it seven cells, just alluded to, continue to enlarge and to differentiate into the typical nurse cells of this species of insect. Hardenberg (1929) has found that Hippoboscidae have seven nurse cells in each mature follicle whereas the Streblidae and Nycteribiidae possess fifteen.

A constriction of the cellular mass now occurs so that the follicle cells separate the oöcyte and its nurse cells from the more anterior remaining cell mass in the vitellarium. The latter are destined to form the second follicle later in similar fashion when they will, of course, be constricted off from the germarium and its contents. The formation of the first follicle in the ovariole seems to check very materially the process of completion and maturity of the second follicle, though Lassmann (1936) reports the discovery of twin ova in the uterus, in two instances, thus showing that retardation may not always occur. Since a first follicle also is differentiating in each of the three other ovarioles of the two ovaries, the same succession of events occurs in all of them. Nevertheless, the eight follicles of the ovarioles do not all arise equally early so that, by observation, one may distinguish between them in regard to their relative maturity.

The oldest follicle now proceeds with its development. It is not only the oldest follicle but is also the largest one in the ovaries. It continues to enlarge and its oöcyte nucleus is located centrally in the deutoplasm. The nurse cells at its anterior end also increase rapidly in size. Their nuclei are larger than the oöcyte nucleus and are rich in chromatin granules. The growth of the follicle and its contents stretches the tunica propria until it may be indistinguishable along the sides of the follicle. It is, however, quite distinct where the follicle ends and the ovariole constricts to a narrow tube between the ripening follicle and the young follicle cell mass above. The tunica propria again is quite evident posteriorly where it is closely applied to the follicle as a continuous envelope, apparently without an opening at this place. As the ovum is discharged later it ruptures the tunica propria as well as the inner peritoneal membrane when it descends into the oviduct.

Just before its liberation the oöcyte grows very rapidly. The nurse cells have attained their maximum volume, but this is not long maintained, for they now begin to recede in size as they transfer their nutrient substances to the oöcyte. At the same time, the follicle cells infiltrate between the oöcyte and the nurse cells and finally enclose the former in a regular, columnar epithelium. The follicular cells surrounding the nurse cells, on the contrary, lose their regular arrangement and, quite evidently, their usefulness is almost at an end. The ovum assumes the typical shape of an insect's egg and the germinal vesicle, losing its nuclear membrane, becomes amoeboid and migrates peripherally. The peripheral, amoeboid nucleus is reduced in size but it has not yet been ascertained how this reduction in bulk is accomplished. The chorion is then secreted around the egg by the cells of the follicular epithelium and the germinal vesicle migrates to a central position with a reconstituted nuclear membrane.

When the ovum is liberated, it is cylindrical in shape with bluntly rounded ends. The dorsal side is very slightly concave while the ventral surface is convex. It is typically muscoid in general appearance. At the anterior pole there is a deep depression in which the micropylar pores may be found. The chorion is composed of two layers and beneath these a vitelline membrane is evident, and Lassmann (1936) assumes the presence of a plasma membrane. The periplasm is clearly perceptible around the egg; anteriorly, however, it is slightly thicker and more distinctly differentiated from the internal substance of the ovum. Posteriorly, it is exceedingly thin and its inner margin cannot be so easily distinguished where it meets the deutoplasm.

The egg plasm within the outer cortical layer or Keimhautblastem forms a network of anastomosing strands. Within its meshes are numerous vacuoles, containing watery yolk spheres. At the caudal pole the plasm is densely impregnated with Blochmann's corpuscles forming the pole plasm which is to receive the cleavage nuclei of the future primordial germ cells (Lassmann, 1936).

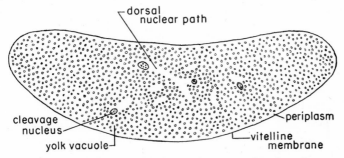

Fig. 37.—*Melophagus ovinus.* Egg with about 10 migrating cleavage nuclei, chorion omitted, longitudinal section. (After Pratt, 1900.)

Cleavage and the Formation of the Blastoderm.—As the oöcyte passes into the uterus it possesses a nucleus in the first metaphase stage of the maturation mitoses. Polyspermy is the rule and, according to Lassmann, four to six complete spermatozoa may be found somewhat posterior to the center of the egg. The polar body is situated near the dorsal side of the egg. During the second maturation mitosis the polar body usually divides at the same time. Thus three polar bodies may be formed, two from the first polar body and a third at the last meiotic division. The haploid somatic chromosome number is eight. The earliest stage of cleavage found by Pratt (1900) contained about 10 cleavage nuclei while Hardenberg (1929) discovered one with approximately 64 nuclei within it (Fig. 37).

At first the cleavage nuclei form an irregularly spaced group near the center of the egg. As they all migrate toward the surface, further cleavages occur. The direction of movement taken by each nucleus is readily observable, for it is surrounded by a clear cytoplasmic area. The clear plasm forms only a narrow space around the nucleus, but behind it the long migration path is marked by the clear plasm which has not yet been invaded by the adjacent yolk spheres. By the time the most advanced nuclei have completed perhaps two thirds of their journey to the surface, there are considerably more than 100 of them within the egg. They are scattered rather irregularly yet their disposition roughly corresponds to the more uniform arrangement found in Muscidae. A few have definitely lagged behind to become the primary yolk nuclei, only their location serving to distinguish them from the cleavage nuclei. Those progressing dorsally arrive earliest in the thin periplasm of the surface. The anteriorly directed nuclei reach the periphery before those of the posterior area. In the later phases of nuclear movement, the migration paths are obliterated through the infiltration of yolk. Blochmann's corpuscles are scattered throughout the egg instead of being confined to the posterior pole as before.

The superficial nuclei, as well as those within the egg, continue to divide so that eventually they are not only more numerous, but very much smaller than formerly. The thin periplasmic layer is only one third as deep as the nuclear diameter, so that quite evidently the nuclei cannot pass directly into it in the usual manner. Nevertheless, they are completely enclosed in cytoplasm for the outer cortical layer forms deep pockets around them as soon as they reach the surface (Fig. 38a). As the superficial nuclei become more numerous they seem to lie even closer to the vitelline membrane, thus producing slight elevations over the surface of the egg. Meanwhile the periplasm gradually thickens. The nuclei, on the other hand, are now only about one third their former size, so that they no longer project deeply into the interior of the egg.

At last the nuclei form a continuous layer over most of the surface of the egg and are spaced at slight intervals from one another (Fig. 38b). No nuclei are to be found directly beneath the micropyle, but at the caudal end of the egg several larger nuclei are distinguishable as primordial germ cells. Lassmann (1936) states that 12 nuclei enter the pole plasm from the egg. They divide to form a total of 24 but this number increases later. These early germ cell primordia push out beyond the general oval contour of the egg as a distinct swelling. Some of the granular plasm of this area concentrates around each nucleus to comprise the distinctive cytoplasm of the germ cell. These germ cells may thus be readily distinguished from somatic cells during their further development and migration. After the germ cell mass has received its quota of cytoplasm and nuclei a definite structureless membrane forms at their bases, thus cutting them off from direct continuity with the internal portion of the egg and its contents. This situation apparently was not observed by earlier investigators of this species.

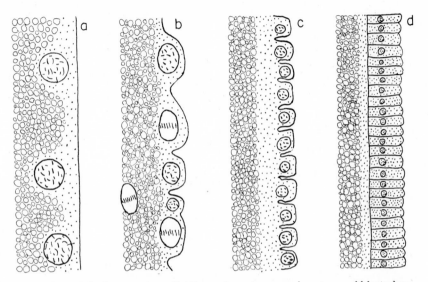

Fig. 38.—*Melophagus ovinus.* Sections of ova in successive stages of blastoderm formation: *a,* cleavage nuclei migrating into thin periplasm which thickens locally to surround them; *b,* nuclei peripheral, surface indentations separating them from one another; *c,* periplasm becomes a wider layer with deep constrictions completely separating nuclei laterally; *d,* lateral constrictions become cell membranes which now entirely enclose cell cytoplasm and nuclei by separating them from underlying cortical protoplasm. Chorion omitted. (Modified from Pratt, 1900.)

The primary yolk nuclei lie, apparently quiescent, deep in the anterior half of the egg. Their period of usefulness is presumably over, for they seem to disintegrate during the remaining steps of blastoderm formation. The production of secondary yolk nuclei is now initiated. These arise from mitotic division of the superficial nuclei, whence they promptly migrate to positions slightly beneath the periplasm. They are more numerous at the anterior and posterior poles and can be distinguished from the more centrally placed primary yolk nuclei by their larger size and by their more transparent condition due to the absence of chromatin in their centers.

The superficial nuclei are slightly larger than before. The periplasm becomes relatively quite thick and the former depressions between nuclei transform into deep grooves because of the close proximity of adjacent nuclei (Fig. 38c). The sides of the grooves finally are pressed together, as further crowding of the nuclei occurs. At these places cell boundaries arise which gradually extend into the lower edge of the periplasm. Constrictions beneath the nuclei ultimately cut off the peripheral layer to complete the blastoderm (Fig 38d). When the blastodermic cells are formed no more secondary yolk nuclei are produced from the surface layer. The interior nuclei apparently multiply to some extent by amitosis. An inner periplasmic layer appears beneath the newly formed blastoderm. It is quite thin in *Melophagus* and arises later than it does in the Muscidae.

At this time some mention should be made of the presence of two cell masses at the egg poles which Hardenberg (1929) describes in detail. Pratt apparently overlooked them entirely, but this omission may be due, in part, to the fact that the embryological development of the insect was a matter of secondary importance to him. However, the subject is of considerable significance because of the apparent participation of these cell masses in entoderm formation.

The blastodermic cells of the anterior and posterior poles of the egg lose their former regular arrangement. The cell membranes disappear and the nuclei become somewhat larger than those of the cellular blastodermic portion. Mitosis occurs freely and a mass of nuclei is formed which pushes as a cone-shaped mass toward the center of the egg. The base of the conical mass is bluntly rounded and projects slightly beyond the margins of the blastoderm (Fig. 39A). The anterior proliferation is the larger although it lags slightly behind the posterior in early formation. In future remarks they shall be referred to simply as the anterior and posterior proliferations since no other name has been applied to distinguish them. Lassmann (1936) also mentions these proliferations but asserts the nuclei of the posterior proliferation have wandered toward their present location while those of the anterior seem to follow a cytoplasmic streaming inward from the micropylar area.

A few nuclei emigrate from the apex of these proliferations and enter the surrounding yolk. These are the tertiary yolk nuclei, which may be differentiated from the secondary yolk nuclei by their larger size and fine chromatin network. In the meantime, the secondary yolk nuclei begin to break down and disintegrate, as the primary yolk nuclei did earlier.

Early in the formation of the tertiary yolk nuclei, the margin of the blastoderm at the caudal pole turns in around the posterior proliferation and grows toward the egg center. The surface of the cone-shaped proliferation, from its base toward its apex, is thus entirely surrounded for a short distance by the infolded blastoderm. A similar investment of part of the anterior proliferation occurs after the appearance of the mesodermic rudiment. Both infoldings are transitory in nature, however, and can no longer be found when the intestinal invaginations arise. Their significance is unknown.

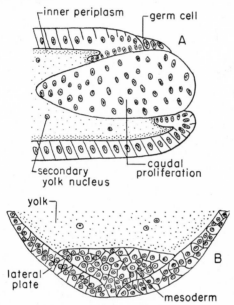

Fig. 39.—*A, Lipoptena cervi,* sagittal section of posterior end of blastoderm stage showing caudal proliferation. Chorion omitted. *B, Melophagus ovinus,* ventral plate in cross section showing formation of mesoderm from proliferating cells of the middle plate. Lateral ectodermic plates will fuse later along the ventral mid-line. (After Hardenberg, Zool. Jahrb. Anat., 50, 4.)

The Ventral Plate, Mesoderm Formation, and Segmentation.—Lassmann (1936) states that by the elongation of the anterior cells the head process is the first to appear as a definite portion of the embryo, distinct from the general blastoderm. Cells along the ventral surface also gradually lengthen and the entire embryonic area is delimited. This is the ventral plate whose anterior and posterior ends extend beyond the ventral surface, the former being continued into the anterior dorsal surface of the egg.

The mesoderm originates from cells in the median longitudinal axis of the ventral blastoderm, the middle plate, which give rise to a large number of cells by transverse mitoses. This process commences near the center of the egg and rapidly proceeds to the polar proliferations. The innermost cells are pushed in toward the yolk as a longitudinal mesodermal strand (Fig. 39*B*). The mesodermal strand flattens out and becomes appreciably wider. Its median portion gradually grows thinner and is eventually removed so that the mesodermal fundament is finally composed of two longitudinal ventrolateral bands of tissue. These are not termed mesentoderm by either Pratt or Hardenberg, for both be-

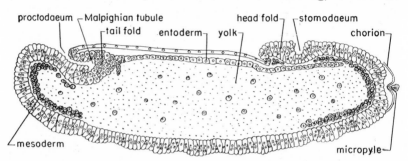

Fig. 40.—*Melophagus ovinus.* Embryo with head and tail folds, stomodaeum and proctodaeum. Diagrammatic sagittal section. (Modified from Pratt, 1900.)

lieve the definitive enteron arises from other cells. The inactive blastoderm cells of the lateral plates, bordering those comprising the proliferating middle plate, approach each other and finally join as the middle plate sinks in toward the yolk. At the same time the blastoderm cells of the lateral plates, including the cells extending halfway around the egg, become taller in contrast to the now flattened dorsal epithelium and also in comparison with the irregularly shaped mesoderm cells. The ectoderm external to the mesodermal rudiment is three to four cells in thickness, but rapidly thins to a layer of single cells on the lateral margins.

The germ band, as the embryo should now be called, continues its growth anteriorly, pushing the anterior proliferation with it. When it reaches the anterodorsal part of the egg it passes posteriorly for a short distance over the dorsal surface. The caudal proliferation is likewise forced to a dorsal position but the posterior end of the germ band then ceases to elongate and extends only slightly over the dorsal surface of the egg (Fig. 40). At its tip the germ cell mass forms a slight enlargement of cellular tissue. The number of germ cells reaches its maximum at this time and only a portion of this number eventually arrives in the gonads.

No embryonic envelopes are formed although Pratt (1900) suggests the possibility that the amnion may be represented by the folds occurring in the dorsal blastoderm where it fuses with the germ band. Hardenberg (1929) denies that the main portion of the dorsal epithelium is the serosa.

The Proctodaeum, Mid-Intestine and Stomodaeum.—Pratt (1900) and Hardenberg (1929) differ essentially in their interpretations of the formation of the alimentary tract. According to the latter, a pair of dorsocaudal invaginations appear, which are the anlagen of the Malpighian tubules. The two are separated by a little space which also invaginates to give rise to the proctodaeum. As it grows further toward the yolk, and ventrally as well, the two rudiments of the Malpighian tubules are drawn in with it. The Malpighian rudiments quickly divide to form four tubules which arrange themselves equidistantly around the inner end of the proctodaeal invagination. Invagination ceases when the inner end of the proctodaeum reaches the yolk. Pratt's view is that the hind-intestine invaginates before the Malpighian tubules appear and the mesoderm at first intervenes between the proctodaeum and the yolk.

The stomodaeum starts developing after the mid-intestine covers about half of the yolk, so the differentiation of the latter will be described first. To do so it will be necessary to recall Hardenberg's observation that the anterior and posterior proliferations were pushed upward beneath the elongating ends of the germ band. The anterior proliferation becomes cellular, whereas it had previously been syncytial in composition. The individual cells exhibit amoeboid movements. Rapid multiplication takes place and the daughter cells spread slightly forward beneath the ectoderm and mesoderm of the anterodorsal part of the germ band. However, their progress caudally beneath the dorsal epithelium is much more rapid than it is anteriorly. They finally unite with a similar strand of cells proceeding forward from the posterior proliferation. The latter was originally situated slightly caudal of the proctodaeal point of invagination; the anterior proliferation, likewise, was located originally beneath the future stomodaeum.

This strip of enteron cells lies dorsally in a median line over the yolk. For the most part it is a single cell in thickness but in the original centers of proliferation beneath the cephalic and caudal regions it is several cells in depth (Figs. 40, 41). Pratt agrees with this description except that he believes the cells of the mid-intestinal dorsal strand have arisen from invaginating ectodermal cells of the proctodaeum with, perhaps, a less pronounced contribution from the stomodaeum.

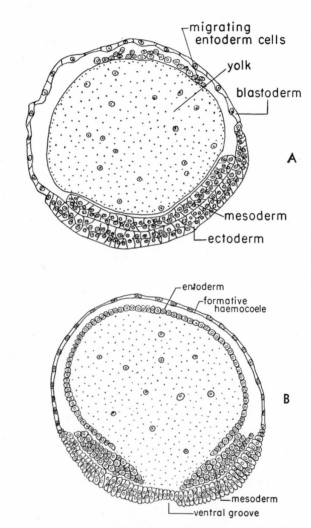

Fig. 41.—*Melophagus ovinus. A,* embryo a little younger than shown in Fig. 40; section across center of the body. Ectoderm and mesoderm circumscribing the yolk laterally while amoeboid entoderm cells lie in a strand above it. (After Hardenberg, Zool. Jahrb. Anat., **50,** 4.) *B,* a slightly older embryo in which the entoderm has spread laterally and mesoderm has thickened; the ectoderm is forming the neural groove. (After Pratt, 1900.) Chorion omitted in both.

The development of the dorsal mid-intestinal strand of cells is not the only direction in which cells have spread from the original centers of proliferation. Some have pushed down between the yolk and dorsal epithelium both anteriorly and posteriorly as a thin sheet of cells. In the cephalic region this layer ultimately covers the entire yolk, dorsally and laterally, for the stomodaeum has not invaginated deeply enough to interfere with it. Caudally, however, the situation is slightly different. Here the proctodaeum has already reached the yolk and the mid-intestinal layer of cells is forced to pass laterally around it. Both centers of lateral growth eventually circumscribe the yolk and posteriorly the cells finally succeed in pushing themselves in between the yolk and proctodaeum. Lateral growth in the dorsomedian part of the egg also continues over the yolk until it is wholly enclosed by the intestinal layer, the ventromedian portion being covered last. Thus the yolk is enveloped by a mid-intestinal layer of cells that originated from the anterior and posterior syncytial proliferations that appeared during blastoderm formation. Pratt agrees in general with Hardenberg in this sequence of events except that the hind-intestine does not lose its connection with the yolk.

Pratt has observed that the proctodaeum opens into direct communication with the lumen of the mid-intestine about the time the latter is completely formed. This continuity persists until some time just prior to the hatching of the larva from the egg, when it is again permanently closed. Hardenberg does not mention this occurrence.

There is little of special interest to be said at present regarding the stomodaeal invagination. It first appears when the mid-intestinal layer covers the dorsal and lateral half of the yolk. Its length is much less than that of the proctodaeum and it at once commences to open at the inner end, where it touches the mid-intestinal layer. Later a common lumen is established between the fore- and mid-intestines so that the intestinal tract is continuous from mouth to anal opening. There may be some doubt, however, whether the lumen is open throughout its length during the entire embryonic period within the egg. Observers are agreed that the inner end of the proctodaeum is closed off from the enteron during the uterine life of the larva.

Hardenberg has contributed only a few comments on the further embryonic history within the egg, but Pratt has included a number of rather disconnected observations that are only incidental to his treatment of the imaginal discs. An effort is made to glean these bits of information from his contributions and to incorporate them, with Hardenberg's, in subsequent paragraphs.

When the blastoderm is complete the inner cortical layer, or inner periplasm, intervenes between it and the yolk. It did not, however, surround the anterior or the posterior proliferation and these remained in contact with the yolk. The tertiary yolk nuclei are immigrants from these proliferations. During the formation of the mid-intestine, the tertiary yolk nuclei gradually left the yolk and assumed positions in the periplasmic layer beneath the entoderm. This is their abode in all later stages of development. There are suggestive and provocative ideas regarding their peculiar behavior for the embryologist who is interested in the concept of gastrulation in the insects, when it is recalled that these tertiary yolk nuclei have, according to Hardenberg, arisen from the same source as the entodermal cells.

Segmentation and Tracheal Invaginations.—Segmentation takes place simultaneously with the invaginations of the intestinal anlagen. Pratt (1900) believes that 12 segments appear altogether, one of which represents the head fold of the early embryo. The head fold exhibits no traces of segmentation, this being entirely confined to the main trunk of the body. Eleven pairs of primary invaginations mark the locations of the tracheae. They seem to be rather large during the early stages of tracheal differentiation.

Nervous System.—The ventral nervous system also develops after the enteron is practically completely formed. Two pairs of prominent ectodermal swellings in a preoral position are the primordia of the optic ganglia and part of the brain (Hardenberg, 1929). It is probable that Pratt (1900) saw these same neural masses but only his observation of their ultimate disposition is carried out in detail. He believes the first pair of anterior ganglionic masses arises from the ectoderm of the head fold just before it invaginates to form the stomodaeum. These are the rudiments of the cerebral ganglia. From the first they are connected with the ventral nerve chain. The second pair originate from the lateral ectodermal body walls opposite the junction of the stomodaeum and the enteron. They migrate ultimately to a position above the stomodaeum where their anterior ends fuse, send a nerve forward to the base of the sucking tongue, and eventually become the sympathetic ganglia of the pharyngeal region. A frontal ganglion results from an invagination of the dorsal stomodaeal wall, but this is an ephemeral structure and later stages of larval life show no traces of it. Two strands of cells arising from the inner layers of the ectoderm extend from the anterior to the posterior ends of the body as the rudiments of the ventral nerve chain. They are pushed up into the haemocoele where they come closer together in the median axis of the body and fuse with the ventral ectodermal ridge. Even before they pass upward away from the ectoderm, however, they show traces of segmentation into ganglionic and commissural portions. The median ventral ectodermal ridge severs its connection with the ectodermal body wall and unites more intimately with the ventral nerve chain. Neuroblasts appear shortly before this event and the nervous system gradually becomes a more specialized structure in subsequent stages.

Meanwhile, the mid-intestine has entirely surrounded the yolk and the lateral body ectoderm has continued to extend dorsally. In later embryonic stages it fuses over the back of the embryonic larva. During its overgrowth the mesodermal tissue pushes upward more slowly and eventually reaches the dorsal mid-line, where the heart forms between its upper margins. The dorsal aorta opens anteriorly over the partly fused ganglia of the pharynx.

When the dorsal body walls fuse and the heart forms, two deep invaginations may be seen laterally, and slightly below, the mouth. These are the rudiments of the salivary glands but they, too, are fugitive and are not to be seen in succeeding stages. At the same time a dorsal evagination projects slightly over the mouth. This structure is, possibly, the labrum mentioned by Hardenberg and also the organ which Pratt (1900) calls the sucking tongue.

The Germ Cells and the Gonads.—It was mentioned earlier that the primordial germ cells make their appearance about the time cleavage nuclei are beginning blastoderm formation by their migration to the periphery of the egg (Lassmann, 1936). Twelve nuclei simultaneously enter the pigmented pole plasm. Several mitoses give rise to a large number of primary germ cells before the embryo has attained the germ band stage. Evidently more nuclei are formed than can be supplied with adequate amounts of this pole plasm because some are eventually lost from the germ cell mass. Upon the development of the proctodaeal invagination the germ cell mass, or a portion of it, is to be found in its lumen. As the proctodaeum lengthens, the germ cells remain near its inner end and so are carried further into the egg. The germ cells seem to penetrate between the cells of the early proctodaeum and so reach the posterior entoderm layer. As the entoderm grows forward over the yolk to fuse with a similar layer from the anterior end, the germ cells are carried along with it to their approximate destination. Here they leave the entoderm to invade the upper portions of the dorsally growing mesoderm as it accompanies the ectoderm toward dorsal closure. The gonadal tissue is formed of this mesodermal sheet and the germ cells are enclosed within. The gonads are paired and no sexual differentiation is yet visible. It should be noted that the ultimate number of germ cells entering the primitive gonads is considerably less than the original number formed at the posterior pole of the egg, for many have strayed or were otherwise unable to maintain contact with the successful cells.

Involution of the Head.—A straightening and shortening of the embryo accompanies its growth and differentiation of parts. The mouth lies at the anterior end of the body and the anal opening is similarly situated posteriorly. The ultimate location of the latter is acquired by its continued migration to a distinctly ventral position. Meanwhile the cephalic portion of the embryo becomes recessed within an overgrowth of the anterior body walls. This is spoken of as the involution of the head, a process which occurs as follows. A little distance back of the organ designated as the labrum, and about equally distant ventrally from the mouth, slight outpocketings or folds of the ectoderm occur (Fig. 42). The folds become increasingly deeper as their outer margins extend and fuse laterally. The folds grow forward, constricting anteriorly over the head to form a new mouth in advance of the former one. A cavity just in front of the labrum becomes the provisional buccal cavity and the labrum, attached only at its base, is the sucking tongue whose rhythmic titillations later effectively force the nutriment from the milk glands into the mid-intestine of the larva.

The Origin of the Imaginal Discs.—The central theme of Pratt's (1893, 1900) investigations was tracing the history of certain adult structures which originate as rudimentary buds in the unhatched embryo and the larva. These are the imaginal discs. To avoid confusion with the history of purely embryonic structures in general, reference to them hitherto has been avoided since they are not essential to larval development. A few imaginal discs appear in the embryo before hatching and these will now be mentioned, while those arising in the larva during its uterine incubation will be reserved for later consideration.

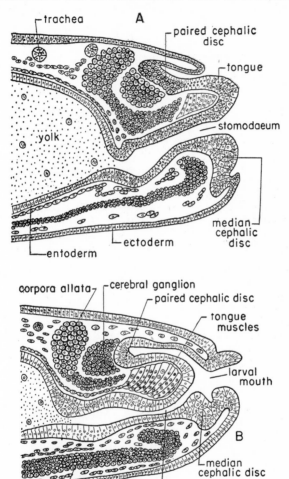

Fig. 42.—*Melophagus ovinus*. The involution of the head. *A,* involution beginning. *B,* involution completed. Sagittal sections cut slightly obliquely. (Modified from Pratt, 1900.)

Three thickenings of the ectoderm arise in the head fold of the embryo at a slightly later stage than that shown in Figures 39B and 40. These are to form the imaginal head. One thickening, slightly posterior to the mouth, is the median disc from

which the ventral portions of the adult head and mouth parts
will develop. It actually arose as paired invaginations which
fused so promptly that no description is necessary. The other
two discs are above the mouth and somewhat laterally placed
on the upper surface of the head fold (Fig. 43). From them will
arise the dorsal and lateral areas of the imaginal head.

The median cephalic disc shifts toward the mouth in later
embryonic stages as the stomodaeum migrates to an anterior terminal position, and is at last
turned in with the involution of
the head so that it then becomes
part of the ventral wall of the
pharynx (Fig. 42B). When it attains this position it thickens
noticeably and starts to invaginate. Part of it extends posteriorly beneath the pharynx as
paired prolongations which later
fuse in the larval stage.

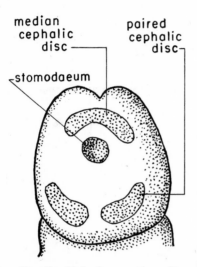

FIG. 43.—*Melophagus ovinus*. Embryonic head fold, surface view showing approximate location of the imaginal discs. (After Pratt, 1900.)

The paired imaginal discs
lying above the larval mouth behave differently. Pratt calls these
the dorsal cephalic discs. These
discs promptly enlarge and each
forms a thickened ectodermal
layer of cells, slightly convex externally and concave internally.
A slight depression in the convex surface quickly invaginates
into a deep groove which penetrates almost to the mid-intestine.
Its cells fuse with the mesoderm laterally and ventrally. On
the inner lateral border the fundaments of the cerebral ganglia
enter at once into permanent and intimate contact with it.
This movement is completed shortly after the mid-intestine
has entirely enclosed the yolk and when the ventral nerve is
just developing (Figs. 44, 45). As the mouth and stomodaeum
migrate further toward an anterior position, the dorsal discs
shift forward so that they no longer lie over the mid-intestine
but in front of it. During this movement the dorsal discs
approach each other in the median line, where their anterior
ends fuse to form a common lumen for the two at this place.
This narrow, slitlike common cavity extends laterally across the

dorsal side of the cephalic region. Posteriorly, however, the dorsal discs remain as separate invaginations, each with an independent cavity of its own. Thus, while fused ectally they are branched, or paired, entally.

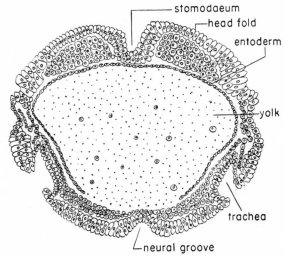

FIG. 44.—*Melophagus ovinus.* Embryo slightly younger than shown in Fig. 40 sectioned through paired cephalic discs. (After Pratt, 1900.)

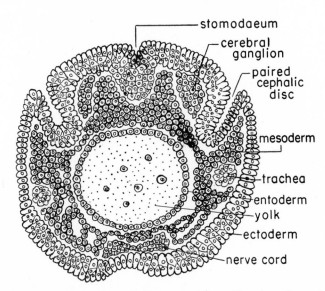

FIG. 45.—*Melophagus ovinus.* Embryo somewhat older than shown in Fig. 40 sectioned through paired cephalic discs. (After Pratt, 1900.)

Six pairs of imaginal discs also appear in the thoracic region of the unhatched embryo, two pairs in each segment. The three ventral pairs arise with the early involution of the head. The other three are somewhat later in differentiating. The primary thickenings of the body ectoderm that delimit these areas soon begin to invaginate at their posterior margins but shortly thereafter the entire marginal portion of each disc is involved in the process. When the discs have sunk beneath the general level of the outer surface of the body, the ectoderm closes over them and they exhibit no further change during this stage or in the subsequent larval life. These discs eventually give rise to the imaginal legs.

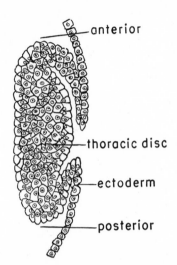

FIG. 46.—*Melophagus ovinus.* Invaginating thoracic disc in frontal section. (After Pratt, 1900.)

The remaining three pairs of thoracic discs lie as thickened areas in the dorsal ectoderm. Their first appearance follows the involution of the head. The prothoracic pair (Fig. 46) are only incompletely overgrown by the ectoderm after their invagination, while the meso- and metathoracic pairs retain their superficial position until some time after the young larva has hatched. The metathoracic pair are fundaments of the halteres while the others remain entirely rudimentary in this species and fail to develop into adult structures.

Two pairs of imaginal discs, representing the rudiments of the adult genitalia, are formed shortly prior to hatching. The larger pair is situated just anterior to the anus and rectum. They have invaginated from the ectoderm beside the rectum. Entally their cavities fuse so that a narrow invaginated sac partly surrounds the rectum ventrally. Their most anterior cellular margins project forward a little way into the haemocoele as separate paired masses. The second pair of discs now develop as ectodermal, superficially placed thickenings that do not invaginate before the embryo hatches.

The Hatched Larva.—Subsequent to its descent into the uterus, the embryo has pursued its ontogenetic history quite independently of the mother, except for the fact that it has been retained and protected from the external environment in the lower end of the maternal reproductive system. The only essential difference between this type of viviparity and ovoviviparity, so far as the offspring is concerned, lies in the fact that here only one egg has been cared for by the parent, while in the ovoviviparous type usually several or many ova developed embryos simultaneously in the mother. Thus far there has been in both types only a single physical differentiation visible to distinguish viviparity from oviparity: the enlarged lower end of the maternal reproductive tract has been turned into an incubatory sac. From the physiological viewpoint, some intangible alteration in the maternal nervous system has no doubt accompanied this physical change because, if not, the egg or eggs of the ovoviviparous and adenotrophic females would unquestionably have been deposited prior to hatching.

Upon the rupture of the chorion and the appearance of the larvae, however, the innate differences between the two classes of viviparity soon manifest themselves, for the adenotrophic larva obtains its nutriment from the mother and continues its ontogeny within the maternal uterus until ready to pupate. Some of the interrelations of the mother and her offspring and the morphological characteristics of the latter will now be considered.

The Maternal Nutrient Glands.—The second, or larger, pair of accessory glands of the female reproductive system is not continually active in its peculiar physiological behavior. Only during periods of gestation does it engage in the actual excretion of its products, which seem to consist of a milky liquid containing numerous refringent granules. Roubaud (1909) and Hardenberg (1929) have shown that a small amount of the material probably consists of fats while the greater portion is albuminoid in nature. The former further points out the possibility of the secretion in *Melophagus* being somewhat different from that in *Glossina* since in the former the non-fatty portion of the product, in the free state, will aggregate into small masses of spherules.

It has commonly been assumed by nearly all investigators that this secretion of the larger pair of accessory glands is the medium supplied to the larva for its growth and further development. One notable exception is the opinion voiced by Berlese (1899). According to him, the larva subsists on the spermatozoa and accompanying voluminous mass of secretion from the male accessory glands, the product of the female nutrient glands perhaps aiding secondarily in this procedure. His preparations have shown objects very closely resembling clumps of spermatozoa in the mid-intestine of the larva. Hardenberg has at least seen spermatozoa very definitely in the oesophagus and mid-intestine of a young larva but he hastens to reject Berlese's theory in connection with his observations. In his view the primary function of the milk glands is to supply a cementing substance that causes the extruded larva to adhere to the sheep's fleece.

Zacharias (1928), however, points out the fact that *Lipoptena* and *Ornithomyia* larvae are not provided with an adhesive substance although their maternal milk glands function as do those of *Melophagus*. It must be admitted that the occasional consumption of seminal fluid and spermatozoa is not unknown among insects and Trouessart (1895) believes this to be an essential requirement in the life of both sexes of the immature stages in the mite, *Chorioptes auricularum*.

But while possibly an accidental, and probably a very incidental, acquisition for the *Melophagus* larva, it seems wholly unnecessary to assume that the consumption of spermatozoa becomes a matter of fundamental importance in the life of this insect. In fact, Roubaud (1909) has pointed out the difficulties in accepting this hypothesis, the principal objections being that copulation must necessarily precede each gestation, traces of spermatozoa cannot be found either on the posterior external body wall of half-grown embryos or at any time within their alimentary tract (which Berlese admits possesses little or no digestive properties). The original quantity of male substance is insufficient to account for the growth of the larva and the volume of its reserve stored food in the mid-intestine. Finally, such a dependence could not be homologized with the nourishment of larvae as it takes place in Glossinidae, relatives with similar reproductive traits, whose succeeding gestations certainly do not require any intervening copulations (Stuhlmann, 1907). It might be well to add to Roubaud's comments the observation that the accessory glands of Pupipara are excessively developed compared with other insects if they function only as cement glands.

One other possible source of food supply is the product of the anterior accessory glands which, with the milk gland, have a common uterine opening. It is probably correct to homologize these anterior glands with the seminal receptacles of the Muscidae as Dufour (1851), Holmgren (1904), Roubaud (1909), and Hardenberg (1929) have done. Zacharias (1928) has reported the presence of spermatozoa in the anterior milk glands of *Melophagus* in a large number of his preparations. Yet there seems, also, to be no question of their supplying substances that now serve to assist in the nourishment of the young where their original function is no longer maintained. *Melophagus* is an example of the nutritional utility of these modified structures. Hardenberg describes their secretion as being physically quite different to that of the posterior glands, for it is mucilaginous in texture. Apparently, however, these glands are neither large enough nor sufficiently active to meet all of the requirements of the larva and, presumably, they play only a secondary part in supplying its food. Aside from the secretions discharged by these two pairs of glands into the uterus there is no evident source of food supply for the developing offspring, and all the evidence at present available leads to the conclusion that they are, in reality, now serving in the capacity of nutrient organs.

External Appearance of the Uterine Larva.—Upon hatching the young larva lies in the uterus with the head and ventral side corresponding to the same aspects of the mother's body. This orientation meets one's expectation from Hallez's law (1886) for the egg stage. It is an elongate, slender, whitish insect whose tapering anterior portion and faintly segmented cuticle causes it to resemble closely the larva of Muscidae. Its length at hatching is relatively very great, and Leuckart (1858) has observed that, while it only doubles in length during its uterine life, further growth consists largely in the acquirement of enormous bulk rather than in continued elongation. Just dorsal to a median lateral line are eight slight depressions, segmentally arranged, in whose centers stigmatic pits are seen. The two anterior depressions occur directly behind the meso- and metathoracic dorsal imaginal discs that were mentioned as occurring in the embryo before hatching. The remaining six pairs of depressions are distributed to each of the first six abdominal segments. These probably are to be homologized with similar organs in the primitive larval forms, but are here no longer functional in the larva.

The mouth opens anteriorly, and a posterior stigmatic plate, containing only a single pair of stigmata, is present at the end of the abdomen. The number of stigmata increases to three pairs after the second molt takes place. The anus is ventral and slightly anterior to the posterior stigmatic plate (Fig. 47).

Berlese (1899) has described the larva as lying within the distended interior of the uterus surrounded by a mass of spermatozoa and spermatic fluid derived from the male. The larva therefore is not in close contact with the uterine walls at first and this condition occurs only later when the larva becomes considerably more robust.

Two molts are definitely known to occur although Leuckart referred to a third, an observation which has not since been verified. The first molt occurs shortly after hatching takes place according to this author, and Pratt (1893) believes that the second takes place when the larva reaches a length of 2.7 mm.

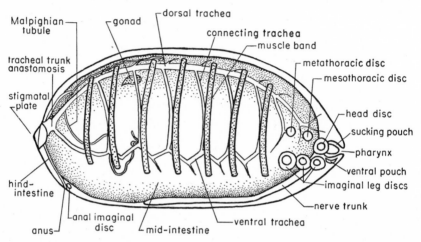

FIG. 47.—*Melophagus ovinus*. Half grown larva, whole mount in lateral view. (After Pratt, Arch. Naturgesch., **59**.)

The larval cuticula increases in thickness with each instar. In the third instar it is, nevertheless, rather thin at first. Some time before birth the hypodermis adds considerably to the thickness of the cuticular layer and the newly formed internal layer is distinctly different in appearance from the cuticular product of the earlier secretion.

When fully grown, however, the larva is far more robust than the early stages. Its length, as given by Pratt (1893), varies from 3.5 mm. to 3.7 mm., the width is about 1.9 mm. and its dorsoventral dimension is 1.6 mm. By this time, too, it has lost practically all of its resemblance to the muscid larva, becoming quite barrel-shaped with a slightly flattened ventral surface. External evidence of its twelve segments has entirely disappeared from the cuticle. Anteriorly, the mouth opens through a conical papilla and on each side of it, just dorsal to the center line, is a small papilla. At the posterior extremity the stigmatic plate bears the functional respiratory orifices. Slightly anterior to the stigmatic plate, on the ventral surface, is the anal opening. A row of seven tiny, slight depressions on the dorsolateral line and a similar row on the ventrolateral line on each side of the body indicate externally the points of attachment of seven muscle bands passing dorsoventrally on each side beneath the hypodermis. Bonnet (1779) originally described them as stigmata but in this he was corrected by Dufour (1845) who recognized their true significance as muscle insertions.

The eight minute stigmatic depressions are still clearly visible, but they gradually fade from view externally as the larva becomes fully grown, with the exception of the two anterior pairs whose minute pits are always distinguishable.

At a point about one sixth of the distance back from the anterior end of the older larva, and slightly dorsal to the center of the side, a narrow depression in the cuticle runs forward, crossing the anterior end of the body at the base of the oral papilla and thence posteriorly to a corresponding position on the other side. This is the arched suture which, opening after pupation, permits the escape of the imago from the puparium. Leuckart (1858) and Pratt (1893) both mention another suture which encircles the very oldest larva at the base of the arched suture just described. The latter believes this ring suture marks the boundary between the thorax and the abdomen (Fig. 48). While the latter is only a shallow furrow, the former is a deep cleft which penetrates to the hypodermis. The cavity of the arched suture appears in cross section to be heart-shaped, with the narrowed portion directed toward the surface. Still later, in the most anterior portion of it, the cleft is transformed into a deep narrow fissure. A row of four hypodermal cells beneath it seem to be different from adjacent hypodermal cells. These peculiar cells excrete a softer matrix which fills the cleft of the arched suture. This suture is characteristic of cyclorrhaphic Diptera.

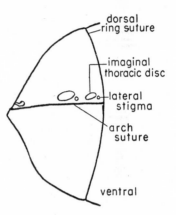

Fig. 48.—*Melophagus ovinus.* Anterior end of old larva showing ring and arch sutures. (After Pratt, Arch. Naturgesch., 59.)

With these descriptions of the external appearance of the youngest and the oldest unborn larvae in mind, some consideration may now be given to certain specific features of their internal organization, especially to the respiratory and digestive systems.

Larval Respiratory System.—Respiration is effected through the stigmata situated on the posterior stigmatic plate. The plate appears subovate in surface view and brownish in color (Fig. 49). There are two deep depressions in its center, separated by a relatively thick dorsoventral chitinous ridge, so that in looking at it from above or below, in a median section, it appears anything but

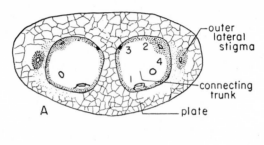

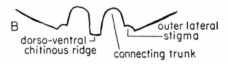

Fig. 49.—*Melophagus ovinus.* *A*, polypneustic lobes of young larva. Numbers 1–3 refer to supernumerary, unnamed stigmata, while No. 4 is the abdominal stigma. (After Newstead, Ann. Trop. Med. and Parasit., **12**.) *B*, same, lateral view, to show cavities in which stigmata occur. (After Pratt, Arch. Naturgesch., **59**.)

flattened. Laterally, outside of each of these cavities is a shallow depression containing the outer lateral stigma. The large cavities each bear four stigmata, rather widely spaced. One is situated near the upper, inner margin, but the others are found near the bottom of the depression, one rather dorsal, one ventral and the fourth is subcentrally placed. The first three are the supernumerary stigmata while the last is known as the posterior abdominal stigma (Newstead, 1918). Pratt (1893) recognizes only three pairs of stigmata in this region.

All of these stigmata, except possibly the first supernumerary which is very small, open into a common large, longitudinal trunk. The paired longitudinal tracheal trunks pass forward on either side of the dorsal mid-line of the body where they end in finer tracheae in the anterior portion. The two main trunks are united

by a short cross trachea near their posterior ends and in the anterior region by two cross connectives which originate beside one
another just behind the dorsal prothoracic imaginal disc. One of
these is a short cross trachea but the second is longer and curves
dorsally toward the body wall.

In addition, each longitudinal dorsal trachea branches shortly
after leaving the posterior stigmatic openings. The branch trachea
passes ventrally and anteriorly for a short distance, in the young
larva, as one of the two longitudinal ventral tracheae. The pair
of ventral tracheae grow longer with the increasing age of the
larva and finally reach the metathoracic region where they, too,
end in finer tracheae. They are spaced somewhat farther apart
than are the two main dorsal trunks.

Lateral connecting tracheae, apparently segmentally arranged
and usually seven in number, develop gradually from the dorsal
trunks as the larva ages. The first lateral pair appears rather
early in the posterior end of the body. Each connective grows
ventrally where it unites with the corresponding right or left
ventral longitudinal trunk. As the ventral trunks pass more
anteriorly in older larvae six additional connecting tracheae, proceeding from the dorsal trunks, meet and fuse with them. Thus
each ventral trunk is a branch from a corresponding dorsal
tracheal trunk and is also united with it at segmental intervals by
a main dorsoventral connective. Smaller tracheae and, finally,
tracheoles, ramify throughout the body from adjacent portions of
the dorsal and ventral pairs of longitudinal tracheae and from the
seven lateral connectives between these two main systems.
Leuckart's figure shows that both dorsal and ventral longitudinal
trunks assume a somewhat zigzag course due to the pull exerted
by the lateral connectives in the distended larva, but Pratt (1893)
mentions this condition only in reference to the ventral tracheae.

In describing the general external aspect of the larva mention
was made of eight rudimentary stigmatic areas along its lateral
line. From each stigma a solid strand of cells extends interiorly.
The two anterior stigmata connect with the dorsal longitudinal
tracheal trunk. These should be considered as belonging to
thoracic segments. The remaining six stigmata are attached to
their respective dorsoventral connecting tracheae in a similar manner and represent the first six abdominal stigmata and their internal main trunks. Thus, according to Pratt (1893), with the three
pairs of terminal stigmata, the larva is found to possess, altogether, a total of eleven pairs of stigmata: two thoracic, six

abdominal, and three on the stigmatic plate. For the sake of completeness it may be noted that a strand also arises from the smaller branch of each longitudinal tracheal trunk in the anterior portion of the body, thus forming a ninth pair of stigmatal cords. These strands fuse with the dorsal prothoracic imaginal discs and, consequently, are not visible exteriorly. They are peculiar to the larval condition and fail to appear in the adult. While the strands of cells extending from the stigmata to the tracheae are said to consist of a compact cord in every case, still Pratt (1893) has found that a fine chitinous thread runs through the center of each. This fact, together with their position, is sufficient evidence to enable him to homologize them with the holopneustic type of respiratory apparatus although the larva is now definitely metapneustic, modified only in the possession of three pairs of posterior stigmata instead of the two pairs which are usually present. These lateral stigmata and their internal strands of cells probably give rise, eventually, to corresponding structures in the imago by forming the imaginal nests from which the tracheoblasts originate during pupation.

The functional tracheae are lined with a chitinous intima, a continuation of the cuticle. In young larvae a taenidium is found only in the main portion of the dorsal longitudinal trunks. The taenidia extend farther along the tracheal lumen as the larva grows and finally reinforce the intima of all of the tracheae. In molting, the tracheal cuticle is cast wherever it occurs, but only the thicker layer of the proximal end of the dorsal trunks is actually removed with the cast cuticle covering the body. The more delicate portions break loose from the external cuticle and remain in place unshed.

The larvae of the Pupipara have been considered as metapneustic since the early investigators had ascertained the presence of the posteriorly placed stigmata. Somewhat recently Newstead (1918) made a more thorough examination of the posterior lobes of this group in relation to the conditions found in Glossinidae and discovered that both groups are actually polypneustic.

The practical utility of this type of respiratory apparatus in the larval stage was clearly recognized by the early students of this insect. Leuckart pointed out the peculiar advantages to be obtained by the presence of depressions in the stigmatic plate which form an air pocket for the ready interchange of gases. The ridge extending between the right and left pairs of spiracular openings further insures against the obliteration of this space through the inpressing of maternal tissues. Pratt (1899) also has called attention to the structure of the vulva and vagina which, together, give the larva ready access to fresh air for respiratory processes. The lateral stigmata, even if functional, could scarcely satisfy the conditions required for this respiration since the larva lies surrounded on all sides, except at the posterior end, by the closely adherent uterine walls and the secretions of the milk glands, either of which would effectually occlude lateral air passages.

Larval Alimentary Tract.—The young larva possesses an intestinal tract not unlike that of the larva of the Muscidae, but there are two important facts regarding the tract which should be noted at once: there are no salivary or other digestive glands which in other types of larvae would serve to convert the ingested food into assimilable substances; and the mid-intestine, which is long and convoluted in most dipterous larvae, is here shorter than the body and lies in a straight anteroposterior direction.

At the anterior end food is acquired through the provisional larval mouth, whose origin before hatching was discussed in the early embryology of the insect. The larval mouth opens in a projection at the anterior end of the body. In older larvae this protuberance becomes ever more definitely conical in contrast to the blunt anterior end of the rest of the body, but the young larva is more slender and tapers anteriorly toward this oral papilla. On either side of the mouth is a small cone which Leuckart (1858) and Pratt (1893) believe are the rudiments of the first maxillae. They have a cellular structure and the cuticula invests them. It is supposed that they assist in acquiring the secretions on which the larva feeds for they become less prominent in older larvae whose ingestion is largely over. They are entirely cast off with the last cuticula at birth.

Immediately behind the mouth is a considerable space formed by the invagination of the embryonic anterior portion of the body. The walls of this cavity are largely composed of cephalic imaginal discs and at its posterior border lies the sucking tongue, already discussed (Figs. 42, 47). The provisional buccal cavity lying before the sucking tongue, and into which the mouth opens, is considered by Pratt (1893) to be a pumping apparatus which, by its rhythmic expansion, becomes filled with nutrient solutions. These substances are in turn passed posteriorly by the sucking tongue into the oesophagus which lies beneath and posterior to it. De Geer (1776) first discovered the titillations of the tongue but

Leuckart originally determined their significance and ascertained that the movements occur normally at the rate of 40 to 50 per minute.

The oesophagus is a simple tube with a lumen that enlarges slightly posteriorly and whose walls are composed of a single layer of epithelial cells. In young larvae it is straight, but as the mid-intestine fills with food in later stages it is bent at right angles in its middle, so that the posterior half then pursues its course dorsally where its cells pass over, histologically, into those of the mid-intestine.

The mid-intestine in the young larva is a straight tube directed posteriorly. As larval feeding continues, however, it becomes greatly distended as a storage reservoir until it completely fills most of the haemocoele. This phenomenon is characteristic of the Pupipara and of Glossinidae, and has been extensively discussed by Roubaud (1909) especially in relation to the latter group. Yet no one seems to have offered what appears to be a simple explanation for it. If one considers that the larvae of other insects feed voraciously, just as do those in the adenotrophic class of viviparity, why do the larvae of the latter type store food in an enormously distended mid-intestine while the former do not? Their nutrient requirements should be approximately the same, in proportion to size, for completion of the pupal and imaginal instars. The solution of the problem apparently lies in a consideration of the kind of food available to the larva and the physiological treatment of the surplus. Larvae of other Diptera obtain nourishment in a form that is perhaps more distinctly foreign to their own cytoplasmic chemical constitution. This is true probably of even those which parasitize other animals, as the Oestridae and is, of course, very different in coprophagous species. In contrast to this, the stored nutrient material of Pupipara and Glossinidae is elaborated for the use of the larva by the maternal uterine glands. One might reasonably suppose that this nutriment, since it is removed from the haemolymph of the mother, would be ready, or almost ready, for direct assimilation by the tissues of either the mother or the offspring and therefore further metabolic activity would be extremely slight and secondary. Thus there is no essential need for anything but simple storage, and there are no bulky waste products.

The food of other dipterous larvae requires a sequence of elaborate metabolic processes before it is prepared for assimilation. Manifestly the intestinal tract of such insects is incapable, ordinarily, of combining the two functions, for the finished product would be heavily contaminated by untreated food. The spatial limitations of the mid-intestine or crop could not retain all of the raw food required for the purpose, since so much of the total bulk is waste. Further, all of the larvae are provided with special reservoirs for the retention of surplus nutriment, as it is absorbed, in the form of fat bodies that are copiously filled with stored products but which are less extensively developed in adenotrophic larvae. Thus, it seems probable that the decreased dependence on the fat body reservoirs in the Pupipara and Glossinidae is the result of a short cut in the insect's economy. Stomach storage is a satisfactory substitute for fat body storage and eliminates several physiological processes from the larva.

Pratt (1893) asserts that about half of the stored food is consumed within an hour after birth of the larva, but that some of the remainder, at least, lasts until the imaginal form has been assumed in the puparium. The larva does not feed after birth.

The mid-intestine ends blindly but it is physically united to the hind-intestine at its posterodorsal end. The hind-intestine continues ventrally around the end of the mid-intestine to the anus whose position has already been described as being posteroventral. The lumen of the upper end of the hind-intestine, where it joins the mid-intestine, is plugged with cells so that there is no possibility of any communication with the lumen of the latter. Its walls consist of an epithelial layer bounded by the tunica propria on one side while on the other lies the secreted cuticular layer in the lumen of the intestine. This chitinous layer, of course, is continuous with that of the lower hind-intestine and the external body cuticle. In older embryos the epithelial cells lining this end become flatter as they are stretched by the distention of the mid-intestine.

Two pairs of Malpighian tubules open into the hind-intestine shortly after it leaves the walls of the mid-intestine. One pair extends dorsally over the stomach for about half its length while the second pair is similarly distributed ventrally. Their secretions are discharged into the hind-intestine and, eventually, to the exterior.

Bacteria.—According to the recent investigations of Zacharias (1928), two species of microorganisms are transmitted to the larva as soon as it begins to absorb the nutrient material from the milk glands. One of these is symbiotic, the other a bacterium which, he believes, belongs to the rickettsia type.

The symbiont is found in great numbers in the lumen of the milk glands but not in the anterior, or smaller, pair of glands. The symbionts presumably enter the lumen of the glands by migrating directly through the walls of the secreting tubules. Here they multiply rapidly into enormous numbers of individuals, yet are not found everywhere equally abundant, and often are completely absent from some of the individual branch tubules. They simply pass down and out with the nutriment secreted by the glands to be picked up when the larva feeds. In the larva they find their way into the taller cells which compose the epithelium of the anterior end of the mid-intestine. They remain as intracellular symbionts during late larval life, and the cells they occupy may be termed the primary mycetocytes. The mycetocytes remain undistributed in the pupa until the imaginal intestine is well developed when they become free and pass posteriorly into it. Then the symbionts emerge in the imaginal intestine where their function seems to be to aid in the digestion of the red blood corpuscles ingested by the adult fly.

The rickettsia organism, which has been found by Zacharias in the secretion cells of the milk glands, is filamentous in shape. Its transmission to the larva also takes place when the latter feeds, but, apparently, not all individuals are infested by the organism. When they are taken up by the larva they are deposited with the stored nutriment in the mid-intestine. They are apparently intracellular in the adult insect, where they inhabit the flat cells of the mid-intestinal epithelium.

The acquirement of symbionts and other microorganisms via the milk glands and their nutrient secretions is a very interesting procedure which is reported for the first time in the paper by Zacharias. He also records the presence of the symbiont in other Pupipara and another microorganism as well.

Larval Musculature.—The principal muscles, and those most readily observed, consist of seven lateral bands running dorsoventrally over the mid-intestine, with their insertions in the cuticula as mentioned in describing the external appearance of the larva. It seems probable that they represent the respiratory muscles of abdominal segments 1–7, for their contraction serves only to depress the body in its dorsoventral dimension. Each band is elongate oval in cross section and is entirely independent, not only from the others on the same side but also from the corresponding muscles on the opposite side of the body, for they do not continue dorsally or ventrally beyond the points of insertion. Apparently Leuckart first ascribed their function as one of respiration. According to Pratt (1893) they operate secondarily in reinforcing the walls of the greatly distended mid-intestine of the older larva.

Two long muscles originate interiorly on the dorsal wall of the provisional pharyngeal cavity which, it will be recalled, is bordered posteriorly by the sucking tongue. They are broad, thin bands which pass dorsally to the body wall and attach themselves to the cuticula, perhaps over the prothoracic region, thence they continue backwards to reattach to the cuticula at three more points, corresponding possibly to the meso- and metathoracic and first abdominal segments. Thus each band consists of a longitudinal dorsal strand of muscle which Pratt believes causes the dilation of the provisional pharyngeal cavity. It seems apparent that the first segment of each muscle could so operate, but it might be suggested also that the last three seemingly segmental attachments would, in contracting, serve to bend the anterior end of the body, of the young larva at least, toward the dorsally situated opening of the milk glands which discharge their secretions into the uterus above its mouth. This possible function is not, however, mentioned by students of *Melophagus* embryology. These muscles show transverse striations in the first three of its segments but not in the last.

The labrum, or sucking tongue, is activated by a single large muscle whose fibrillae converge dorsally. Pratt believes this muscle is attached ventrally to the epithelium of the labrum rather than to its cuticula; dorsally, it ends in the epithelium of the ventral wall of the dorsal pharyngeal cavity (Fig. 42). A small muscle also runs from left to right at the base of the lip.

The mid-intestine may have small, scattered muscle fibers around it, as Roubaud (1908) has described in the Glossinidae, but this has not been definitely ascertained. The heart has six pairs of muscles near its posterior end. Their function and arrangement are typical. Having apparently no other muscles, at least of the segmental, voluntary type, the larva is forced to lie immobile in the maternal uterus. This is quite in contrast with the larva of Glossinidae which possesses some ability to migrate after birth and, also, may contract various regions of the body in the uterus of the mother and assist likewise in its deposition. By contrast, most dipterous larvae are exceedingly active.

Larval Circulatory System.—The dorsal aorta extends practically the length of the body, directly above the mid-intestine.

Throughout most of its length it consists of a simple tube with the muscles distributed nearer the posterior portion of it. The anterior end enlarges somewhat only to constrict again to a small orifice opening directly over the supraoesophageal ganglia. Pratt thinks it possible that two pairs of ostia also are present in the anterior end just back of the infundibulum.

The blood is aggregated principally in the anterior and posterior portions of the larval haemocoele, since comparatively little blood space exists among the fat cells and oenocytes surrounding the mid-intestine.

Larval Fat Body Cells and Oenocytes.—While these cells may be found in other parts of the haemocoele they are especially aggregated between the mid-intestine and the hypodermal walls. The fat cells vary greatly in size and sometimes form a layer of tissue as, for example, around the sexual cells. The oenocytes are rather large and easily distinguished. They are circular, containing granular cytoplasm and a large nucleus with a distinct nuclear membrane.

Larval Gonads.—The first appearance of the primordial germ cells was outlined in the discussion of the early embryo. In the very young larva they are found again arranged in two small masses containing only relatively few cells, similar in shape, and surrounded externally by a single epithelial layer. In older larvae these appear as a single compact pair on the dorsal side of the body between the fifth and sixth muscle bands. They are evident throughout larval life. The male organs each consist of a pear-shaped mass of cells, the outermost of which form an epithelium. A spherical small group of cells, staining more deeply, is situated in the center of the gonad (testis). Posteriorly, the pear-shaped testis constricts to meet one of the paired seminal ducts, a solid strand of cells which runs posteriorly. The vas deferens and posterior portion of the testis are covered by a thin tunica propria.

The ovaries are likewise paired and similarly situated but they vary from the testis in shape. Externally each appears elongate and pear-shaped but the tapering half of it is bent at almost right angles to the direction taken by the larger portion. In microscopical section each shows a rather thick outer cortex composed of small cells which also invaginates inward from the broad end, thus constricting the interior into two somewhat cone-shaped spaces in the posterior half of the gland. Each of these cone-shaped portions probably delimits the future pair of ovarioles possessed by each ovary in the adult. The internal spaces, together with the narrowed proximal half of the ovary, are filled with larger cells which, however, become smaller distally where they lessen in size to match the cortical cells. The paired oviducts are constructed in the same manner as was explained for the vas deferens, but the ultimate destination of neither system has been followed in the larva.

Larval Nervous System.—A pair of supraoesophageal ganglia, which are firmly united by a cross commissure, lie close together above the oesophagus. A commissure descends ventrally from each ganglion to fuse with the suboesophageal portion of the ventral trunk. The latter, in young larvae, has a more definitely segmental arrangement than is visible in the later instars. Gradually the more posterior ganglia diminish in relative size as the anterior ones enlarge and all finally are gathered into a continuous paired strand of ganglionic substance, extending below the mid-intestine for about two thirds of the body length. Broad cross commissures between the pairs render it very difficult to identify individual ganglia of the right and left sides while the longitudinal commissures are no longer visible. All of the ventral ganglia but the last three have lateral branches which proceed obliquely backward. The posterior ganglia give rise to a pair of large nerves which continue caudally along the ventral median line of the body.

The sympathetic nerve arises from either end of the supra-oesophageal cross commissure which, being above the oesophagus, bends dorsally with the latter. Very little is known concerning the paths of the lesser fibers leading from the main ganglionic centers.

Larval Imaginal Discs.—The early appearance of several imaginal discs was described in the embryo prior to hatching from the egg. Of these, the cephalic and thoracic discs may be briefly considered here, a detailed summary probably being unnecessary. The cephalic and prothoracic discs, especially, are pushed somewhat anteriorly by the gradual distention of the mid-intestine. The paired dorsal discs fuse into a common disc anteriorly but their posterior portions unite later. The ventral cephalic disc, which in the embryo was a single cavity below the tongue with two posteriorly directed extensions, gradually increases in size and in the older larva also fuses into a single large pouch below the sucking tongue and the anterior half of the oesophagus.

Eventually the dorsal and ventral discs in turn coalesce so that one large pouch surrounds and includes the provisional pharynx and the anterior half of the oesophageal epithelium.

By this union of the discs arises the imaginal cephalic vesicle, whose tissues later evaginate to become the definitive head of the imago. The imaginal proboscis develops rather precociously in the cephalic vesicle as paired conical projections derived from the median epithelium of the posteriorly directed extensions of the ventral cephalic disc. It was pointed out before that the pharyngeal region and the sucking tongue are, in reality, only invaginated portions of the anterior ectodermal wall.

The three dorsal and three ventral pairs of thoracic discs are not materially altered during larval life, except for some increased growth in the ventral pairs and a shifting in position due to internal pressures. They are, indeed, crowded forward until they come to lie external to the cephalic discs. This area, naturally, will be the thoracic portion of the body when the cephalic vesicle is finally evaginated to form the imaginal head. The dorsal discs will give rise to part of the thoracic hypodermis and to rudimentary halteres according to Pratt (1893), but to this Stange (1907) has properly taken exception. He says halteres are absent but in their place a deep fold is produced, the upper part of which eventually gives rise to imaginal dorsal hypodermis of the metathorax while the lower portion of the fold bears a stigma. The ventral discs form hypodermis and the imaginal limbs. It may be interesting to note, according to Pratt, a slight evagination of the wall of the mesothoracic discs which suggests the former development of imaginal buds of wings which are no longer present. Nor do halteres appear in the adult *Melophagus*.

The preceding imaginal discs were produced in the embryo through invagination of the ectoderm. But other imaginal discs should now be mentioned. The abdominal discs, except the anal discs, are simply thickenings in the various parts of the larval hypodermis. They are the anal discs, the cell islands, and the discs of the intestinal tract. The early differentiation of the anal discs occurred in the embryo and has been outlined. In the old larva the larger, inner pair become large tubes surrounding the anus. The interior wall of each disc invaginates into its own lumen so that a section through it gives the appearance of two tubes, one lying within the lumen of the outer main portion of each disc. The outer pair of discs arose in the embryo as thickenings of the ectoderm. These proliferate interiorly during late larval life and become hollow tubes through the subsequent rearrangement of their cells. All of the anal discs retain their connection with the hypodermis of the larva.

Several pairs of cell islands distributed over the abdominal wall of the larva are imaginal discs of the adult hypodermis. Pratt (1897) claims that they and the ventral thoracic discs are homodynamous organs. Seven pairs are to be found on the lateroventral wall near the insertion of the dorsoventral muscles, while two pairs are situated beside their dorsolateral insertions. One of the dorsal pair is approximately twice as great in diameter as its companion. They are more readily seen in young larvae, being quite inconspicuous or invisible after the second molt.

The imaginal discs of the anterior portion of the alimentary tract of *Melophagus* have been identified by Pratt (1893) as an imaginal mouth ring and the imaginal epithelium of the oesophagus, mentioned in connection with the imaginal discs of the head. Posterior discs are the imaginal epithelium of the posterior part of the hind-intestine, and in connection with it the imaginal ring of epithelium surrounding the anus. Imaginal discs have not been found either in the posterior portion of the oesophagus, in the mid-intestine, at the base of the Malpighian tubules, or in the anterior portion of the hind-intestine.

Swingle (1913) has found that an adult female may live from four and one-half to six months. According to him, also, during her reproductive period a female may give birth to a mature larva, ready for pupation, every eight days.

Finally, some comment should be made regarding the birth product. Several have observed that the prepupa, or the puparium, is formed before birth (Root, 1921; Drake and Jones, 1930). Others speak of puparium formation very promptly after that event (Swingle, 1913). It must be realized, however, that the actual disintegration of larval tissues, histolysis and regeneration into the adult by reorganization and the growth of imaginal buds are the true physiological expression of the pupal stage. These activities may be initiated before birth but it is probable most of them, and the most critical steps, occur during the free, quiescent pupal period. Details of this borderline situation in development await investigation.

Many interesting facts have been ascertained concerning larviparity, the structure of the reproductive system, symbionts, and other microorganisms in the remaining families, Nycteribiidae and Streblidae. Sufficient embryological data, however, have not accumulated to warrant their presentation.

LITERATURE CITED

Berlese (1899, 1909), Blanchard (1846a, 1846b), Bonnet (1779), Comstock (1925), De Geer (1776), Drake and Jones (1930), Dufour (1825, 1845, 1851), Hallez (1886), Hardenberg (1929), Holmgren (1904), Lassmann (1936), Latreille (1805), Leuckart (1854, 1858), Massonnat (1909), Metcalfe (1933), Newstead (1918), Osten-Sacken (1881), Pratt (1893, 1897, 1899, 1900), Réaumur (1742), Root (1921), Roubaud (1908, 1909), Von Siebold (1837), Stange (1907), Stuhlmann (1907), Swingle (1913), Trouessart (1895), Wheeler (1889), Zacharias (1928).

Order Diptera   Family Nycteribiidae

While members of the Hippoboscidae were being subjected to the investigations just outlined, other families of the Pupipara also were examined to ascertain whether they, too, were viviparous. Westwood (1835) dissected one of the *Nycteriba* and found what he imagined to be a pupa within the maternal uterus. The offspring was similar to that of the Hippoboscidae and he was convinced that this genus of the Nycteribiidae was pupiparous. Almost fifty years elapsed before Osten-Sacken (1881) corrected Westwood's observations by showing that the genus was larviparous.

Since it has now been definitely ascertained that fully developed larvae are deposited which quickly pupate without seeking food, they must have had access to nutriment in the female uterus. As the milk glands appear similar to those of Hippoboscidae it is assumed that these glands also function as nutrient organs. Rodhain and Bequaert (1915) have added materially to the evidence of adenotrophic viviparity in this family. The ovaries are described by Scott (1917) as being asymmetrical due to activities exactly like those described for *Glossina* and *Melophagus*.

LITERATURE CITED

Osten-Sacken (1881), Rodhain and Bequaert (1915), Scott (1917), Westwood (1835).

Order Diptera   Family Streblidae

Kolenati (1862) asserted that Streblidae were oviparous but Speiser (1900) has since ascertained that they, too, give birth only to larvae. According to Muir (1912) the female appears to nourish the larva in the uterus, for only fully grown larvae are deposited, which form their puparia within a few minutes after deposition. Ferris (1923) was probably the first to furnish a detailed though brief description of one of the peculiar larvae dissected from the uterus of the female.

LITERATURE CITED

Ferris (1923), Kolenati (1862), Muir (1912), Speiser (1900).

Order Diptera   Family Braulidae

The situation has been quite the reverse for Braulidae, the remaining family that has often been included in the Pupipara. Réaumur described the only species that represented this family some 200 years ago (Massonnat, 1909). In 1914 a second species, *Braula kohli,* was described by Schmitz (1914) and the family then contained two species. Because little was known about the life history or habits of *Braula,* and on account of its tentative position among the Pupipara, it had been assumed that this group also was viviparous. Indeed Assmuss (1865), in reporting his results, claimed to have dissected over 100 females. He described the developing larvae within the reproductive tract and recognized well-developed nutrient glands in the mother's body. Müggenberg (1892) denied the presence of nutrient organs and found no larvae within the females he studied. However, Skaife (1921) definitely proved that *Braula cœca* is oviparous when he found the eggs in the wax comb and described the embryological development of the species. Arnhart (1923) later supported Skaife's general observations when he, too, discovered eggs and larvae in the comb of the hive. Argo (1926) was, perhaps, the first to study *Braula* in the United States and his observations caused him to conclude that the species here was likewise oviparous. He suspected that the American and European specimens belonged to the same species but he did not have them studied by a taxonomist.

LITERATURE CITED

Argo (1926), Arnhart (1923), Assmuss (1865), Massonnat (1909), Müggenberg (1892), Schmitz (1914), Skaife (1921).

Chapter 9

HAEMOCOELOUS VIVIPARITY—DIPTERA
(CHIRONOMIDAE, ETC.)

Two orders of insects show examples of haemocoelous viviparity. Of the Diptera represented, *Miastor* has furnished a classic example which has not only focused attention on paedogenetic reproduction for the first time but has also proved to be of prime importance in tracing the germ track. Relatives have also been used in problems of experimental research. This type of viviparity is, presumably, universal in the Strepsiptera.

Haemocoelous viviparity is characterized by the haemocoelous development of the parthenogenetic ova and larvae, the destruction of the mother by the haemocoelous feeding of the predatory dipterous larvae, and the emergence of offspring through other openings than the reproductive orifice. In the Diptera, the life cycle is complicated by the seasonal appearance of oviparous products and in the Strepsiptera there is a high degree of hypermetamorphism in the larva, subsequent to emergence.

Order Diptera   Family Cecidomyidae

The astonishing fact that larvae of certain insects may give rise to daughter larvae, viviparously born, and that these, in turn, may continue the reproductive cycle in a similar manner was discovered by Wagner in 1861. After finding numerous larvae under the decaying bark of linden, elm, and ash trees, he subjected them to careful scrutiny and was surprised to find that some contained smaller larvae in the haemocoelar space. He at first thought the young were parasites, but ultimately grasped their true relationship to the mother larvae. A paper was prepared giving the results of his observations and was sent, with specimens, to Von Siebold in November, 1861, for publication in the *Zeitschrift für wissenschaftliche Zoologie*. Apparently the preparations were ruined, for Von Siebold found nothing in them to support Wagner's statements in the manuscript, nor could he find similar insects in his own neighborhood. It seems that in the meantime

Wagner (1862) presented the paper for publication in the *Scientific Memoirs* of Kasan University, where he held a professorship in zoology. Although a colleague, Professor Owsiannikow, substantiated Wagner's observations his paper still encountered criticism and disbelief.

The essential points recorded by Wagner are these. A very small dipterous larva reproduces by forming reproductive elements from the fat body tissues. Such elements are elongate, ellipsoidal, and filled with yolk. In them the embryos rapidly arise. Usually seven to ten young larvae are developed which, during their embryogeny, absorb the fat body contents. During their larval life in the maternal haemocoele they entirely destroy the mother's internal organs and she dies. The young escape by rupturing the maternal cuticle and at the end of about five days of independent life, they, in turn, continue the reproductive cycle by the production of daughter elements within their own bodies. Five larval forms have been found but none appears to present sexual differences.

Reproduction extends from August until June of the following year, at which time the latest larvae, somewhat smaller than their predecessors, complete their growth, pupate, and shortly emerge as imagoes of either sex. The female emerges with five large, well-developed eggs in the reproductive system.

There is no doubt that the fat body functions in a nutritional capacity. The weakly developed tracheal system, coupled with sluggish movements in the mother-larva, assists in the conservation of the stored fat.

From this summary of the part of Wagner's paper which concerns us, it appears that he had correctly observed many of the main points in the economy of the species. Moreover, he located the ovaries without recognizing them as the genital organs. His brief descriptions of a few stages in the embryonic history are scantily illustrated. The figures show, among other stages, the young egg with its large nutrient chamber but Wagner failed to analyze its parts correctly. His observations, we may conclude, were remarkably accurate as to detail, but his interpretation of what he saw was in some respects erroneous. His conclusions may well be viewed with leniency, for one seldom investigates new fields with absolute accuracy.

Opposition to Wagner's statements, voiced especially by Professor Brandt, and the skepticism at first expressed by Von Baer coupled with Von Siebold's own doubts in the matter, caused Von

Siebold to postpone publication of the original manuscript (Wagner, 1863). However, when Von Baer (1863) finally examined actual specimens, he was readily convinced that the essential facts had been correctly recorded by Wagner and quickly obtained local recognition, at least, for the latter's original discovery. Meanwhile, Von Siebold received a second collection of specimens from Wagner in 1863 with further correspondence (Wagner, 1865). From these he was able to verify the latter's observations and to corroborate the fact that the larva probably belonged in the Cecidomyidae.

Further verification of Wagner's work was not long in appearing from other sources. Meinert (1864a, 1864b) supplied a description of the species, calling it *Miastor metroloas*. His material was obtained from a beech stump and seemed to be identical with Wagner's specimens. He found definite groups of cells in the fat body which undoubtedly were the ovaries but, like Wagner, failed to recognize their true significance. The mesodermal nutrient cells were observed by him and their possible function was tentatively suggested. He supported Wagner's concept of the origin of the embryonic elements in the mother larva, which he compared to a kind of budding process (Meinert, 1865b). The primordial germ cells, which were seen by him, held no interest or significance at all. In later articles (Meinert, 1866, 1870, 1872) his views were somewhat modified by the discoveries of other investigators, but even in his last paper he insisted that ovaries may clearly be found only in those larvae which transform into the imagoes of summer.

Pagenstecher (1864) obtained larvae from sugar-beet pulp with the same kind of reproduction, but apparently belonging to a different species. His paper contains a description of larval anatomy and constant comparisons with Wagner's observations. The latter's belief that budding from the maternal tissue takes place was opposed by Pagenstecher, who maintained that the reproductive elements are true ova, derived from a definite, but undetermined reproductive center located somewhere in the posterior end of the mother larva. About 15 eggs are formed, four or five of which usually complete their development and become larvae.

Ganin [1865 (Hanin, 1865)] discovered the ovaries in the eleventh segment of a species of larva closely resembling the one studied by Pagenstecher. He described and figured eggs with a polar organization of cytoplasm and nurse cells. The young, he claimed, developed from these eggs in a manner quite analogous to the embryonic history of other Diptera, except for partheno-genesis. In this he was quite correct.

The bark of an apple tree gave Leuckart (1865a, 1865b) speci-mens which agreed with those collected by Pagenstecher. This species was later described by Meinert (1866) as *Oligarces para-doxus*. Leuckart's careful observations yielded additional ana-tomical details of the ovaries, which he identified independently and simultaneously with Ganin's discovery of them. Eggs with their nurse cells and follicular epithelium also were described, but he hesitated to give them full recognition as ova, preferring to call them pseudova. Perhaps this was because of his interest at the time in the development of the Hemiptera, among which the aphids received most attention. Only shortly before, Lubbock (1859) had proposed the term pseudovum to designate the repro-ductive elements from which viviparous aphids arise. This con-cept was carried over by Leuckart into the terminology of the eggs involved in cecidomyid larviparity. At any rate, he soon turned this work on Diptera over to his student, Metschnikoff (1865, 1866) who traced some of the embryogeny of the insect far more completely than any worker hitherto had been able to do. While highly diagrammatic, Metschnikoff's figures show quite well the essential features in segmentation and blastoderm formation. He recognized the germ anlage and traced the primordial germ cells to their final position in the developing larva.

About this same time summaries of the observations of early workers in this field of investigation appeared (Wagner *et al.*, 1865; Carus, 1866). Von Baer (1866) was the first to come to a definite conclusion regarding this method of reproduction after carefully reviewing the earlier contributions. He decided that it represented an entirely new type of multiplication to which he applied the name paedogenesis.

Other writers were active in preparing papers of less originality, but of interest to us. Loew (1864, 1865) was interested mainly in the taxonomic questions involved. Schwabe (1866) summarized the results of preceding publications on this subject, with em-phasis upon Ganin's researches. Mäklin (1865) also gave a his-torical review, while Gerstäcker (1865) made a study of old daughter larvae in specimens found near Berlin. Lubbock (1867) reflected the widespread interest in these insects by his comments upon the embryogeny and the use of the term pseudovum. Bal-biani (1882, 1885) later confirmed the earlier comments regard-ing the origin of polar cells, or primordial germ cells, and their precocious segregation in the embryonic history through his studies of an oviparous chironomid.

For some time, the attention of embryologists was drawn to other fields of investigation and no details of the embryology of paedogenetic Cecidomyidae were forthcoming until quite recently. Interest in the subject was revived, however, when Kahle (1908) published his results, which will be reviewed later. Felt (1911a, 1911b, 1912) discovered paedogenesis in *Miastor americana* and gave a brief account of it. Hegner (1912, 1914a, 1914b) immediately placed new emphasis on the subject in his treatment of the germ cell cycle in these insects. Apparently these insects still remain the only animals in which all of the steps intervening between successive generations of primordial germ cells have been ascertained.

Several species of Cecidomyidae are now known to exhibit paedogenesis. In addition to his descriptions of *M. metroloas* and *O. paradoxus,* Meinert (1865a) also described the paedogenetic species *Meinertomyia (Pero) fasciata.* Karsch (1887) found *Miastor subterraneous* likewise to be paedogenetic and Zavřel (1907, 1926) discovered similar conditions in the genus *Tanytarsus,* while numerous other examples have been summarized by Barnes (1929). Klyver (1931) called attention to a very curious case of an undetermined species in California which apparently shows larval paedogenesis and oviparous paedogenesis, both by mother larvae and by pupae. This instance, if verified, should prove to be exceedingly interesting. It recalls the situation found in the oviparous paedogenetic multiplication by pupae of *Chironomus grimmii,* described by Grimm (1869, 1870, 1873). To this statement, however, Schneider (1885) takes strong exception, claiming the pupa has no external genital opening. More recent writers (Zavřel, 1926; Vandel, 1931) seem to accept Schneider's interpretation of the facts in the case. Schneider, by the way, reports the species as being possibly parthenogenetic in the imaginal stage. This last example is very similar to the case of *Tanytarsus dissimilis* cited by Johannsen (1910a, 1910b), the larvae of which are paedogenetic, while the adult females occasionally are parthenogenetic.

During the past few years attention has been directed more especially to experimental problems relating to the influence of the environment on the production of paedogenetic larval forms. An introduction to this interesting phase of the subject is contained in the papers of Springer (1917) and Müller (1912) on reversal of function due to the effects of light; Harris (1923, 1924, 1925) on the effects of crowding; Gabritschevsky (1928, 1930) and Ulrich (1934, 1936a, 1936b) on the influence of several environmental factors. Reitberger (1934) and especially Kraczkiewicz (1935, 1936, 1937) have interested themselves in the cytological phenomena accompanying parthenogenesis, paedogenesis, and the development of adult males and females.

Before concluding this discussion, the complexity of the larval life history should not be overlooked. Ulrich (1936) described the larvae of *Oligarces* as of three general types: thelyotokous, producing mainly females; amphiterotokous, which may develop into either sex; arrhenotokous, from which come males. But this simple statement does not sufficiently suggest the very complicated sequence of larval stages which may intervene between successive adult generations, and Ulrich's paper should be consulted for fuller details. *Micromalthus* has been shown to possess similar larval stages and a few of their characteristics have been included with that insect.

Female Reproductive System

Since the adult females are oviparous we need not concern ourselves with the embryogeny of their ova and our attention will be centered on reproduction by the larvae. According to Kahle (1908), the larvae reproduce paedogenetically throughout the year except for a period of severe winter weather, when all reproductive activity is suspended. Upon emergence from the mother, the young larva varies from 1.5 to 1.75 mm. in length; when fully grown, and with young larvae in its own body cavity, it attains a total length of about 4 mm. The large fat bodies lie principally between segments 6 to 14, although there is a small amount anteriorly in the fifth segment. Harris (1923) described several other larval forms, for the species is polymorphic in this stage, and Ulrich has effectively described the entire life cycle of the insect.

The Ovary.—The ovaries consist of two ovate bodies lying in the tenth or eleventh segment, but their exact location fluctuates with the movements of the insect. The individual ovary, when mature, is primarily only a one-layered epithelial sac containing the germ cells, with their attendant nurse cells, and· a number of mesodermal supporting cells (Fig. 50). Hegner (1912) has determined the number of oöcytes in the ovary of *Miastor americana*

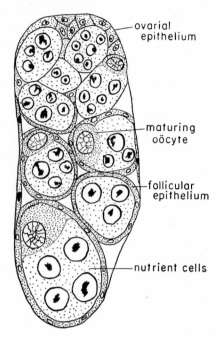

FIG. 50.—*Miastor metroloas*. Larval ovary greatly distended by maturing follicles that will eventually rupture its wall and scatter throughout the haemocoele, longitudinal section. (After Kahle, Zoologica, 2, 55.)

as 32, and a like number exist in the ovary of *M. metroloas* according to Kahle. When reproductive activity commences the ovaries rupture and liberate the ova into the haemocoele. Movements of the mother larva cause the eggs to disperse throughout the haemocoele, where development continues and, of course, the ovaries can no longer be identified. The balance of the reproductive system is lacking (Fig. 51).

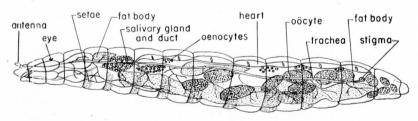

FIG. 51.—*Miastor metroloas*. Mother larva showing haemocoelous ova in various developmental stages; digestive system omitted. (Modified from Kahle, Zoologica, 2, 55.)

Development of the Embryo

The Egg.—The function of the investing membrane, which is a simple epithelium derived from maternal mesoderm, is analogous to the follicular cells of other insects. Definite polarity is exhibited by the egg for at one end is a mass of nurse cells, about 24 in number, while the opposite pole, the posterior end of the egg, contains the pole-plasm (Fig. 52A). It should be noted here

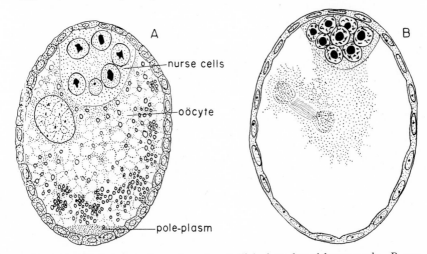

FIG. 52.—*Miastor metroloas. A,* mature follicle from larval haemocoele. *B,* egg in telophase, first division; yolk omitted, longitudinal sections. (After Kahle, Zoologica, 2, 55.)

that the nurse cells are mesodermal elements, derived from the mother larva, and are not formed from contemporary germ cells as in most insects. The germinal vesicle lies usually in the anterior half of the egg and is subcentrally located. The inclusions of the egg are far from being homogeneous. A dense granular portion of cytoplasm is visible immediately beneath the nurse cell mass, from which it probably came. A concentration of granular material may be seen around the nucleus and the pole-plasm, already mentioned, is likewise granular. No periplasmic layer is visible and no chorion is secreted by the follicular epithelium. The rest of the egg presents fine radiating strands of cytoplasm among which are crowded deutoplasmic vacuoles of various sizes and kinds. The cytoplasm of the nurse cells appears to be definitely separated from that of the egg, except in certain restricted places where the cytoplasm of the two areas seems to be continuous.

Consequently, the nutrient materials of the former may pass directly into the egg.

The nuclei of the nurse cells are quite distinctly different from the germinal vesicle. They are smaller, round, with large chromatin particles and contain a prominent nucleolus. The egg nucleus is relatively large, with a fine network of chromatin particles, but no nucleolus is visible.

The nuclei of the follicular epithelium are typical of those found in many insects. While large in comparison with the size of the cells, they are very much smaller than those of the eggs or nurse cells. They, too, possess conspicuous nucleoli.

Maturation, Cleavage, and the Formation of the Primordial Germ Cells.—The nucleus, lying near the periphery, undergoes one maturation division so only one polar body is given off. In this division, whole chromosomes first associate together in tetrads which, with other data, has led Kraczkiewicz (1935) to assume the cell to be tetraploid or, perhaps, octoploid, a condition derived from six original pairs of chromosomes. He has determined the present number of chromosomes in the paedogenetic ovum to be 48, although Kahle believed there were about half this number (Fig. 52B). The chromosomes split lengthwise and one portion of each chromosome passes into the polar body zone. As a result, no reduction division occurs and the number of chromosomes remains constant. The polar body subsequently attempts to participate in a second mitosis, which is only partially completed. It finally suffers gradual disintegration and is absorbed by the egg cytoplasm at about the 58-cell stage. The nucleus reforms after maturation and is found to be again subcentrally situated.

During the interval devoted to the maturation process the nurse cells also have been active. A large amount of nutrient substance has passed from the nurse cells into the egg and may be seen in the latter as an elongate mass of granular material extending to its center. The cleavage nucleus lies embedded in this material. Because of the loss of its stored substance the nurse cell chamber has become much reduced in size, while the egg has grown proportionately larger.

The first cleavage figure is oriented so that the spindle coincides with the longitudinal axis of the egg. There is the usual spindle formation but no observable centrosomes or centrospheres. Remnants of the spindle persist after the daughter nuclei are formed, then gradually disappear. When mitosis is completed the daughter nuclei lie along the main axis of the egg, separated from each other by an intervening area of deutoplasm. The cone-shaped, granular mass of cytoplasm, formerly extending from the nurse cell chamber to the center of the egg, has now condensed into two equal portions, one about each cleavage nucleus.

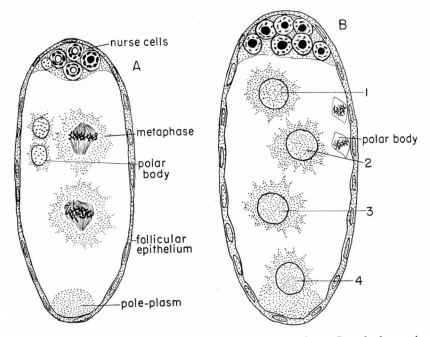

FIG. 53.—*Miastor metroloas. A,* second cleavage, metaphase. *B,* end of second division, nucleus No. 4 entering pole plasm. Polar bodies exhibit karyokinesis, yolk omitted. (After Kahle, Zoologica, **2,** 55.)

The spindles of the second cleavage division generally lie, one above the other, in the same axis as the first (Fig. 53*A*). In some of his preparations Kahle found centrioles in this cleavage. At the end of cleavage four nuclei are present which, for purposes of convenience in the discussion, may be numbered in anteroposterior sequence. The granular cytoplasm again has been divided so that daughter nuclei 1, 2, and 3 are equally supplied with it, but the fourth nucleus has rather little. Nucleus 4, nevertheless, quickly acquires its share by coming in contact with the pole-plasm, and a portion of this cytoplasm invests it (Fig. 53*B*).

Very little cytoplasm remains with the nurse cells by this time and their nuclei reveal signs of degeneration. Their chromatic portion is formed into heavy short threads but the nucleoli remain unchanged. The egg, itself, continues to elongate and is now about 0.24 mm. in length, which is approximately twice its original longitudinal measurement. There is, however, no equivalent increase in diameter. The cleavage nuclei were quite reduced in volume during maturation and the first cleavage divisions, but they are now found to be regaining their original size.

The third cleavage division offers several peculiarities. The separation of nuclei 1, 2, and 3 into the six daughter nuclei is accompanied by chromatin diminution in which a portion of this material is left in the equatorial area of each spindle. Kraczkiewicz (1935) has shown that during this process the chromosomes are so distributed that 36 remain at the equatorial plate, divide, and there disintegrate, while only 12 actually undergo equatorial division and migrate to the poles in the later stages of karyokinesis. Reitberger (1934) had previously discovered this to be true also for *O. paradoxus*. He carefully explained that in this first diminution stage not all of the chromosomes were eliminated to attain the correct reduced number (10 in this species) but that further elimination occurred in a later cleavage. Kahle originally described the continuance of diminution through successive cleavages but believed each chromosome left some part of itself behind. The later concept involves, on the contrary, the sacrifice of entire chromosomes in this process. Perhaps a more complete study of the chromosomal constitution of the species and genera of this family of flies would reveal some explanation of speciation based on simple multiples or duplication of chromosomes as has been suggested for certain plants.

Nucleus 4 shows somewhat different end products. As this nucleus divides no chromatin reduction occurs, yet one daughter nucleus remains in syncytial relationship to the other six nuclei. The second daughter nucleus, on the contrary, migrates farther into the pole-plasm. The pole-plasm with its nucleus, and some deutoplasm, now forms a separate cell, very much smaller than the syncytial egg. Thus, at this time, there are seven syncytial nuclei in the egg, six with reduced chromatin and one with the full amount. The eighth nucleus, with its full complement of chromatin, occupies the pole-plasm and is part of a separate cell. It is the primordial germ cell of the embryo (Fig. 54*A*).

During the fourth cleavage the six syncytial daughter nuclei, derived from nuclei 1, 2, and 3, undergo a second chromatin reduction. The syncytial daughter cell of the egg, descending originally from nucleus 4, also loses part of its chromatin in a division that occurs with the others. The egg now contains 14 cleavage nuclei with reduced quantities of chromatin; the primordial germ cell did not divide. Therefore, the embryo consists of 14 cleavage nuclei and a germ cell.

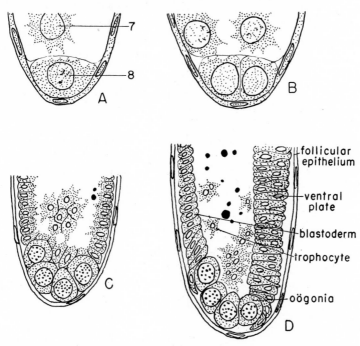

Fig. 54.—*Miastor metroloas.* *A,* posterior end of embryo with 8 nuclei, the lowest being the primordial germ cell (No. 8). *B,* same, with 28 somatic nuclei and 2 germ cells. *C,* blastoderm stage, vitellophags arising from blastoderm cells. *D,* older, with embryonic mesoderm beginning to enclose the oögonia. Longitudinal sections. (Modified from Kahle, Zoologica, 2, 55.)

This reduction of the chromatin seems to have a peculiar significance in the embryonic history. According to Kahle, the somatic nuclei of the embryo always exhibit an actual reduction in the number of chromosomes so that only the haploid number is present. This process, he claims, is precisely the same as in the reduction maturation stage of amphigonous eggs; here, however, it is deferred to a later period and involves only the primitive somatic nuclei. Their descendants, of course, are thus all haploid and only the germ cells retain the full complement of chromosomes.

The fifth cleavage yields 28 somatic nuclei and two germ cells, since the primordial germ cell participates in the division (Fig. 54*B*). Some variability in the rate of cleavage is frequently manifest at this stage, for a few of the somatic nuclei lag behind others although complete agreement is often lacking even in earlier cleavages. This irregularity increases in succeeding cleavages. The nuclei are beginning to migrate toward the surface, also, in order to initiate blastoderm formation.

Formation of the Blastoderm.—The succeeding cleavage produces the 56-nuclear stage with two primordial germ cells, or oögonia as we shall now call them. Most of the somatic nuclei have wandered to the egg surface and eventually all arrive in this position. At first the nuclei comprise a loose syncytium with large gaps which are filled with deutoplasm and cytoplasmic strands, but with successive divisions a uniform blastodermic layer ultimately covers the egg. Concomitantly the blastodermic nuclei have become smaller and are separated superficially by typical cytoplasmic constrictions into definite cellular areas. The residual chromatin, cast from the first seven cleavage nuclei, still stains deeply; in fact, this substance is evident throughout the early embryonic history.

Shortly after 56 somatic nuclei have arisen, the two oögonia divide, but one lags slightly behind the other. The four oögonia again pass through a mitotic division to form eight. With the attainment of this number further division ceases in them for a considerable time while the embryo proceeds with its development.

A series of mitotic divisions in the superficial cells of the egg soon results in the completed blastoderm whose cells are now contiguous and small, so that all assume a cuboidal shape approximately uniform in size (Fig. 54*C*). They are separated from one another by cell membranes on the superficial and lateral surfaces, but not basally. The eight oögonia lie outside of the blastoderm and the cells of the latter are slightly pressed in opposite them. At this time a few cells are seen to pass from the blastoderm back into the internal yolk mass. Their nuclei are pale and surrounded by little cytoplasm. In the interior of the egg their cytoplasm becomes stellate, as each is transformed into a typical vitellophag.

The Ventral Plate and the Germ Band.—The cells of the blastoderm now become definitely separated on all sides, so that complete cells are formed. Those along the ventral side of the egg assume a tall columnar shape with their nuclei so disposed that some of them appear to be near the surface while others are placed at a deeper level in the blastoderm. This is rendered necessary by the active cell division that continues in this area with the consequent crowding of the cells. Over the rest of the egg the blastoderm remains flat, with cuboidal cells.

The thickened portion may be called the ventral plate. At its anterior end the plate is wider for a short distance where the anlagen of the cephalic lobes appear laterally. Posteriorly, the oögonia adhere closely to the blastoderm, pressing in and upward until they lie within the blastodermic portion above the end of the ventral plate. During this operation the blastoderm cells immediately opposite them are separated from all contact with the adjacent cells of the blastoderm and the ventral plate. They are pushed into the interior of the egg before the oögonia where they become, perhaps, part of the vitellophagous cells. Simultaneously, in other areas individual cells, or groups of cells, may be detected which also make their way into the interior for the same purpose. The gap left in the posterior end of the egg is quickly covered by the overgrowth of blastodermic cells which unite with the cells of the ventral plate (Fig. 54D).

While the development just described is taking place the embryonic envelopes begin forming in the typical manner by overgrowth, the only feature requiring mention being that this process is initiated first, and grows faster, in the anterior region over the cephalic lobes. Kahle (1908) is quite certain the embryonic envelopes are completely formed but calls attention to an earlier statement to the contrary made by Metschnikoff (1866). The latter admits the appearance of the amniotic folds but claims the envelopes are rudimentary and incomplete, a view adopted by Korschelt and Heider (1899) and Dawydoff (1928). Subsequent investigators have likewise supported this view or, in some cases, have failed to comment on the matter.

During this time the ventral plate has grown enormously in length in the posterior region. This portion, after reaching the end of the egg, turns dorsally and then anteriorly, until longitudinal growth ceases, with the posterior end reaching almost to the cephalic end of the embryo. While growing, it has carried the oögonia before it, where they are to be seen lying dorsally and slightly anterior to the tip of the embryo.

The mesoderm arises from a few cells along the mid-line of the ventral plate. This row is about five or six cells wide. As these median cells are crowded dorsally into the interior by the lateral plates, they round up into typical mesodermal elements and the lateral plates fuse beneath them as they migrate inwards. At first they form a solid strand, but quickly spread out to become a flat sheet one cell in thickness. In the later phases of this growth we may correctly speak of the embryo as being in the germ band stage. The next few paragraphs will present an account of some of the most important changes that occur in this stage.

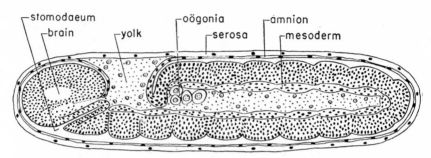

Fig. 55.—*Miastor metroloas*. Germ band showing metamerism, greatest length with dorsally flexed telson almost reaching the head. Parasagittal section. (After Kahle, Zoologica, 2, 55.)

Segmentation, the Stomodaeum and Proctodaeum.—The definitive segmentation of the embryo proceeds posteriorly from the cephalic lobes. The intersegmental furrows are very deep in the anterior body region and become successively shallower behind. The exact number of segments seems to be undetermined, but Kahle has found 18 in some embryos (Fig. 55).

The stomodaeum invaginates earlier than the proctodaeum. It grows posteriorly from the first segment and finally reaches the yolk. The proctodaeum arises at the very extremity of the embryo so that its posterior wall is continuous with the amniotic envelope. As it invaginates it passes dorsally over the oögonia and thence anteriorly until it, too, presses against the yolk. Neither of these invaginations has supernumerary cells that might correspond to the primitive entodermal anlage, their inner ends consisting only of the single-layered ectodermal tissue.

With the ingrowth of the proctodaeum the eight oögonia separate into two masses, each containing four cells that are arranged longitudinally, one behind the other. They lie close together and are pressed down by the proctodaeum against the mesodermal rudiment that lies ventrally beneath them. In this situation they are invested by mesodermal cells.

The Nervous System.—The primitive nervous system differentiates shortly after the mesodermal layer is formed. As the lateral plates fuse in the mid-line the ectoderm in this vicinity becomes many layered and a deep but very narrow furrow persists along the line of fusion. Within the ectodermal layers, on either side of the groove, a few large cells are seen at first as the neuroblasts. Mitosis in this area produces a bilateral ridge of cells which projects internally, causing no external swelling of the ectoderm. This ridge is the anlage of the ventral nerve cord.

The Coelomic Pouches and Blood Cells.—The neural swelling projecting into the interior leaves two depressed areas lying between it and the lateral parts of the embryo. The mesodermal cells fill these furrows with a multilaminar mass of tissue, being connected with each other only by a single layer of similar cells lying dorsal to the neural swelling and forming a mesodermal middle plate. Some cells of the middle plate grow larger, dissociate, and later are recognizable as blood cells.

The cells of the lateral strands of mesoderm continue to multiply, however, and this tissue finally becomes many layers in thickness intrasegmentally. At the segmental margins it is very definitely constricted into thin interconnecting plates. The cells in each intrasegmental area assume an epithelial, ovate arrangement, one cell in thickness, in the center of which a narrow cleft may appear to represent the remnant of the coelomic pouch.

Blastokinesis.—Kahle considered anatrepsis to be represented in the *Miastor* embryo by the dorsal and anterior extension of the ventral plate and the germ band, during which the embryonic envelopes are formed. Katatrepsis follows when the embryo reaches the complexity which has just been described. Both are rudimentary movements.

In katatrepsis, the embryo simply shortens and straightens itself until its entire length reaches only from one end of the egg to the other, along its ventral surface. At the end of katatrepsis the egg is much longer than before, also narrower. Naturally, several changes in external and internal organization accompany this movement (Fig. 56). The embryonic envelopes are not ruptured. While the amnion remains exceedingly delicate and thin, the serosa is transformed into a very thick membrane whose nuclei are round instead of flat as formerly. The cytoplasm immediately surrounding them is stellate and, according to Kahle, amoeboid. It now plainly exhibits a nutritional function since a large number of vacuoles, containing nutrient substances, give it the appearance of a coarse meshwork. It is believed that the contents of these vacuoles are discharged into the interior of the egg. The vitellophags are largely gathered between the yolk and the embryo where, presumably, they are converting yolk spheres into assimilable substances.

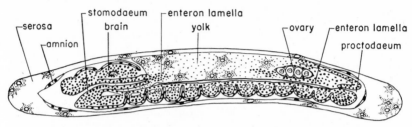

Fig. 56.—*Miastor metroloas*. Embryo after katatrepsis, parasagittal section. (After Kahle, Zoologica, 2, 55.)

Organology.—A few observations may be made here in order to continue more briefly with the morphological differentiation of various organs. Actual formation of definitive tissues begins about the time katatrepsis is initiated. The external shape of the larva is acquired by the overgrowth of the lateral body walls and their dorsal fusion. This one-layered epithelium at once becomes the hypoderm and secretes the cuticle exteriorly. The longitudinal nerve trunks lose their intimate connection with the ectoderm and move farther into the body cavity. Here they develop into ganglionic masses and their connectives, and are surrounded by the ventral musculature. Smaller nerves arise and extend to various parts of the body. Oenocytes and tracheae originate from ectodermal elements as is usual for other dipterous insects.

The Digestive Tract.—The formation of muscle tissue, heart, fat body, and blood cells offers nothing new upon which to comment. The development of the mid-intestine and the fate of the yolk, however, are of interest to us. It will be recalled that the yolk possesses numerous vitellophags owing to the immigration of many cells from the blastoderm and the addition of a cluster of cells pushing into it with the earliest migration of the oögonia. These vitellophags have, by this time, grown rather large, approaching the germ cells in size. The yolk nuclei with their interconnecting cytoplasmic strands compose an elaborate, loose syncytial meshwork enclosing masses of yolk. The main portion of each vitellophag, with its nucleus, generally occupies a peripheral position on the yolk. Kahle suggests that this condition, in which the central yolk mass is surrounded with a loose syncytial layer, resembles a mucosa of the embryonal yolk-intestine.

When the embryo initiates katatrepsis, the yolk fills all of the dorsal part of the embryonic space in the egg. Anteriorly, it presses against the brain and stomodaeum, while posteriorly it reaches to the proctodaeum. In fact, both the stomodaeum and the proctodaeum already have penetrated into the yolk slightly with their single layer of epithelial cells. Ventrally the yolk is squeezed into the shape of a narrow ridge where it lies against the ventral nerve chain. Posteriorly it passes between the gonadal masses. From the stomodaeal end, and later from the proctodaeal region, a layer, only four or five cells in width, appears on each side of the ventral yolk ridge (Fig. 56). Cells are added to them from the anlagen of the fore- and hind-intestines. As these lamellae extend posteriorly from the stomodaeum they meet and fuse with the corresponding lamellae proceeding anteriorly from the proctodaeal end. In this manner they unite the fore- and hind-intestines by means of two narrow bands of cells on either side of the yolk ridge. Lateral overgrowth by them encloses the yolk with the definitive mid-intestine in due time. Thus Kahle derives the mesenteron directly from ectoderm, but observes that not all of the intervening steps in the process have been distinguished in his preparations.

The Formation of Ovaries.—No consideration has been given to the origin of the ovaries since the position of the oögonia was mentioned in connection with the segmentation of the embryo. In katatrepsis these two cell masses are pushed forward until they come to lie in the eleventh and twelfth segments with the proctodaeal invagination between them. Each still contains four very large oögonia that are pressed close together (Fig. 57A). The mesodermal layer investing them is one cell in thickness except at the ends, where small clumps of cells are present. Both the oögonia and the cells of their mesodermal investment now enter upon periods of activity which cease just before the embryo attains its complete larval form.

The germ cells may be summarily disposed of for the present by stating that they pass through three more mitoses, whereby they become, in succession, 8, 16, and 32 cells in number in each rudiment of the ovary. This is the definitive number of oöcytes (Figs. 50, 57B).

In the meantime, the mesodermal elements have proliferated actively. Migrating daughter cells have pressed in and separated the much larger oögonia from one another. Anteriorly, a group of cells arrange themselves in the form of a long strand reaching from the ovary to the ninth segment, probably representing a

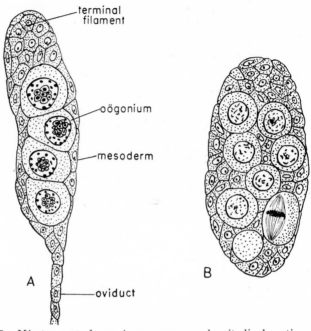

FIG. 57.—*Miastor metroloas. A,* young ovary, longitudinal section. *B,* older ovary. Twelve oögonia of the 5th order, another in metaphase. (After Kahle, Zoologica, 2, 55.)

structure analogous to the terminal filament of other insect ovaries. A similar posterior extension forms the rudiment of a paired oviduct. Both of these structures are ephemeral, being resorbed later, so that the mature ovary is held in place entirely by the fat body cells, nerves, and tracheae.

The embryo now ruptures the embryonic membranes and emerges as a free-living larva in the maternal haemocoele. The rudiments of its ovaries continue with their development into mature organs. Five to ten mesodermal cells in the immediate vicinity of each oöcyte aggregate into a compact mass, lose their cell membranes, and adhere closely to the adjacent oöcyte. These form the nurse cell body whose total syncytial nuclei finally number about 24. The additional nuclei are obtained through amitotic division of the few nuclei first organizing this body. The nurse cell mass grows relatively very large, compared with the adherent oöcyte. Additional contributions of a few cells from the mesodermal area of the ovary enclose each oöcyte and its nurse cell body in a thin epithelium, the follicular membrane. With increasing differentiation, some of the most external mesodermal cells of the ovary transform into a very thin cellular envelope around the entire ovary.

Kahle calls particular attention to the fact that 32 oöcytes are formed in each ovary, but fewer than this number may become fully mature and be provided with a nurse cell body as well as a follicular membrane. Further, the oöcytes located most posteriorly and most superficially reach maturity first. These seem to exert some kind of inhibiting action upon those more anteriorly or more centrally situated, so that the acquirement of maturity by many of the oöcytes is much retarded or entirely checked. For this reason it frequently happens that there are, in reality, less than 32 oöcytes actually capable of reproduction.

When the moment arrives for these eggs, in turn, to commence their development into embryos of the following generation, those of greatest maturity, or better supplied with nutriment, will complete their embryonic history in advance of the others. Those lagging behind in embryonic growth will not survive.

The Young Larva.—The young larvae emerging from the egg lie free in the maternal haemocoele. Here they commence to feed upon the vestiges of the maternal fat body and other tissues. They also consume their unfortunate sisters that are retarded in their development and fail to hatch with them. Eventually the mother's body is almost entirely devoured, leaving only the cuticular body wall, portions of the nervous system, and heart. The young larvae succeed in rupturing the maternal cuticle and emerge to take a more independent part in the gregarious, phytophagous behavior of the insect community.

Literature Cited

Von Baer (1863, 1866), Balbiani (1882, 1885), Barnes (1929), Carus (1866), Dawydoff (1928), Felt (1911a, 1911b, 1912), Gabritschevsky (1928, 1930), Ganin [1865 (Hanin, 1865)], Gerstäcker (1865), Grimm (1869, 1870, 1873), Harris (1923, 1924, 1925), Hegner (1912, 1914a, 1914b), Johannsen (1910a, 1910b), Kahle (1908), Karsch (1887), Klyver (1931), Korschelt and Heider (1899), Kraczkiewicz (1935, 1936, 1937), Leuckart (1865a, 1865b), Loew (1864, 1865), Lubbock (1859, 1867), Mäklin (1865), Meinert (1864a, 1864b, 1865a, 1865b, 1866, 1870, 1872), Metschnikoff (1865, 1866), Müller (1912), Pagenstecher (1864), Reitberger (1934), Schneider (1885), Schwabe (1866), Springer (1917), Ulrich (1934, 1936a, 1936b), Vandel (1931), Wagner (1862, 1863, 1865), Wagner et al. (1865), Zavřel (1907, 1926).

Chapter 10

HAEMOCOELOUS VIVIPARITY—STREPSIPTERA

This order is exceptional among insects in that all of its species are viviparous. Thus Pierce (1909) has been able to use viviparity as an ordinal characteristic in separating it from the others. The species are internal parasites of insects and their attack seems to be limited to the orders Orthoptera, Homoptera, Heteroptera, and Hymenoptera (Pierce, 1909). The adult males are swift fliers and have been infrequently observed only when on the wing or while mating, so little is known of their activity or actual longevity. The sexually mature females are invariably neotenic and sedentary and only the anterior end of their bodies protrudes from the abdomen of the host. Von Siebold (1839) gives credit to Burmeister for surmising that only the males are winged. Smith (1845) also claimed that all of the winged specimens of *Stylops* are males, thus corroborating Von Siebold's (1843) own conclusions.

Order Strepsiptera   Family Xenidae, etc.

The earlier observers suffered much confusion regarding the method of reproduction of these parasites. Klug (1810), as well as many others, believed the triungulinid form to be parasitic upon the larva-like female Strepsiptera. Westwood (1836) considered the females, which he found in their hosts, to be larvae. After further investigations, he observed the actual emergence of triungulinids from some of the larviparous females. While he suspected their true significance as progeny of the strepsipteran he was observing, he was still somewhat influenced by the thought that they might, perhaps, be parasites rather than offspring (Westwood, 1837). Thus he just missed making the discovery of viviparity in these insects. This method of reproduction was left for Von Siebold (1839) to suggest, although the idea seems to be not entirely his own for, according to Meinert (1896a), Burmeister already had hinted to Von Siebold that they possibly were offspring of Strepsiptera. Von Siebold apparently had examined the females critically, for he not only verified the presence of the brood canal first reported by Jurine (1818) but also found ducts leading into it from the maternal abdomen. Within the abdomen of the larva, as the female was termed at that time, he saw an enormous number of egglike bodies, apparently surrounded by choria.

This investigator continued his studies of Strepsiptera and finally was able to publish the principal steps in the life history of the group (Von Siebold, 1843). He stated positively that the female is viviparous and never leaves the body of the host. He described the ovaries and their location in the fat body. They are ruptured in the mature female and the eggs are distributed throughout the haemocoele during the entire subsequent development. The young triungulinids finally escape through funnel-shaped canals, which are accurately described, and reach the outside through the space between the maternal abdomen and the persistent last larval cuticle. This space Von Siebold designated the brood canal. He discovered that it opens by a narrow slit over the anterior end of the mother. The general appearance of the entire reproductive system of the male insect also was described by him. The male never overwinters while the female does, with her brood slowly passing through their embryonic history within her abdomen.

Von Baer (1866) had used the term paedogenesis to cover the reproduction of young by physically immature females whose reproductive systems develop precociously. This idea was seized upon by Von Siebold (1870) who maintained that Strepsiptera, too, were paedogenetic. Nassonov believes these insects to be pseudo-paedogenetic rather than paedogenetic for, he maintains, female development lies between the larval and imaginal stages of growth (Nassonov, 1910, pp. 28, 118, 171). It may now, however, be held that this order is an example of sexual dimorphism with neotenic development in the female, a view which Comstock (1925, p. 194) already enunciated.

These interesting observations on the peculiarities of strepsipteran development and metamorphoses should long ago have subjected the order to a sustained and critical study of their embryological development, but such was not the case. The chief difficulty probably consisted in finding sufficient numbers of any one species for a complete study of conditions in them. In fact, Newport (1851) did give figures showing several of the embryonic stages of *Stylops aterrimus*, for which he has not received due credit in the literature, together with a short account of the embryology gleaned from a very few specimens. However, it was not until Brues (1903) published an account of the early embryogeny of *Acroschismus wheeleri* Pierce (*Xenos peckii* Kirby) that any of the finer details concerning it were known, and his studies again were greatly restricted on account of the scanty material available.

Hoffmann (1913, 1914) contributed materially to our knowledge concerning their development in his studies of *Xenos bohlsi* Hoffmann, with some comparative notes on other species. His papers gave descriptions of the later events in development which were lacking in the account by Brues.

Noskiewicz and Poluszyński (1924) discovered that polyembryony exists in *Halictoxenos* (*Halicostylops*) in which at least as many as forty individuals apparently may develop from a single egg. They have also contributed to our knowledge of strepsipteran embryology in an excellent study of *Stylops spp.*, collected from several hosts, Noskiewicz and Poluszyński (1927). This paper together with Brues' (1903) and Hoffmann's (1913, 1914) contributions will be used as the principal sources of information with regard to the embryology given here. But before entering upon this phase of the subject two additional points of interest should be discussed in order to avoid devoting too much space to these questions in the strictly embryological section.

The first of these is the matter of the possible parthenogenetic or amphigonous condition of the egg. The method of mating in these insects has provoked much discussion from the very first, since the male is winged and free, while the female remains in an endoparasitic, apodous larviform condition, with the abdominal region projecting into the haemocoele of the host. Von Siebold (1843) wrote that spermatozoa were present in the male insect and briefly described them. Later Meinert (1896a) again emphasized the fact that viable spermatozoa were present in the male, and suggested that copulation might occur through the brood chamber. In a few instances notes have appeared of mating between the sexes, some of which certainly seem to be carefully recorded from critical observations. Matings have been reported by Sagemehl (1882), Crawford (1902–6), Muir (1906), Pierce (1909), Perkins (1918), Hofeneder (1923), and Hughes-Schrader (1924). On the other hand, Brues (1903) and Smith and Hamm (1915) contend that parthenogenesis occurs in the species with which they worked. Hughes-Schrader and Noskiewicz and Poluszyński (1927) carried out cytological investigations and their papers offer rather convincing data to show that Smith and Hamm perhaps missed the cytological evidences for fertilization, while Brues' investigations have been revised and superseded by Hughes-Schrader's more recent work on the same species of insect. Yet Smith and Hamm's conclusions are not entirely unsupported by other, less direct, evidence. The males of certain species seem to be at times either exceedingly rare or entirely absent from a colony of infected bees. Thus, Wheeler collected a number of stylopized *Halictus albipennis* Robertson. The 139 specimens showed the presence of 225 female Strepsiptera but no males. The present situation with regard to these data allows us only to conclude that fertilization of the eggs of certain species normally occurs, and that parthenogenetic development of eggs in other species still awaits verification.

Hubbard (1892) showed that male Strepsiptera emerged very early in the morning, and died after flying about actively for a few minutes. Hughes-Schrader (1924) determined that the life of adult males of *Acroschismus wheeleri* covered about three hours. At the same time, she found that mating could occur only on the fourth or fifth day after the female had exserted the cephalothorax through the abdominal wall of the host. Mating lasted twenty to fifty seconds, but undoubtedly actual insemination required only a portion of this interval. Muir (1906) had observed that copulation lasted six seconds or less. These data explain, in part, why actual mating has been so infrequently recorded.

Hughes-Schrader further established the fact that the spermatozoa were introduced into the brood canal, whence they migrate through the genital canals into the haemocoele of the female insect. Since the brood canal consists of the last larval cuticle, which is unshed by the female, and since the genital ducts, numbering from three to five according to the species, are purely ectodermal, independent of any reproductive system and far removed from the normal placement of a bursa copulatrix, we see here a very remarkable modification of the fertilization process. Nassonov (1892) compared the ducts of the female Strepsiptera to the unpaired ducts of the annelids and applied the term "genital canals" to them, which is the name to which we shall adhere. Enteman (1899) since has come to the conclusion that they are modified apodemes of intersegmental origin. At any rate, the spermatozoa of these insects are distributed over the external ventral surface of the body and must force their own way into the female. This is an occurrence not found elsewhere among insects; perhaps the nearest approach to it is the insertion of sperm into the bursa copulatrix of certain insects, or into the peculiar organs in *Cimex* described by Ribaga (1897), Berlese (1898, 1899), Carazzi (1902), Cragg (1920), and which Jordan (1922) has discussed in the Clinocoridae.

The second point relates to the degree of development obtained at any definite time by the embryos within the haemocoele of a single female. Brues (1903), working with *Acroschismus wheeleri,* and Noskiewicz and Poluszyński (1927) investigating species of *Stylops,* found that all of them developed isochronously, and this is true also in *Stylops melittae,* according to Smith and Hamm (1915). However, Noskiewicz and Poluszyński have observed in their specimens that the older embryonic stages showed distinct differential rates of development, so that many of the embryos completed their early growth and were ready to emerge long before others within the mother's body were able to do so. Newport, as early as 1851, showed definitely that *Stylops aterrimus* females contained eggs with all stages of development represented simultaneously; and in *Xenos bohlsi* the embryos present similar conditions, according to Hoffmann (1913). The same likewise is true for several species examined by Pierce (1918, p. 402). We may conclude, therefore, from the evidence of Newport, Hoffmann, Noskiewicz and Poluszyński, Pierce, and others that the early maturity, and possibly the immediate emergence of the more advanced embryos, do not seriously affect the mother's metabolism or the survival of the remaining offspring.

Female Reproductive System

The Ovary.—The female sex organs consist of two or three ovarial strands extending longitudinally on each side of the intestinal tract (Brues 1903, Hughes-Schrader 1924). In the sexually mature female they connect with no oviducts but, after the eggs ripen, the ovaries are disrupted and the ova are distributed throughout the haemocoele, which they largely fill because of their enormous numbers.

Noskiewicz and Poluszyński (1927) studied members of a genus which they believed to be *Stylops* but the specific names were not definitely determined. One species was thought to be *S. bimaculata* Perkins, and the remainder were named provisionally for the *Andrena* species from which they were collected; thus they list *S. gwynanae, nycthemerae, ovinae, parvulae, praecocis* and *xanthurae* for the remaining forms, in order to distinguish between them.

A. Development of the Embryo from Eggs with Little Yolk

The Egg.—The youngest eggs found were undergoing maturation. They vary in size from 43 microns in diameter for *S. parvulae* to 56 microns for *S. ovinae* and are enveloped by two cellular membranes. The outer envelope consists of loosely arranged cells but the cells of the inner form a syncytium, which is quite thin and bulges slightly at intervals because of the relatively large nuclei within. Although the origin of these membranes was not ascertained, they doubtless serve as nutrient organs for the embryo which develops in the enclosed egg.

The egg plasma consists of a uniformly distributed, finely granular ground substance in which larger chromatic bodies appear. Fatlike substances also occur throughout the egg with some tendency to accumulate in the vicinity of the nucleus. The absence of yolk is a characteristic of the eggs of all the species examined. The nucleus of the youngest egg in the first maturation stage was invariably situated at the periphery, forming a barrel-shaped spindle perpendicular to the surface, and contained eight elongate oval chromosomes arranged in an equatorial position. The chromosomes are enclosed independently in cylindrical, tapering sheaths which extend the entire length of the spindle and give the latter its barrel-like outline. No spindle fibers are present nor are there any centrosomes, so that the figure is of the anastral type. In a transverse section of a spindle at this stage the chromosomes are paired and distributed in the form of a circle with one or, occasionally, two pairs in the centers. One pair always appears to be substantially larger than the others. The germinal vesicle pauses in the above-described metaphase stage of the first maturation division until one or more spermatozoa penetrate the cytoplasm, when it immediately continues with the formation of the first polar body. This it does by greatly lengthening the spindle figure, and the sheaths enclosing the chromosomes are transposed into spindle fibers. The polar body lies outside of the egg beneath the inner enveloping membrane, where it very quickly disintegrates. It may remain attached to the egg for a short time by means of a long stalk. However, if no spermatozoon enters the egg while it is in the metaphase stage, the latter eventually breaks down and no development takes place.

Immediately after the formation of the first polar body the chromosomes of the egg nucleus advance to the metaphase stage of the second maturation division, omitting prophase. The second polar body is much larger than the first and remains within the egg, where it is very quickly resorbed into the cytoplasm. The remaining chromosomes become vesicular and a nuclear membrane surrounds them to form the female pronucleus. It then moves toward the center of the egg where it finally comes in contact with the male pronucleus.

The sperm nucleus brought two centrosomes into the egg. They constantly remain in association with it and for this reason, when the two pronuclei first meet, they are readily distinguishable. At this time, and before the initiation of the first cleavage spindle, there is a marked rearrangement of the cytoplasmic inclusions of the egg. The fat globules assort themselves as a broad sphere around the two pronuclei, which lie in a finely granular cytoplasm with their two attendant centrosomes. Outside of the layer of fat vacuoles the cytoplasm is still finely granular except for a few large clear areas which show a fibrillae-like substance that is always oriented with the long axes parallel to the future axis of the first spindle.

Cleavage.—The first cleavage occurs in the center of the egg and it, as well as succeeding cleavages, is of the astral type, presumably resulting from the centrosomes introduced with the spermatozoon. As the first cleavage spindle forms, the nuclear membranes of the two pronuclei disappear and the typical figures of division follow in sequence (Figs. 58A, 58B). It may be observed that the elongation of the spindle in the first illustration has caused the spherical mass of osmiophilic substance to expand in the equatorial plane in order to conform to the shape of the enclosed material, including especially the altered dimensions of the cleavage figure. When cleavage is completed these enveloping substances infiltrate into the space between the daughter nuclei. All of the osmiophilic substance eventually accumulates between the metaphase figures of the second cleavage (Fig. 58C). The two second cleavage spindles are always perpendicular to the position assumed by the first, but are not necessarily parallel to each other. One of them may be rotated to any extent up to 90° from the orientation taken by the other. With the initiation of the second cleavage, furrows appear on the egg surface, and, beginning with the 4-celled stage, separate the blastomeres from one another except in the central portion of the egg, where the concentration of the osmiophilic, fatlike substance delays their complete formation. In the 4-celled stage the blastomeres fill

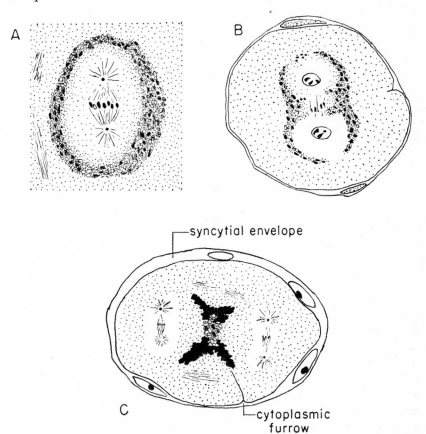

FIG. 58.—*Stylops bimaculatae.* Eggs showing: *A*, metaphase of first cleavage; *B*, early 2-cell stage with osmiophilic substance infiltrating between nuclei and cytokinetic furrow; *C*, second metaphase with osmiophilic granules central, fibrillar substance in cytoplasm. (After Noskiewicz and Poluszyński, 1927.)

the entire egg mass, and their long axes are thus tangential to the egg surface. The succeeding cleavage spindles are, in consequence, also tangential to the surface. Cleavage therefore multiplies the number of cells extending from the egg surface to the center and has the effect of making each daughter cell approximately half the size of the cell from which it was derived. At the fourth cleavage (16-celled stage) the blastomeres are beginning to constrict and to become separated from the centrally situated nutrient substance of the egg.

The fifth cleavage brings about several important changes in the embryo. As the cells have become more numerous it logically follows that some of them cannot maintain their long axis parallel to the egg surface. Even in the 16-celled stage it is sometimes observable that the spindle of one blastomere assumes a radial position in relation to the egg, although recognition of this altera-

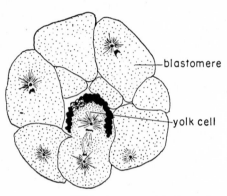

Fig. 59.—*Stylops gwynanae.* Fifth cleavage with the yolk cell moving toward the interior with the osmiophilic substance. (After Noskiewicz and Poluszyński, 1927.)

tion in orientation normally occurs in the fifth cleavage (32-celled stage). This blastomere, with its radially directed spindle, sinks somewhat below the egg surface so that the circumference of the latter is slightly flattened or even depressed at this point. At the next cleavage this cell divides so that one daughter cell encloses the nutrient substance and remains in the center of the egg. The other will lie above it yet somewhat below the egg surface; it will be mentioned in the next paragraph. During this division, the fatlike nutrient substance again becomes rearranged, this time forming a hollow bowl into whose lumen the aster and chromatic portions of the daughter nucleus migrate (Fig. 59). The osmiophilic material redistributes itself evenly throughout the peripheral cytoplasm of the newly formed yolk cell. The nucleus of the yolk cell undergoes mitosis twice in subsequent stages and forms a syncytium with four nuclei, since no cytokinesis accompanies karyokinesis. The term yolk cell is suggested simply to distinguish this cell, containing the fatlike osmiophilic substances, from the other cells. Noskiewicz and Poluszyński

(1927), however, really consider the nuclei to be primary entoderm nuclei which, with their cytoplasm, formerly possessed the
ability to form the entoderm.

The other daughter cell remains sunken in position. An imagi-
nary line drawn from its center through the center of the sister
cell (now the yolk cell) and thence through the egg would project the future dorsoventral axis of the embryo. Therefore, one
of the principal axes of the embryo is determined either at the
16-celled stage, or more frequently, at the 32-celled stage, depending upon the cleavage stage in which this condition is attained.

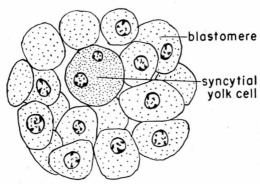

Fig. 60.—*Stylops gwynanae*. Embryo with approximately 60 blastomeres and
4 syncytial yolk nuclei (two shown). Yolk cell is migrating dorsally from original
position in preceding figure. (After Noskiewicz and Poluszyński, 1927.)

Upon completion of the fifth cleavage a few more blastomeres
have changed their main axes so that their next spindles will be
radial in position. These cells lie adjacent to the sunken cell
described in the preceding paragraph. After the sixth cleavage
has taken place 64 cells are present and, because of the radially
directed spindles of some of them, more blastomeres are to be
found in the interior. As a result of this partially two-layered
condition of the embryo, it is evident that the yolk cell is pushed
further toward the periphery of the cell opposite to the position
of the original blastomere from which it arose. The fatty substances within it have suffered extensive modification for they
no longer stain with osmic fixatives. It may be presumed that
they have been converted into other forms of nutrient materials
by the activity of this syncytial yolk cell.

During the multiplication of the blastomeres they have become relatively smaller and spherical, or oval, in shape (Fig. 60).
After the seventh cleavage, the embryo consists of a superficial

layer of blastomeres and the yolk syncytium which has been pushed to the surface. The interior is filled with the remaining ovate blastomeres arranged somewhat irregularly into three layers, counting from the surface toward the yolk syncytium (Fig. 61). These inner blastomeres are descendants of the cells which had radially placed spindles in later cleavages. The nuclei of all blastomeres are distinctly larger than the four in the yolk cell, and their chromatic portions stain deeply.

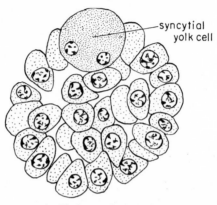

Fig. 61.—*Stylops praecocis.* Embryo of approximately 128 cells, Syncytial yolk cell arriving at prospective dorsal side. (After Noskiewicz and Poluszyński, 1927.)

The actual number of blastomeres may vary slightly beginning with the fourth or fifth cleavage, depending upon the initial appearance of the yolk cell. If the latter is set aside in the fourth cleavage stage there will be 15 blastomeres and the yolk cell. At the close of the seventh cleavage, therefore, 120 blastomeres and one yolk cell syncytium with four nuclei are found. If, on the other hand, the yolk cell appears in the fifth cleavage 31 blastomeres and a yolk cell are present, while in this event, at the end of the seventh cleavage the embryo consists of 124 blastomeres with the same sort of yolk cell.

During all this multiplication of blastomeres no increase has occurred in the size of the egg. However, different eggs within the same mother may vary from one another in relative size, presumably because of the more favorable situations which some attain within the maternal haemocoele. The type of cleavage, too, is intermediate between the superficial cleavage of most insect eggs and the total cleavage less frequently met, although it closely approaches the latter type and may, perhaps, be classed as a form of total cleavage (Noskiewicz and Poluszyński, 1927).

Formation of the Germ Disc and the Embryonic Envelope.—
Blastomere formation ceases for a time after the seventh cleavage
stage and a process of cell rearrangement and differentiation follows as the next step in embryonic development. The blastomeres
change to a cuneiform shape and those in the central portion of
the egg take a superficial position with the others, except that
some cells are unable to reach that portion of the surface occupied
by the relatively large yolk cell and are, therefore, forced to lie

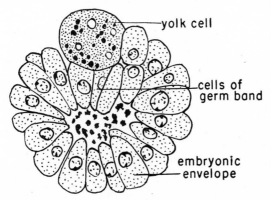

FIG. 62.—*Stylops praecocis.* Early germ band formation through reversal of
polarity and rearrangement of cells immediately beneath syncytial yolk cell.
Ventral surface below, yolk dorsal. (After Noskiewicz and Poluszyński, 1927.)

beneath it (Fig. 62). The migration of the blastomeres to the
surface leaves a hollow central cavity that is gradually filled,
apparently, by secretions from the inner ends of the cells. This
conclusion is drawn from the altered appearance of the polarized
substances that were evident in the cytoplasm during the earlier
stages of this shifting of the blastomeres to their present positions.
At first the inner, pointed ends of the blastomeres have very indistinct boundaries and the cytoplasm between the nuclei and
the inner ends is filled with osmiophilic inclusions. Later the
cells shorten and thereby enlarge the central egg cavity; the
fatty substances no longer are found in them but in the central
space, and the inner cell membranes are clearly observable. All
of the cells are essentially similar in size and shape but do not
long remain so. Those immediately beneath the yolk cell are
crowded in toward the center of the egg, and this causes them to
taper distally and enlarge a little at their inner ends. They tend
to form a cuplike invaginated mass surrounding the lower half
of the yolk cell. This mass is the definitive germ disc and rep-

resents the future ventral surface of the embryo, while the remaining cells, forming all of the convex portion of the egg, constitute the primordium of the embryonic envelope.

Shortly after the cells have rearranged themselves to form two bowls, one within the other with the yolk cell filling the center of the inner one, cell multiplication is again resumed. This activity is especially conspicuous around the lip of the outer bowl where it is continuous with the inner one. While at first all of the other cells are of approximately the same size, those engaged

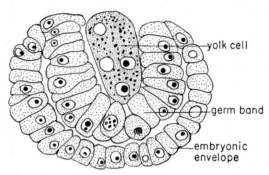

FIG. 63.—*Stylops gwynanae.* Germ band, cross section; yolk cell gradually becoming cone-shaped. (After Noskiewicz and Poluszyński, 1927.)

in a series of mitoses necessarily become smaller and tend to encompass the yolk cell as they proliferate. Cell differentiation quickly involves all of the cells on the outside, which are to form the embryonic envelope, and they become gradually very much smaller than those immediately enclosing the yolk cell (Fig. 63). The central cavity has become a very narrow cleft, and the fatty inclusions have disappeared.

This interesting succession of events culminating in the formation of the germ disc has varied greatly from the usual procedure followed by oviparous as well as viviparous insects. In some respects they might be compared, in part, with the early embryogeny of certain parasitic Hymenoptera and with *Hemimerus talpoides.* But one specific alteration, especially, should again be called to attention: the relation of the yolk cell to the blastomeres immediately adjacent to it. Originally, the slight accumulation of nutrient material was centrally situated when the first blastomeres were formed. This position is typical for all insect embryos and the inner ends of the blastomeres are always in contact with it in blastoderm and germ band formation. In the Strepsiptera, however, this polarity of the blastomeres in relation to the yolk is definitely reversed. The yolk cell comes to lie outside of them in the early differentiation of the germ disc and, upon its completion, the former outer ends of the cells forming the embryo lie adjacent to the yolk cell. As a result, the outer ends of the cleavage cells have now become the inner ends of the cells that are to form the embryo. From these inner ends the mesentoderm eventually must arise. The space that is normally enclosed within the embryo of other insects is here interposed between the germ disc and embryonic envelope. It thus becomes an extraembryonal cavity, a space usually known as the amniotic cavity.

The Germ Disc and Dorsal Curvature of the Embryo.— The embryo shown in Figure 63 has developed to a point where it is ready to change from a single layer of cells into a multilaminar condition. It very definitely exhibits a dorsoventral axis. The section has been cut in a sagittal plane, so the anteroposterior axis is also seen. The anterior and posterior ends of the embryo are not yet sufficiently differentiated to enable one to distinguish them. The germ disc itself is clearly delimited by the contrast between its cells and those of the embryonic envelope. When stained, the nuclei of all of the resting cells no longer show chromidia; they now exhibit large and conspicuous nucleoli which formerly were never evident. These are shown even by the yolk cell nuclei.

The cells of the germ disc, in the longitudinal axis, almost encompass the yolk cell, which is becoming distinctly conical in shape, with its broad base projecting dorsally. Examination of the germ disc in cross section during this and subsequent stages shows that cell division has not occurred so frequently laterally as at the anteroposterior poles, for the germ disc is narrow, and consequently encloses less of the yolk cell.

Figure 64 shows a slightly older embryo which is now converted into a multilaminar one, but the process involved is unknown. However, from the figure, it may be concluded that cell proliferation has occurred more rapidly in the posterior than in the anterior portion of the germ disc, for more cells are present there. This area is considerably thicker than the anterior end and is, therefore, readily recognized. Cell multiplication laterally continues to lag behind the activity shown in the anterior and posterior ends, so that the width of the embryo is considerably less than its length. Nevertheless, measurements indicate that the egg is not larger than it was in the preceding stages.

The embryonic envelope stretches in order to surround the germ disc and its cells become very thin as they increase materially in surface area during this change. No further cell division is visible in them. Anteriorly, the envelope unites superficially with the outer cells of the germ disc, but posteriorly it passes over the outer germ disc cells to fuse with them in the vicinity of the yolk cell.

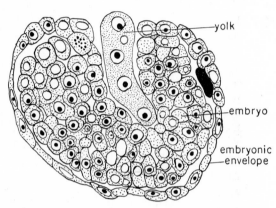

Fig. 64.—*Stylops praecocis.* Multilaminar germ band, sagittal section; yolk cell elongated. (After Noskiewicz and Poluszyński, 1927.)

As the germ disc continues to elongate in its dorsally curved longitudinal axis, the anterior and posterior ends approach each other and finally almost meet. Increasing pressure upon the enclosed yolk cell causes it to elongate in a dorsal direction and, at last, a substantial quantity of the nutrient material, with two or three of the nuclei, is extruded and comes to lie above the ends of the embryo. The two portions of yolk eventually lose contact, the outer undergoing dissolution beneath the egg membranes while the inner, smaller mass is ultimately enclosed by the midintestine as soon as it develops (see Figure 66).

Formation of the Germ Band and the Segments.—When the germ disc has assumed the position just described, in which the anterior and posterior ends almost touch dorsally, the anterior end remains stationary while the opposite end continues to elongate. This longitudinal growth is accomplished, without interference from the anterior portion, by the spiral curling of the lengthening posterior extremity. When it has attained its maximum length the embryo makes two complete spiral turns and part of a third, as illustrated by Figure 65. In the course of this growth the germ band, as it has now definitely become, has increased to a total length of about 80 microns without materially enlarging the area which it originally occupied. This great extension of the germ band is not brought about entirely through cell multiplication but, to a large degree, by the regrouping of the cells already present in the middle and posterior portions of the embryo. This is shown by the fact that the germ band has become relatively much thinner dorsoventrally, being only two or three cells in thickness in some places.

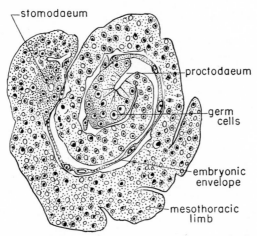

Fig. 65.—*Stylops gwynanae.* Old germ band stage, sagittal section. (After Noskiewicz and Poluszyński, 1927.)

At the completion of the first spiral a slight indentation appears on the surface of the anterior part of the embryo. This delimits the cephalic lobes, which thereupon begin to extend laterally over the surface of the egg. They enlarge and become huge flaps covering the lateral portions of the embryo outside of the spirals composing the abdominal region of the germ band. Shortly afterwards, additional transverse depressions indicate that segmentation is proceeding generally in a posterior direction from the mandibular to the thoracic and abdominal areas.

The appendages now arise, but nothing regarding the method of origin or of the order in which they are formed in these species has appeared in the literature.

The changes occurring in the embryonic envelope merit some consideration here. The appearance of this structure and of the germ disc has been described as two bowls, one within the other, the inner representing the germ disc (Figs. 63, 64). Where the rims of the two touched, their cells fused, so that there was cellular continuity between them around the margin. By the differentiation of an anteroposterior axis, followed by the spiral prolongation of the abdominal portion, that part of the envelope covering the abdomen was carried along with it and remained attached to it laterally and in the region of the telson. The anterior part of the envelope, where it united with the cephalic lobes of the embryo, was firmly pressed against its middle portion at the place where it also covered the abdomen. The spirally curved half of the envelope fuses finally to the head of the embryo where this contact was made so that there are now two

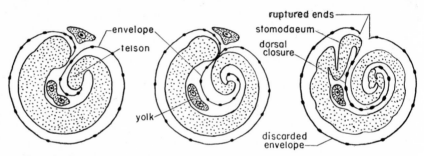

Fig. 66.—Diagrammatic formation of provisional dorsal closure by cephalic adhesion of the posterior end of the trophamnion and its subsequent rupture. Its external, ventral portion is later lost. (Modified from Noskiewicz and Poluszyński, 1927.)

envelopes formed from the original one. The first envelope is a large outer membrane covering the ventral surface of the embryo, the other is a smaller one extending from the head, over the dorsal part of the embryo, to the telson (Fig. 66). During the further growth of the embryo the outer envelope ruptures and gradually disintegrates so that no trace of it can be found in a stage represented by Figure 65. On the other hand, the inner envelope, which has persisted, extends from the cephalic lobes laterally to the edges of the germ band and posteriorly to the telson. Thus it forms the membrane of the provisional dorsal closure of the body in a manner quite like the original amnio-serosal envelope of oviparous insects, in cases where these membranes are ruptured during katatrepsis, but persist over the dorsal yolk until the embryonic body wall is completed (Noskiewicz and Poluszyński, 1927). Emphasis should be placed on the entire absence of a dorsal envelope which previously, in other forms, protects the yolk from contact with the follicular epithelium or the chorion of the egg. Throughout the embryonic development of most insects an embryonal membrane is present, though a few other exceptions occur, as *Hemimerus talpoides, Oöphthora semblidis* and the Strepsiptera. The embryos of the Polyctenidae also have no covering around them for a short time just after katatrepsis.

At a stage of growth of the germ band represented in Figure 65, the stomodaeum makes its appearance as a simple invagination whose inner end always extends to the inner yolk mass, although the present figure fails to show it since it is cut not quite in the median plane anteriorly. Posteriorly the proctodaeum also is visible, but this invagination is shallower than the former. How they arise and when they may first be discerned are unknown. Shortly after they have developed, a single group of cells with characteristic staining reactions may be identified as the primordial germ cell mass. These cells are invariably seen in their earliest visible stage at the interior end of the proctodaeum.

Blastokinesis and the Form of the Older Embryo.—No distinct movement of the early embryo can be distinguished as anatrepsis unless this is represented by the spiral growth of the posterior part of the embryo. Katatrepsis, however, consists essentially of the shortening of the embryo with a consequent elimination of the spiral position of the abdominal region. In this process, the dorsal wall develops by the upward extension of the lateral and posterior body ectoderm. Fusion of the two lateral walls takes place along the mid-dorsal line, first in the posterior segments and thence forward to the cephalic region, where the head folds have already contracted and rounded to form the head in conjunction with the mandibular segments. The provisional dorsal membrane, formed from a portion of the original embryonic envelope, is thus pushed forward and its cells are eventually replaced by true ectoderm. When last observed, the envelope is still connected anteriorly with the head region, but the larger part of it has become massed above the yolk cell remnant to form the dorsal organ. Nothing further is known regarding its ultimate fate.

The Mid-Intestine.—The stomodaeum gives rise to the entoderm by means of cells that appear at its inner end and which gradually extend over and beneath the residual yolk cell mass. Growing laterally, these cells eventually complete the formation of the mid-intestine. It is not known whether the entodermal cells originally came from mesentoderm cells situated at the end of the stomodaeum, or whether they arose by mitosis from the ectodermal cells of the fore-intestinal invagination. Later, the lumen of the stomodaeum becomes continuous with that of the mid-intestine. There is no evidence that the proctodaeum plays any part in the formation of the mid-intestine and these two portions of the digestive system never develop a common lumen.

The Late Embryo.—At length the embryo assumes a definite and characteristic position in which the abdominal half is flexed ventrally and applied closely against the head and thoracic sections of the body. This alteration in position must occur with great rapidity, for no intermediate steps in the ventral folding of the abdominal region could be found. The nervous system is enormously developed and fills a very large part of the haemocoele. A most peculiar characteristic is the strong posterior shifting of the brain to a position opposite the second thoracic segment. The very slender fore- and mid-intestine extend through the center of the embryo. Ventral to the posterior end of the mid-intestine the gonadal anlage has taken a definite position in the embryonic haemocoele. Most posteriorly the rather large proctodaeal invagination is seen to end blindly at its inner end, as described. Organology has never been completely followed in these species.

B. Development of the Embryo from Eggs with Abundant Yolk

The development of embryos from eggs with a large amount of yolk originally present offers several essential variations from the history recorded by Noskiewicz and Poluszyński (1927). The eggs studied by these workers contained very little yolk.

Brues (1903) described the earlier steps in the development of *Acroschismus wheeleri* Pierce (*Xenos peckii* Kirby), which was supplemented by Hughes-Schrader (1924) who clarified our knowledge of the maturation processes and the fertilization phenomena of the same species. Hoffmann (1913, 1914) furnished information on the later development from his studies of *Xenos bohlsi* Hoffmann, which also has eggs with abundant yolk.

Primitive Eggs.—According to Brues, the reproductive systems of the two sexes are precociously developed in the early larval forms. In a late larval stage the eggs are still enclosed in the follicular epithelium of the ovarial tubules extending along the alimentary tract, as previously mentioned for the ovary of species with little yolk. These he calls the primitive eggs to distinguish them from the definitive eggs arising later; and in this terminology Hughes-Schrader concurs. Each egg consists of a definitely arranged spherical mass of cells, with their apices directed inwards. According to Brues, no yolk is present, but Hughes-Schrader believes that a very small amount is deposited. The nuclei are large and contain conspicuous nucleoli (Fig. 67).

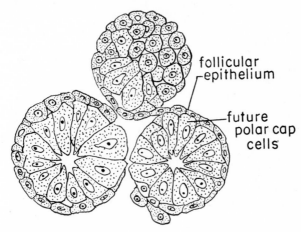

follicular epithelium

future polar cap cells

Fig. 67.—*Acroschismus wheeleri*. Primitive eggs in cross section, a third in tangential section. (After Brues, Zool. Jahrb., **18**.)

In a still later stage, just before the sexual maturity of the female, the primitive egg masses accumulate a very large number of nurse cells in their interior, but the means of acquiring them was not ascertained. The eggs finally break into fragments, each piece consisting of a substantial number of nurse cells with some of the original cells of the primitive eggs forming a cellular cap on one side of them (Fig. 68). Fragments of the follicular epithelium are retained outside of the polar cap of cells which apparently reconstitute an epithelium entirely surrounding each piece. These will be the definitive eggs. When the female projects the anterior end of her body through the cuticle of the host she rapidly becomes sexually mature. In fact, according to Hughes-Schrader (1924), this is accomplished within four or five days.

Upon the approach of maturity the eggs become scattered throughout the maternal haemocoele with cells of the fat bodies interspersed among them. Within each definitive egg the deposition of yolk takes place through the disintegration of the nurse cells, the cells of the polar cap and, without doubt, through some intake of nutritive substances from the maternal fat body cells. When all cellular organization has disappeared, except for a small mass of degenerating nurse cells at one end, the germinal vesicle may be recognized for the first time, although its earlier presence and history could not be detected by Brues. In her material, however, Hughes-Schrader found it to be present in the earliest stage of definitive egg formation.

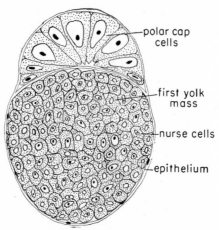

Fig. 68.—*Acroschismus wheeleri.* Median longitudinal section of egg prior to secretion of yolk. Polar cap cells are derived from fragments of primitive eggs; parts from original follicular epithelium reconstitute the new epithelium enclosing the egg. (After Brues, Zool. Jahrb., **18**.)

The Mature Ovum.—The egg is invested by two membranes, the outer one probably being derived from part of the original follicular membrane. The inner membrane, the chorion mentioned by Brues, appears to be syncytial. Hughes-Schrader believes it arises from cells of the polar cap and the nurse cell group. The bulk of the egg is slightly increased through the absorption of more of the maternal fat body substance in which the inner membrane, at least, seems to take an active part as indicated by its vacuolar appearance. This membrane also becomes definitely thicker and remains so until after blastoderm formation. Except for a short time during the early formation of the embryo, as just observed, it is a very thin membrane which persists until hatching of the triungulinid.

The germinal vesicle is large and prominent. A granular and stellate cytoplasm surrounds it and from the latter cytoplasmic processes extend into the egg. Its position is peripheral and generally equatorial. The yolk spheres are quite large and entirely fill the egg so that little cytoplasm is seen between them nor is a periplasm present at the surface.

Maturation and Fertilization.—These phenomena have been very carefully described by Hughes-Schrader (1924) in great detail and most of the essential part of her work was given in the discussion of these events in the embryogeny of *Stylops spp.* since, in the main, the results of the later work of Noskiewicz and Poluszyński (1927) agree with hers. Here are added only those points which apply especially to *Acroschismus wheeleri*. The number of chromosomes and the polar body formation are practically the same as already described. Polyspermy is as typical of this genus as it is of *Stylops*, several entire sperms entering the egg where all but one disintegrate. However, upon the completion of polar body formation, the egg chromosomes become highly vesicular, forming eight small bodies closely aggregated at the periphery of the ovum. This aggregation constitutes the large female pronucleus. The fertilization path of the sperm is oriented directly toward the cytoplasm surrounding the female pronucleus. Near it the sperm tail disintegrates and the sperm head forms a large vesicular pronucleus beside that of the egg. After the completion of fertilization the zygote nucleus migrates toward the center of the egg and cleavage follows.

Cleavage, the Blastoderm, and the Germ Band.—During cleavage in *A. wheeleri* all of the daughter cells finally migrate to the surface to enter into the blastoderm. Brues (1903) emphasizes the fact that no yolk nuclei, or vitellophags, remain behind. Six or seven later return to become vitellophags, whereupon the yolk segments into a similar number of distinct masses, each of which contains one vitellophag. Hoffmann's (1913, 1914) specimens, *X. bohlsi*, on the contrary, always possessed three, or unusually four—vitellophags which develop from nuclei that never passed to the surface. The blastoderm covers a very large part of the egg surface with large, flat cells spaced rather far apart and connected with each other only by extended cytoplasmic processes. The yolk is entirely exposed at one pole (Fig. 69). The blastodermic cells contract locally to form a polar cap of contiguous cells instead of stellate, spaced cells over the end of the egg. This cap then sinks into the yolk and becomes an oval, morula-like hollow mass representing an immersed type of germ band (Brues, 1903). This stage is transitory, for the cells slowly migrate again toward the egg pole where they assume a symmetrical, spherical form with the individual cells conical in shape, broad on the outer surface and tapering toward the central cavity of the sphere. Simultaneously, an outer layer of apparently structureless and homogeneous yolk substance is visible, surrounding the entire egg including the spherical mass of cells. The sphere of cells quickly begins to show a lumen within as its component cells expand in their lateral dimensions. The sphere also alters its shape, becoming first dome-shaped with a flat base, then

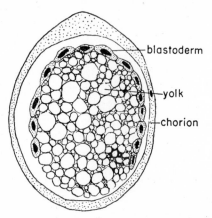

Fig. 69.—*Acroschismus wheeleri*. Blastoderm stage with approximately 86 cells. (After Brues, Zool. Jahrb., **18**.)

an oval mass of very long and extremely narrow cells whose number has greatly increased through mitoses. The large lumen remains in the center of the cell group. At this time the vitellophags, previously mentioned in this paragraph, make their first appearance and macromeres are formed of the yolk.

Brues' (1903) material revealed only fragments of the later development of this species and we must turn to Hoffmann (1913, 1914) for further light on the embryogeny of a yolk-rich type of egg. But it will be necessary to review the principal points in germ band formation in *X. bohlsi*, for these steps do not duplicate those of *A. wheeleri*, although the blastoderm is quite similar in both (Fig. 69).

Formation of the Germ Band in Xenos bohlsi.—The blastoderm with its widely spaced cells begins to contract, a process which continues until the cells shape themselves into a bowl-like cap on one pole of the egg. The polar bodies are still visible at the opposite end (Fig. 70). A cone-shaped cavity in its center is filled with metamorphosed yolk nutrient but no vitellophags are present in this region for they are few in number and confined solely to the macromeres of the original yolk mass. This cellular cap is the polar disc or primitive ventral plate.

Cell proliferation now commences at the margin of the cap of cells on the egg. We should expect the new cells to extend gradually over the egg surface and at last compose the blastoderm as in other insect eggs. Such, however, is not the case. The original

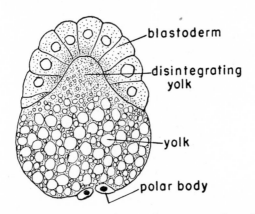

Fig. 70.—*Xenos bohlsi.* Germ band somewhat younger than shown in preceding figure, longitudinal section. (After Hoffmann, Nachr. v. d. K. Gesellsch. Wiss. Göttingen, Math.–Phys. Kl., 3.)

cell mass nevertheless represents the embyronic rudiment of the ventral plate. The daughter cells form a sheet of cells which reverses the usual process by folding up over the ventral plate until it meets above the plate and fuses into a single layer whose cellular elements are somewhat smaller than those of the cell cap. The ventral plate may now be called the germ band and the cellular layer above it the embryonic envelope. The yolk, meanwhile, has greatly increased in amount by the transference of nutrient substances into it from the maternal haemocoele. Except for the very great disparity in the yolk contents of the two kinds of eggs, this stage quite closely resembles those of *Stylops sp.* as described by Noskiewicz and Poluszyński (1927), and shown in Figure 63. Its presence however, has come about by a very different process in the two cases despite their eventual similarity; and, especially, the cells in the germ band of *X. bohlsi* have not reversed their polarity in relation to the yolk.

It would appear that the dorsoventral axis of the *Xenos* egg in Hoffmann's material is established during the maturation of the egg nucleus since the blastoderm forms first at the opposite pole. *A. wheeleri* eggs show a definite dorsoventral axis only when the blastoderm arises.

Segmentation and the Embryonic Appendages.—The newly formed germ band immediately begins to elongate in an antero-posterior direction over the egg. Thus another axis is at once recognizable. When the germ band has encompassed about half of the yolk as a comparatively narrow band of ectodermal cells, covered by an embryonic envelope, it continually becomes thinner as it extends over a greater area. The anterior portion may be distinguished by the lateral growth of the cephalic lobes. Shortly afterwards the embryo may be divided roughly into the three major body regions, due to the appearance of constrictions in its width in certain places. While the elongating embryo circumscribes the yolk, the abdominal end approaches the cephalic portion on the dorsal yolk. As this growth continues, the cephalic lobes appear to shift somewhat laterally and the telson moves slightly in the opposite direction in order to pass over the yolk without contact with the head. Only a little more than one complete circumscription of the yolk occurs before elongation ceases. Meanwhile the vitellophags have formed large yolk cells about themselves, each completely distinct from the others although closely pressed together in the space at their disposal. Thus the entire yolk is divided into as many yolk cells as there are vitellophags, usually three in this species.

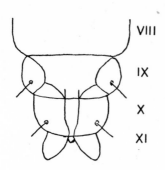

Fig. 71.—*Xenos bohlsi.* Four posterior segments of an old embryo showing cleft segment XI. (After Hoffmann, Verhandl. deut. Zool. Gesellsch., Leipzig, **24**.)

When the germ band ceases to elongate further after it has surrounded the yolk cells, it is still a rather narrow embryo except for the expansion of the cephalic lobes and the broad telson. Bulges with deep depressions between them are now conspicuous, the depressions serving to mark off the primitive segments of the embryo. Hoffmann (1914) believes that eleven abdominal segments are formed (Fig. 71), while anteriorly the intercalary segment could not be distinguished. The appendages arise, as do the segments, in the general anteroposterior sequence of other insects and shift later to their definitive positions. The antennae show a very rudimentary growth and are resorbed when pigmentation appears in the eyes. The first maxillae become the most elongate of all of the buccal appendages. Nevertheless, only one portion of them, the palpus rudiment, remains in the triungulinid, while the second maxillae are completely resorbed. The mandibles are also retained by the larva. Just posterior to the invaginating stomodaeum, of which we shall speak later, a tonguelike glossa is found. Abdominal appendages appear as in most insect embryos only to prove fugitive, too, with the exception of the terminal springing bristles on the eleventh segment. Of these appendages, the pleuropodia show most prominently at this time (Fig. 72). Two bristles also appear on the ninth and on the tenth abdominal segments which are retained by the hatched triungulinid.

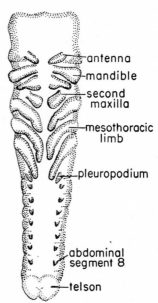

FIG. 72. — *Acroschismus wheeleri*. Young embryo with developing appendages, ventral view. (After Brues, Zool. Jahrb., 18.)

With the appearance of segmentation and the evagination of the appendages, the germ band begins to shorten into the definitive shape of the embryo. The telson is drawn back until it again lies in front of the head and both extremities resume a median sagittal position. At the same time, the lateral overgrowth of the yolk is completed and the latter is now entirely enclosed within the haemocoele. The fate of the embryonic envelope is not made clear, but apparently it begins to undergo dissolution as the appendages evaginate, a fate indicated by its great vacuolization.

The Mesoderm.—There is no visible invagination of a portion of the ventral plate to give rise to the mesentoderm. This layer is apparently formed by the occasional transverse mitotic division of ectodermal cells whose innermost daughter cells gradually migrate toward the interior, for the germ band only slowly becomes multilaminar. According to Hoffmann (1914), this inner layer of cells represents the true mesoderm anlage, for he claims that the entoderm does not develop from it.

Stomodaeum, Proctodaeum, and Entoderm.—As the appendages evaginate, the stomodaeum, and later the proctodaeum,
invaginate from the superficial ectoderm in the customary manner. The interior ends of both intestinal portions project inwards
and press firmly against the yolk. They remain in this condition
until after the ventral flexure of the abdomen occurs. Now a most
interesting transformation is evident in the yolk macromeres.
Their sharply distinguishable boundaries disappear and the shape
of the entire yolk mass is changed to a cylindrical form, owing to

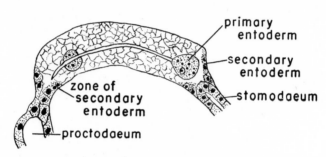

Fig. 73.—*Xenos bohlsi.* Union of stomodaeum and proctodaeum with cylindrical yolk mass enclosed in primary entoderm, old embryo. Secondary entoderm
will arise from anterior and posterior zones. Embryo ventrally flexed following
blastokinesis. (Modified from Hoffmann, Nachr. v. d. K. Gesellsch. Wiss. Göttingen,
Math.–Phys. Kl., 3.)

the pressure of the enormous ventral nerve below and the contracting dorsal body walls laterally and dorsally. One vitellophag,
in the largest dorsal macromere, migrates to an anterior position
near the stomodaeum while two others proceed to the vicinity
of the proctodaeum where they remain side by side. If four
vitellophags occur, two migrate forward and two back. Apparently a long cytoplasmic process extends posteriorly from the
anterior vitellophag through the yolk mass and unites with a
similar strand progressing anteriorly from those situated in
front of the proctodaeum. The strand seems to possess a narrow
lumen which, Hoffmann (1914) suggests, is reminiscent of ancestral yolk entoderm formation (Fig. 73). After a time this
structure breaks down and disappears together with the vitellophags and the yolk. The yolk itself has greatly diminished in
amount through liquefaction and, probably, through absorption.
At any rate, upon completion of the secondary entoderm much
less is present in the embryo than formerly. At the inner ends of
both stomodaeal and proctodaeal invaginations the cells are at

first large and cylindrical. Later, smaller cells are formed ventro-laterally at the inner end of the stomodaeum, and somewhat later still, a similar condition is seen in the proctodaeal area. These smaller cells slowly pass along the yolk and finally fuse to complete two lateral strands of cells. Dorsal and ventral extensions in growth eventually enclose the yolk within the definitive secondary enteron, or mid-intestine. This is fully formed about the time eye pigmentation occurs. An opening leads from the stomodaeum into the mid-intestine but the proctodaeal junction remains permanently closed. The proctodaeal lumen forms a narrow duct leading to the outside, but the inner end is considerably dilated. A few of its ectodermal cells are enlarged, perhaps in order to function as excretory units since the Malpighian tubules are either entirely absent, or are only very slightly developed and probably functionless.

The Nervous System.—There is little to add to the account already given for the formation of the ventral nervous system. It is comparatively enormous in size in the embryo but later becomes quite restricted in the adult, as illustrated by Smith and Hamm (1915). It appears from the first as a continuous single mass and shows exteriorly no traces of segmental arrangement, as it does in most insect embryos. Internally, it seems to consist of five or six fused ganglionic pairs. Two commissures connect it anteriorly with the paired cerebral ganglia, which are very large. During later development the brain shifts posteriorly into the thoracic region and the ventral portion contracts until it no longer extends beyond the mesothorax anteriorly. The ventral cord portion ends at the fourth abdominal segment instead of the eighth, in which it was first found.

Mesoderm and Blood Cells.—The cells derived from the ectoderm to form mesodermal tissues by a process already described are found scattered at random in the epineural sinus which lies between the developing nerve cord and the yolk macromeres. These differentiate in two directions after becoming stellate, rich in lymph, and often united by thin cytoplasmic extensions. A few of them become associated into strands of muscle tissue, and at one stage during this change, coelomic pouches have been observed. The remaining mesoderm cells achieve permanent independence and finally become blood cells. The details of these processes have not been followed. None of the cells have been seen to form any part of the mid-intestine.

Definitive Position of the Embryo, Hatching, and Birth.—
Early in the formation of the stomodaeum and proctodaeum and,
therefore, before most of the other internal differentiations have
taken place, the telson of the embryo elevates from the yolk. As
the embryo shortens it tends to straighten out at both ends. The
anterior portion, including the head and thorax, remains permanently straight but the posterior half of the abdomen continues
its movement until it is flexed strongly along the anteroventral
half of the abdomen.

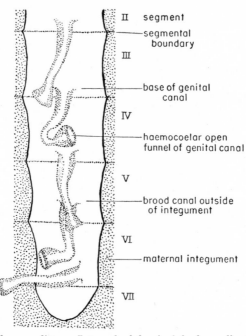

II   segment

segmental
boundary

III

base of genital
canal

IV

haemocoelar open
funnel of genital canal

V

brood canal outside
of integument

VI

maternal integument

VII

Fig. 74.—*Stylops melittae*. Internal abdominal body wall of adult female,
ventral view, showing brood and genital canals. The latter lie between the thin,
semi-transparent maternal integument and the last larval cuticle which remains
unshed; canals are integumentary invaginations. (After Nassonov, Ber. Naturwiss.–Med. Vereines in Innsbruck, **33**.)

Since embryonic development varies in age for the different
eggs, it follows that hatching of some of them continually occurs
until all have escaped from the eggs. The genital canals (Fig. 74)
leading from the maternal haemocoele to the brood canal remain
closed at their inner ends until some time before hatching takes
place. They then open and the young escape through them into
the brood canal. According to Hoffmann (1914), an elastic
tonguelike projection across the exterior end of each genital canal

enables the offspring to emerge but prevents their later return to the interior. They make their way to the outside through a crescentic slit in the anterior wall of the brood canal.

C. Polyembryology

Noskiewicz and Poluszyński (1935) give some of the essential details of polyembryonic development in a new species, provisionally named *Halictoxenos simplicis,* which occurs as a rather rare endoparasite of *Halictus simplex* Bluthg. This species also possesses comparatively abundant yolk in the egg even though it is quite atypical since it appears more cytoplasmic than definitely deutoplastic. For convenience the contents will be termed the yolk.

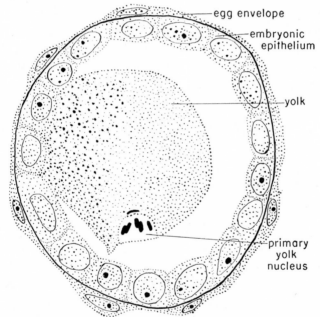

Fig. 75.—*Halictoxenos simplicis.* Primary embryonic rudiment, a blastula-like epithelial sphere with central nutrient mass and fluid of unknown function. (After Noskiewicz and Poluszyński, Zool. Poloniae, Lwow, 1.)

The Primary Embryonic Rudiment.—The cleavages are thought to be typically superficial although no examples of these stages could be found. A primary embryo is produced which is enclosed within two cellular envelopes, as previously mentioned for the preceding species in this order. The outermost envelope disappears quite early. The embryo consists of a spherical, blastula-like epithelial layer containing approximately 100 cells. Within the central cavity lies the mass of nutrient material containing at one margin a large nuclear area showing five or six sheath-enclosed chromosomes radially directed (Fig.75). Whether this nucleus invaded the yolk from the more superficial epithelium or was left there originally is unknown. At any rate, a considerable number of yolk nuclei appear, probably derived from the first yolk nucleus, which may often be differentiated into two types. Both are not always present in any given embryo. One type consists of smaller nuclei with a few large chromatin masses and frequently without visible cytoplasm surrounding them. In the other type the nuclei are larger and reticulate, containing numerous small chromioles which are enclosed by the so-called yolky material. The former are usually first to form, being followed later by nuclei of the second type.

The Trophamnion.—The yolk is eventually converted into cellular masses by yolk cleavage, and the resultant cells migrate through the layer of the primary embryonic rudiment to assume positions peripheral to the latter (Fig. 76). This process also reverses the polarity of the cells of the embryo, as explained for some other Strepsiptera. Migration of the yolk cells through the embryonic cell layer may occur at various places simultaneously or mainly at one location, in the latter case causing a distinct opening of the blastula-like embryo at this point. The yolk cells spread out and form a continuous syncytial trophamnion over the primary embryonic rudiment. The nuclei of this trophamnion are of two types: a peripheral, spindle-shaped one, next to the membrane, with numerous chromatin granules; the other lies more deeply and is elliptical or more rounded in shape, is paler in staining reaction, and contains a nucleolus. It is thought the latter type of nucleus retains yolk cell potentialities while the former has lost this capacity and is now limited solely to a trophic function. With the advent of the trophamnion the cellular envelope of the egg becomes a very thin membrane.

The trophamnion with its two types of nuclei in certain cells has been said to form a complete, circumferential covering over the embryonic rudiment. This is particularly true for the more superficial cells. The cells more deeply situated and possessing greater potentiality are more scattered in their distribution over the embryonic rudiment. They represent yolk centers at the various locations where they appear. This is quite different from previously described conditions for Strepsiptera, wherein the en-

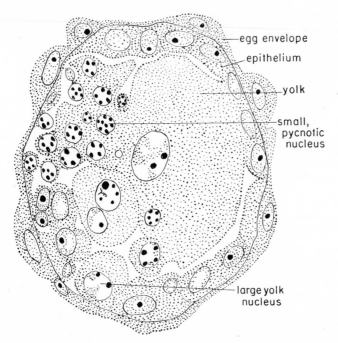

FIG. 76.—*Halictoxenos simplicis.* Rupture of primary embryonic epithelium by migration of large yolk cells peripherally. Migration results in reversing the polarity of embryonic cellular tissue. Pycnotic nuclei may not be enclosed in nutriment, the larger nuclei are invariably enclosed. (After Noskiewicz and Poluszyński, Zool. Poloniae, Lwow, 1.)

tire yolk mass exhibited polarity in relation to the embryonic rudiment and was aggregated at one side of the young rudiment.

Secondary and Tertiary Embryonic Rudiments.—The activating source of polyembryonic development within the egg is unknown, but opposite each of the scattered yolk centers of *Halictoxenos* the epithelial layer of the primary embryonic rudiment now initiates a rapid cell proliferation. Details of this process are still lacking and cannot be discussed more fully. Each center of activity, usually less than five in number, may become a secondary embryonic rudiment (Fig. 77). It is thought these centers of secondary embryonic proliferation are, for the most part, further subdivided, though the actual sequence of events has not been followed. Before definitive embryos are formed the small number of secondary proliferation centers is increased, presumably by fission of cell masses, into 40 or more independent tertiary embryonic centers (Fig. 78).

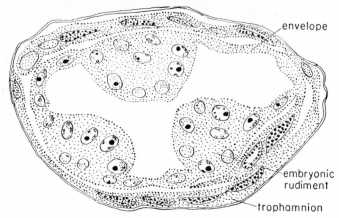

FIG. 77.—*Halictoxenos simplicis*. Three secondary embryos within a germ vesicle, peripheral yolky trophamnion and an inner envelope. (Modified from Noskiewicz and Poluszyński, Zool. Poloniae, Lwow, 1.)

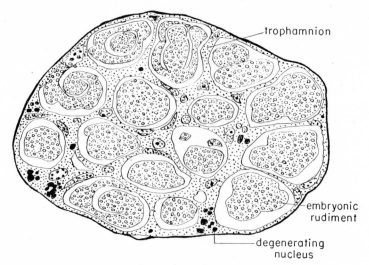

FIG. 78.—*Halictoxenos simplicis*. Tertiary embryos arising by budding of secondary embryonic rudiments shown in preceding figure. Each embryo is enclosed in a vesicle formed by ingrowth of the trophamnion derived from the yolk cells. (Modified from Noskiewicz and Poluszyński, Zool. Poloniae, Lwow, 1.)

As each tertiary definitive embryonic anlage is formed it is, of course, still connected with adjacent similar rudiments by a thinner continuation of the primary embryonic epithelium which has remained a single layer of cells at these places. The separation of tertiary embryonic rudiments from one another and their enclosure in separate trophamniotic vesicles seems to be accomplished by invasions of trophamnion and yolk cell elements toward the more central portion of the egg. These points of in-growth occur between the tertiary embryonic rudiments, or defini-tive embryonic masses, and carry before them the thin connecting layer of primary embryonic epithelium. As the partitioning trophamniotic and yolk cells press inward, the primary embryonic epithelia are also necessarily pushed in over the tertiary embry-onic rudiments. The fold of primary embryonic epithelium on one side of an embryonic rudiment eventually comes in contact with a similar one from the other side when they fuse to form an embryonic membrane. The embryonic membrane thus formed is, at first, similar to a typical amnion in shape, position, and man-ner of attachment to the tertiary embryonic rudiment, though not formed quite the same.

Trophamniotic Vesicles.—In the preceding paragraph refer-ence was made to the inward growth of portions of the troph-amnion. This process continues until the inner ends of the trophamnion meet and fuse. This fusion serves to divide the interior of the egg into numerous vesicles, each enclosed by troph-amniotic tissue to which yolk cells are adherent. Within each

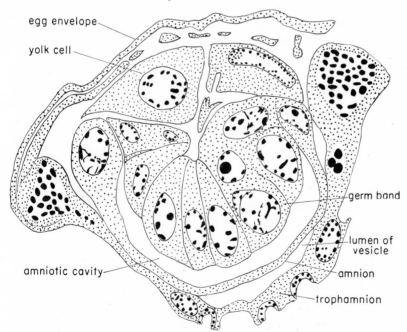

Fig. 79.—*Halictoxenos simplicis.* Definitive polyembryonic embryo in germ band stage, cross section. Newly formed envelope appears to be a typical amnion. (Modified from Noskiewicz and Poluszyński, Zool. Poloniae, Lwow, 1.)

vesicle formed by the trophamnion lies a definitive embryonic rudiment (the tertiary embryonic rudiment) which was derived from the primary embryonic rudiment. The embryo is covered ventrally by an amnion-like embryonic membrane which was formed from extraembryonic epithelium formerly connecting the embryonic rudiments to one another.

Development of the Definitive Embryo.—The tertiary rudiment may now be considered an early germ band stage of development, covered ventrally by one embryonic membrane (Fig. 79). As further development occurs, the dorsal portion receives about five yolk cells which assume the position typical of yolk cells of Strepsiptera. These come directly from the trophamniotic membrane in the case of the superficial vesicles but were carried into the deeper positions by the ingrowing trophamnion at the time of vesicle formation, as previously mentioned.

As the germ band elongates and acquires the curvature of the *Stylops* form of spiral germ band, the embryonic membrane comes to cover the whole of the embryo, thus comprising a combination of amnio-serosal functions and providing the provisional dorsal closure of the embryo.

Comments.—The early development, including the formation of the primary embryonic blastula-like epithelium, and the peripheral migration of the yolk and trophamnion cells, take place in the fall of the year. With renewed activity in the spring, the secondary embryonic rudiments appear and subsequent developmental stages rapidly follow. The relatively small amount of yolky material and few yolk cells, no doubt reflect the transference of the nutrient function to the trophamnion. This nutrient organ, however, is as yet incapable of providing adequately for all of the embryonic growth centers when 40 or more vesicles are formed, and it is thought several of the more deeply situated embryos actually do disintegrate.

LITERATURE CITED

Von Baer (1866), Berlese (1898, 1899), Brues (1903), Carazzi (1902), Comstock (1925), Cragg (1920), Crawford (1902–1906), Enteman (1899), Hofeneder (1923), Hoffmann (1913, 1914), Hubbard (1892), Hughes-Schrader (1924), Jordan (1922), Jurine (1818), Klug (1810), Meinert (1896a), Muir (1906), Nassonov (1892, 1910), Newport (1851), Noskiewicz and Poluszyński (1924, 1927, 1935), Perkins (1918), Pierce (1909, 1918), Ribaga (1897), Sagemehl (1882), Von Siebold (1839, 1843, 1870), Smith (1845), Smith and Hamm (1915), Westwood (1836, 1837).

Chapter 11

PSEUDOPLACENTAL VIVIPARITY—DERMAPTERA

With the consideration of the embryogenies of insects that display the pseudoplacental type of viviparity, we encounter examples of extraordinary modifications of structures to insure the adequate nourishment of the embryos. The haemocoelar incubation and nutrition of the offspring is, in itself, remarkable. Essentially, in haemocoelar viviparity, the embryo is suspended in nutriment which simply passes by diffusion or osmosis through trophic membranes into the egg from the surrounding medium. The pseudoplacental type of embryo has established new contacts with its food supply or has recalled to activity some degenerating organ whose original utility is lost, that it may assume the function of a nutrient organ.

The young, though few in number, are born individually or in very small populations at any one time. Reproduction continues over a relatively long duration of the mother's life as an adult and the birth of young does not terminate her existence. Moreover, the mother's reproductive system has often become so modified that the embryos, either singly or in groups, find lodgment in enlarged portions of it during the greater portion of their embryonic history. The apparent ease with which parents give birth to relatively enormous offspring, often equipped with numerous setae is, in itself, a very surprising condition.

The greatest contrast with haemocoelous viviparity, however, lies in the fact that the embryos of this class are not directly exposed, except for their membranes, to adjacent food supplies. Sometimes they are even enclosed in a practically impermeable chorion. They must, therefore, by some means supply themselves with organs by which nutriment can be obtained, usually long before their own digestive system is formed. Unlike the adenotrophic type of viviparity where the larva is retained and nourished, these offspring are expelled when they attain a stage equivalent to the hatched offspring of ovoviviparous species.

In the following pages the nutrient structures will be described and their relation to the insect's ontogeny will be shown.

261

Order Dermaptera   Family Hemimeridae

Dermaptera usually exhibit maternal care and protection of eggs and young in oviparous species. Two genera, *Hemimerus* and *Arixenia,* contain viviparous species of the pseudoplacental type. Both genera are apterous and the eyes are much reduced or absent. The incomplete metamorphosis is so slight that the prenatal embryos, the nymphs, and the mature stages of development closely resemble one another.

Hansen (1894) discovered a case of viviparity in the order Dermaptera when he was preparing specimens of *Hemimerus talpoides* Walker for taxonomic study. A female insect was removed from caustic potash and cleared in glycerin. It still contained cuticular structures that obscured Hansen's observations, so he dissected them out and examined them. Upon sorting this material he found that he had before him the exoskeletons of a number of young insects. These he assumed to be offspring of *Hemimerus* because of the close resemblance between them and the adult insect. He immediately opened another female that was still untreated. This time he was rewarded by the presence of six young in the reproductive system. The embryos were firmly attached to maternal tissue by means of the membrane between the head and the protergum. Jordan (1909a) thinks it probable that this area later becomes the plate covering the occipital foramen. The structure was diagnosed as a nutrient organ for the offspring. The significance of this kind of reproduction was at once recognized by Hansen and he asserted that it was fundamentally different from the conditions described for viviparous Blattidae and Pupipara.

Jordan (1909b) obtained specimens of this species and gave a detailed account of the reproductive systems of both sexes. His material was not in such a state of preservation that any of the embryological history could be given, but he believed the embryos are retained in the ovarioles until ready for birth. During their development they are connected to the nutrient chamber by means of the nuchal organ, as Hansen previously had determined. Individual birth of the offspring occurs, although two, one from each ovary, may possibly be born almost simultaneously. It should be observed that Jordan is convinced these insects feed upon adhering spores and the dead epidermis of their host, an African rat. This opinion is interesting in comparing the food habits of other adult insects generally infesting mammalian fur.

Heymons (1912) has confirmed Jordan's conclusions relating to the food habits of this insect, having, indeed, supplied a list of such a variety of objects consumed that one may assert that they are practically omnivorous.

Finally, Heymons (1909, 1912) obtained sufficient material to give a very satisfactory account of the nutrient organs and some details in the embryogeny of the insect. The first paper contains a description of the nutrient organs and a little embryological data. A portion of it also is devoted to a discussion of fertilization of the egg and some comparisons with other viviparous insects. In the second article we find a much more detailed narration of the activity of the nutrient organs. In the pages immediately following, a review of the embryogeny of *Hemimerus talpoides* will be taken from the excellent observations made by Heymons.

Female Reproductive System

The Ovary.—The common oviduct is short. From its distal end the two long, slender paired oviducts pass through the fat body to the region of the metathorax. From ten to twelve ovarioles lead from each paired oviduct on its dorsal side. These are equally spaced in a single dorsal row along the oviduct. The first ovarioles stand rather erectly on the oviduct, but the angle of departure becomes constantly more acute until the most distal, or anterior one, is prolonged in the direction taken by the oviduct. Each ovariole ends distally in a terminal filament, which passes forward and joins the next one. The terminal filaments finally unite into a common filament which is attached, Heymons (1912) believes, to the pericardial septum.

The basal end of the terminal filament is enlarged and contains a few nuclei where it joins the germarium of the ovariole. A slight contraction of the surface marks this union. The germarium is comparatively short. Within it at the upper end are a few transverse nuclei, but no cell membranes are visible that would serve to distinguish individual cells, nor can the presence of primary germ cells be definitely established. A single epithelial layer lines the germarium but, again, the cell boundaries are not visible. Its numerous, oval nuclei are irregularly placed and are often massed in groups which may be widely spaced. Outside the follicular epithelium there is a thin, structureless tunica propria which, of course, covers the entire ovariole. With another slight constriction the germarium passes over at once into the vitellarium.

The vitellarium has been designated as the egg chamber by Heymons (1912), for it is in this portion of the ovariole that the egg matures and embryonic development takes place. The walls of the vitellarium consist essentially of a single layer of cells in the absence of pregnancy. When reproductive functions are being carried on it is capable of great distensibility and peculiar modifications of its tissues. These characteristic changes will be described in their relation to the embryo. The basal end of the vitellarium is very sharply and strongly constricted where it opens into the peduncle.

The fourth portion of the ovariole, or peduncle, is a short, thin-walled tube which connects the main portion of the tubule to the oviduct. A few circular muscles around its upper portion probably assist in expelling the embryo at the proper time. While Heymons considers the peduncle separately in his discussion, it is probably only a modified part of the oviduct which prevents the obstruction of the latter by the developing embryo in the vitellarium above the oviduct.

All of the ovarioles are surrounded by a relatively thick layer of tissue which is rather spongy in nature, but nevertheless shows definite compact outer and inner lamellar margins. The ovarioles are supported in their relative positions by the terminal filaments, nerves, and exceedingly numerous tracheae. It is Heymons' belief that only five or six of the ovarioles in each ovary bear embryos, the others, more apically situated, being partially or wholly inactive.

Development of the Embryo

The Oöcyte.—The central portion of the germarium is occupied by two or three young oöcytes which, compared with the size of the follicular cells, are relatively enormous. The germinal vesicles of the oöcytes are also huge. Each oöcyte has adjacent and anterior to it a nurse cell of equally voluminous proportions, chiefly recognizable by the weak staining reaction of its nucleus.

The Mature Egg and Nurse Cell.—Unlike most eggs, no chorion is secreted around the egg of *Hemimerus* by the follicular epithelium. Another unusual condition is the absence of yolk in the cytoplasm. Nevertheless, it has increased tremendously in size through the addition of another kind of nutrient material that Heymons describes as a fatlike substance. This is dispersed throughout the cytoplasm in the form of small ovate droplets, giving the egg a foamy appearance. The superficially placed nucleus is clearly visible about halfway between the two ends of the elongate egg (Fig. 80).

The nutrient cell lies at the anterior end of the egg and occupies almost two fifths of the space enclosed by the follicular epithelium. It is greatly reduced in cytoplasmic content but the nucleus is gigantic. The latter has now become lobate as a first step toward degeneration into the *corpus luteum* of subsequent stages.

The follicular epithelium enclosing the egg with its attendant nurse cell is composed of a single layer of tissue except for a small area at the posterior end. Because of the compactness of this tissue, the nuclei are distributed at different depths in alternating cells. A double layer of very small cells interposes itself as a disk between the nurse cell and the egg. The cytoplasmic continuity of the two areas is not interrupted in the most central portion, however, for the follicular disk does not extend quite so deeply as to completely isolate the ovum from its nurse cell. The outer edge of the upper concave

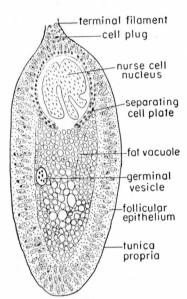

Fig. 80.—*Hemimerus talpoides.* Vitellarium containing nurse cell with degenerating nucleus and a mature oöcyte, longitudinal section. (Modified from Heymons, Zool. Jahrb. Suppl. 15, 2.)

layer of this cellular disk extends around the nurse cell, thus apparently separating it from the follicular epithelium (Fig. 80).

A small plug of transversely placed cells effectually closes the lumen of the vitellarium immediately above the follicular epithelium that covers the nurse cell. A similar stoppage of the lumen intervenes at the junction of the upper and lower halves of the vitellarium (the egg chamber and the peduncle of Heymons) beneath the posterior end of the egg. The nuclei of the cells in the basal position are, however, very elongate and rather more obviously differentiated in relation to their peculiar function.

The Follicular Epithelium and Maternal Pseudoplacentae.—
Before presenting any information regarding the cleavage stages,
certain alterations in the organization of the follicular epithelium
should be given, since they precede cleavage in time.

After the egg is mature and embryonic development begins,
the cells of the follicular epithelium are rearranged irregularly
into two or three layers. The nuclei also greatly increase in number but mitotic figures have not been found. This multiplication
of nuclei is especially true at the egg poles. At the anterior end
the follicular cells press in between the egg and the epithelial
diaphragm that encloses the nurse cell, thus finally completely
isolating the two. Other follicular cells above the nurse cell give
rise to a very large accumulation of cells that are smaller than
those derived from other areas. These form an amorphous mass,
without any distinct organization, that Heymons designates as
the anterior maternal placenta. The nurse cell nucleus disintegrates and dissolves in its cytoplasm. This cell soon fails to
retain cytoplasmic stains, rounds up into an ovate body and may
then be called the corpus luteum. It persists in this condition
throughout embryonic development. A similar mass of cells
appears at the posterior end of the egg, but, since there is no nurse
cell here, the corpus luteum is absent. This is the posterior
maternal placenta (Figs. 81, 82).

Hagan (1931) already has pointed out the fact that the term
placenta is pre-empted for use in indicating a specific organ in
mammals. The nutritional functions in these two nutrient masses
described by Heymons are supplied by specialized parts which are
not, in any sense, homologous to placental organs, therefore it
might be well to call the structure in *Hemimerus* the pseudoplacenta, as another such nutrient structure in the Polyctenidae
has been already designated.

The pseudoplacentae possess no tissue differentiation, each
simply constituting a prominent mass of cells which are smaller in
size than the cells in other portions of the egg follicle. They are
round rather than cylindrical and the cytoplasm is spongy, thus
they may be clearly distinguished in preparations.

While no mitotic figures could be found to account for the increased number of cells in the follicular epithelium and the
pseudoplacental masses, there is some evidence that multiplication takes place through amitotic division. The tunica propria,
too, is thickened around the vitellarium of a gravid ovariole. Just
within the latter a few scattered cells seem to be closely applied

to the tunica in order to assist it in protecting the embryo from the effects of external pressure.

Cleavage.—The maturation of the egg and fertilization have not been observed. Although the egg contains no yolk, cleavage is incomplete. The ovum changes to a spherical shape and shows no cytoplasmic cleavage furrows whatever in the early stages. When several nuclei are present, a few seem to distribute themselves subperipherally over a part of the egg, a lesser number are grouped near the opposite side, while only a very few remain situated interiorly. At this stage, none of the nuclei shows any differences in appearance or activity, but it is possible that the first assortment will enter into amnion formation, the second foreshadows the embryonic rudiment, while the central nuclei will become trophocytes (Fig. 81).

During cleavage, the pseudoplacentae have assumed a more definitely barrel shape with bluntly rounded ends projecting toward the egg. Due to the enlargement of the entire follicle the ovum itself is relatively smaller. This creates a space around the latter which is occupied by the cytoplasm of the follicular cells. Their nuclei are in the outer ends of the cells.

The Germ Band and the Amnion.—A young embryo in the early germ band stage is composed of a single layer of columnar, wedge-shaped cells. It is uniformly bent around two sides of the rest of the nutriment and egg plasm not used in forming cleavage cells (Fig. 82). At its margins the cells pass over into those of the amnion. The amnion is formed before the serosa in *Hemimerus,* which is quite contrary to the condition found in most insect embryos that possess two envelopes. The succulent cells of the amnion are round or quadrate, and from them long pseudopodial processes extend out to the follicular cells. These probably serve in two capacities: to anchor the embryo securely in position, and to obtain nutriment for further embryonic development.

The space between the embryo and its amnion is the amniotic cavity. Another space is evident surrounding the entire embryo, its amnion, and egg plasma. This may be known as the pseudoplacental cavity. The latter apparently is caused by the rapid enlargement of the entire follicle without a corresponding increase in size of the embryo and its accessory parts. It seems to be filled with nutriment in liquid form.

The egg plasm lies on the dorsal side of the germ band. Within it the trophocyte nuclei are relatively enormous in size. They have not yet formed macromeres from portions of the egg plasm but they may be considered as equivalent, in every respect, to the vitellophags of other insects, even if no yolk is present. They vary from eight to ten in number.

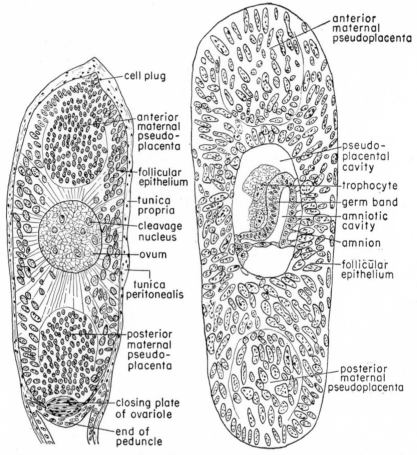

Fig. 81.—*Hemimerus talpoides.* Vitellarium showing maternal pseudoplacentae and early cleavage of the ovum, longitudinal section. (Modified from Heymons, Zool. Jahrb. Suppl. 15, 2.)

Fig. 82.—*Hemimerus talpoides.* Vitellarium with germ band, sagittal section. (Modified from Heymons, Zool. Jahrb. Suppl. 15, 2.)

The ectodermal cells in a slightly older germ band are still arranged in a single layer, but their nuclei are very irregular in position. The germ band is now curved in the shape of a horseshoe about the plasm occupied by the trophocytes. At its posterior end is a small group of primordial germ cells (Fig. 83).

At this time the amnion appears to be actively engaged in the absorption of nutriment from the pseudoplacental cavity, for its cytoplasm is vacuolar. The same conclusion may also be drawn for the trophocytes since they, too, show large vacuoles within them. The plasm of the trophocytes probably has come in contact with the anterior maternal pseudoplacenta and its nutriment no doubt is obtained from this source. Thus, at this early stage, the embryo depends upon nutritional substances that are derived from extraembryonal supplies.

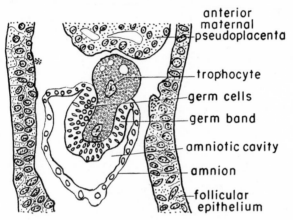

anterior
maternal
pseudoplacenta

trophocyte

germ cells

germ band

amniotic cavity

amnion

follicular
epithelium

FIG. 83.—*Hemimerus talpoides.* Vitellarium containing germ band in sagittal section; somewhat older than preceding figure. (Modified from Heymons, Zool. Jahrb. Suppl. 15, 2.)

Both pseudoplacentae give evidence of the drain placed upon them for nutriment. Their shape is no longer symmetrical and the cytoplasm shows fissures that constantly enlarge as development proceeds. The innermost cells of the follicular epithelium likewise exhibit signs of degeneration. Their nuclei are losing their normal outlines and are granular in nature. Even a few solid particles of cells are cast out into the liquid of the pseudoplacental cavity, although it is possible that these cell remnants come from the pseudoplacentae.

Mesoderm.—The mesoderm was already present in a slightly older embryo. The latter has greatly elongated and now consists of two layers, but the method of forming the inner layer has not been observed. The germ band has grown decidedly longer so that its posterior end is in contact with the anterior pseudoplacenta. The cephalic margin extends forward almost an equal distance but approaches the follicular wall, where the amnion actually touches a projection of the latter (Fig. 84). The cephalic portion is somewhat broader than the rest of the germ band but no large cephalic lobes arise from it, contrary to the condition found in most insect embryos.

The trophocytes have divided the original egg plasm into several cellular masses whose long axes extend anteroposteriorly toward the pseudoplacentae. They lie entirely within the curvature of the germ band but the most anterior trophocytes still adhere to the anterior maternal pseudoplacenta.

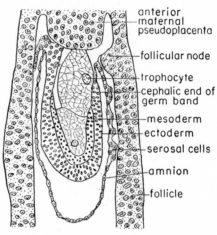

anterior
maternal
pseudoplacenta
follicular node
trophocyte
cephalic end of germ band
mesoderm
ectoderm
serosal cells
amnion
follicle

FIG. 84.—*Hemimerus talpoides.* Older germ band with mesoderm, sagittal section. (Modified from Heymons, Zool. Jahrb. Suppl. 15, 2.)

The Serosa and its Nutrient Function.—The amnion gives rise to the serosa, which is quite unusual for insect embryos. At first, anterior and posterior margins of the amnion cut off a few cells by transverse mitoses. These gradually spread out in the form of a true embryonic envelope, especially as their numbers increase through cells derived later from other parts of the amnion.

The functional activity of the trophocytes is rapidly coming to a close. The nuclei, especially, are approaching early disintegration for they are becoming irregular and acutely lobate. The serosa completely surrounds the embryo and is beginning to assume its role as a nutrient organ. It lies as a loose sheet of cells between the amnion and the follicular cells. Here and there its cells may be clearly seen to be attached to the follicle by means of cytoplasmic processes. In certain places, too, it is more than one cell in thickness. This condition occurs particularly in the gap that exists between the anterior and posterior ends of the germ band. The serosal cells have succeeded in separating the trophocytes from the projecting node of follicular tissue at this point, and the node itself is slowly subsiding to the general level

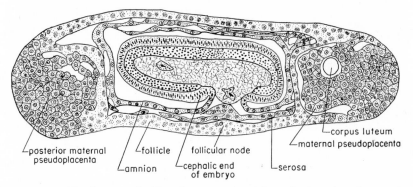

posterior maternal pseudoplacenta — follicle — amnion — follicular node — cephalic end of embryo — serosa — corpus luteum — maternal pseudoplacenta

FIG. 85.—*Hemimerus talpoides.* Late germ band in sagittal section, degenerating follicular epithelium and corpus luteum in the anterior maternal pseudoplacenta. (Modified from Heymons, Zool. Jahrb. Suppl. 15, 2.)

of the follicular layer. On the inner surface of the serosa contact with the amnion is very frequent and intimate so that, at times, the two seem to be fused almost into one layer (Fig. 85). From now on, these envelopes bear the function of transporting nutriment to the embryo and they may, therefore, be considered as the trophamnion and the trophserosa.

Anatrepsis.—A still older germ band almost fills the pseudoplacental cavity. The orientation of the embryo quite definitely shows that anatrepsis has gradually occurred simultaneously with the development of the germ band to the present stage. The anterior end lies ventrally near the central margin of the cavity while the future abdominal area is anterior. The whole embryo is strongly curved at both ends while the ventral middle portion is turned uppermost.

Fate of the Follicular Epithelium and Pseudoplacentae.— The more deeply situated cells of the follicular epithelium continue undergoing dissolution and histolysis is likewise invading the pseudoplacental masses of cells far more strikingly than before. Decomposition is evident first in the nuclei of all of these cells; they become granular, irregular in shape and, finally, the nuclear walls break down. Numerous spaces occur in the pseudoplacentae where cells have altogether disappeared. It is entirely possible that the embryonic envelopes, pressing so closely against the maternal tissues, may somehow assist in their further disintegration but no evidence of phagocytosis has been detected.

Later Embryology.—Heymons (1912) states that further embryonic development follows, in general, the pattern outlined for the oviparous genus *Forficula*. No details are given for the conditions that are identical, nor for those that may slightly differ in the two examples, hence several very important steps in the embryogeny are omitted. These include, at this point, segmentation of the germ band, the origin of the appendages, the nervous system and the intrasegmental aggregations of the mesoderm with their coelomic pouches.

Katatrepsis.—While the embryos of most insects are migrating to their definitive position in the egg, the embryonic envelopes are destroyed. *Hemimerus* offers another of the less frequently observed cases where this does not occur. Indeed, after katatrepsis there are still further modifications in store for them, as we shall see presently. It may be noted that, in general, the amniotic cells, and especially the nuclei, are smaller than similar structures in the serosa.

During katatrepsis, the anterior end of the embryo gradually moves forward and dorsally to a position opposite the anterior pseudoplacenta. The embryo shortens as the abdominal region progresses posteriorly and, finally, the embryonic orientation corresponds to that of the ovariole except for the later ventral flexure of the abdomen (Fig. 86). The cerci, which have arisen from the eleventh abdominal segment, are bent dorsally over the abdomen but they cannot be shown in this figure as it cuts the embryo in the median sagittal plane. Rotation is not yet complete for the abdomen is not flexed ventrally.

Simultaneously with katatrepsis, the lateral ectodermal body walls have grown upward and fused dorsally, except in the occipital region; a condition which will be treated later with the discussion of the nutrient organs. The nervous system presents the typical ganglionic concentrations with three in the thorax and ten such masses in the abdomen. Some of these have already started to fuse together. The mid-intestine is formed and joined to the stomodaeum and the proctodaeum. The trophocytes are rapidly breaking down within it, for their nuclei have lost their identity and the chromatic particles are bunched in large masses. The dorsal vessel, or heart, is present and, since a musculature invests it, blood circulation probably occurs. Effective distribution of the blood is necessary to the embryo after the dorsal closure of its hypodermis, for fresh nutrient material enters the head region and must be dispersed throughout the voluminous body cavity for the developing tissues and organs.

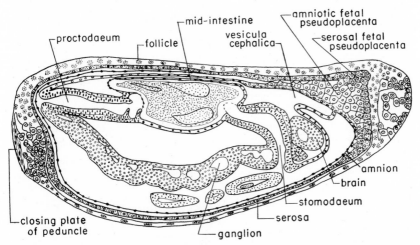

Fig. 86.—*Hemimerus talpoides*. Embryo nearing end of katatrepsis, sagittal section. (Modified from Heymons, Zool. Jahrb. Suppl. 15, 2.)

At this stage of embryonic development, the follicular wall is reduced to a very thin layer of epithelium so that it scarcely contributes any further to the nutritional function. The maternal pseudoplacental masses, too, have become very much smaller and within them the lymph spaces have increased both in size and number.

The Fetal Pseudoplacenta and Cephalic Vesicle.—The embryonic envelopes now play an even more active part as nutrient organs. Opposite each maternal pseudoplacenta, with which they are intimately in contact, they proliferate a multitude of cells. The outer layers resemble serosal cells while the innermost layers seem to have descended from amniotic elements. These two masses are the fetal pseudoplacentae, of which the anterior is considerably the larger.

Previously it was remarked that complete closure of the embryonic dorsal body wall did not occur in the occipital region. The haemocoele of the embryo is thus continuous with a large space that occupies the anterior fetal pseudoplacenta, the cephalic vesicle. At first the cephalic vesicle is bounded only by amniotic cells, but Heymons (1912) believes it is lined later by a thin mesodermal diverticulum from the cephalic blood space. Any nourishment passed into it by the adjacent pseudoplacental cells, therefore, would at once enter into the general circulation from this organ. The posterior fetal pseudoplacenta has no such prominence in nutrition. It is quickly dissolved and absorbed into the amniotic cavity, where it probably reaches the embryo by diffusion through the delicate body wall.

The Older Embryo.—The embryo continues its growth and the posterior abdominal segments flex ventrally opposite the anterior abdominal and thoracic segments. The well-developed legs and the antennae are folded compactly between them, but the cerci extend forward on either side of the head. The hypodermis secretes the cuticle and the setae while the internal organs complete their development in anticipation of birth. The trophocytes have been entirely digested and absorbed, so that the mid-intestine is empty.

The maternal and fetal pseudoplacentae are almost entirely consumed by histolytic processes. However, a small remnant of the anterior masses and the corpus luteum persist in front of the very restricted head vesicle. It is presumed that the latter is withdrawn and the occipital region is closed only shortly prior to birth.

Most peculiarly, a small projecting egg tooth, or egg burster, was discovered on the head of the embryo by Hansen (1894) and its presence has been verified by Heymons (1912). Its exact function under the present conditions in the *Hemimerus* embryogeny is wholly a matter of conjecture at present. Heymons (1912) suggests that possibly the embryo employs it to irritate the mother's tissues, whereby her musculature is stimulated into peristaltic contractions that expel the offspring.

LITERATURE CITED

Hagan (1931), Hansen (1894), Heymons (1909, 1912), Jordan (1909a, 1909b).

Order Dermaptera   Family Arixeniidae

This family consists of two known species, *Arixenia esau* first described in 1909 and *A. jacobsoni* which was described later. They are characterized as rather robust insects, being decidedly

larger than *Hemimerus* and more nearly approaching the general external conformation of the Forficulidae than does this genus. The eyes are greatly reduced, the wings are lacking, and they are viviparous. The species are cavernicolous, predatory and often, apparently, cannibalistic. Their study is especially interesting because they seem to possess modifications for the viviparous condition which differ from those shown by *Hemimerus*.

Specimens of the first species, described by Jordan (1909), were originally discovered on a bat, *Cheiromeles,* in Sarawak, on the island of Borneo. Since the four specimens received were immature, efforts were made to obtain additional material. A new lot eventually arrived from south-central Java but these proved to be a different species which Burr (1912) described as *A. jacobsoni.* These were in a better state of preservation, therefore the recipients were able to give considerable details regarding the reproductive system and the viviparous condition (Burr and Jordan, 1912). Still more recently, *A. jacobsoni* has been found in a cave in western Java and the writer wishes to acknowledge the receipt of two lots collected and shipped through the courtesy of Dr. Karl Dammermann and Dr. M. A. Lieftinck of the Zoological Museum and Laboratory, Buitenzorg. One lot, unfortunately, was not quickly penetrated by the fixative so the distorted and pycnotic nuclei were unsatisfactory for study. The second lot, while well preserved, contained nearly mature embryos within the maternal reproductive tracts of nearly all those so far examined. A few, however, proved to have younger embryos and unfertilized eggs, hence some data are available to us.

Female Reproductive System

There are three very short functional ovarioles in a linear series situated dorsally on the massive, muscular paired oviduct. The germarium tapers distally to a fine filament traceable for a short distance. The oviducts are directed posteriorly, forming a horseshoe shape with the somewhat parallel sides represented by the right and left oviducts. They approach each other posteriorly to join the common oviduct, a short, robust tube opening almost immediately to the outside between the seventh and eighth sternites. When viewed from the side, the paired oviduct bulges slightly just below each ovariole even when no embryo lies within (Fig. 87). The distal or third ovariole is attached before the end of the oviduct which terminates in a bluntly rounded bilobed projection which may represent abortive ovarioles.

The entire reproductive system is surrounded by a dense mass of tracheae exactly as Heymons (1912) has related for *Hemimerus*. Lesser branches lie in the folds of the oviducts, as shown in Figure 88, which also affords some idea of the thickness of the wall of the paired oviduct, its folds, and its consequent ability to expand and encompass the large embryos during part of the

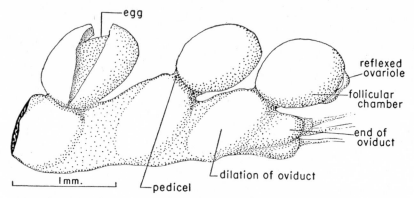

FIG. 87.—*Arixenia jacobsoni.* Major portion of severed oviduct and attached ovarioles, whole mount. Left ovariole is cracked by gentle pressure to reveal the contained oöcyte.

gestation period. The wall of the paired oviduct consists of a comparatively thick epithelium of columnar cells with small, slightly ovate nuclei each containing a central nucleolus, peripheral chromioles, and clear nucleoplasm. Externally there is a wide band of striated muscle which is not distinctly arranged into circular and longitudinal layers. Instead, some muscles also seem to run diagonally, perhaps because of folding. While groups of muscle fibers are often aggregated, at no one elevation will those extending one way lie in a separate spatial relation to those directed elsewhere. This intermingling is, perhaps, influenced considerably by the tracheal plexus. Outside the muscles are found great masses of fat body tissue but these are not nearly so densely impregnated with tracheae as are the oviducts.

Each ovariole rests on a pedicel and consists of an enlarged ovate vitellarium whose distal end is distinguished by being much smaller and reflexed slightly along the top of the vitellarium. Apically, it becomes the germarium. The tip of the latter tapers into a filament. It is possible that the ovariole is so robust and short that anchorage by means of a filament is unessential, or that the filament may be attached to dorsal fat body tissue in the immediate vicinity.

Beginning with the lumen of the ovariole one may distinguish a follicular epithelium supported by a prominent basement membrane or tunica propria. An external tunica peritonealis consisting of scattered muscle fibers comes next and, outside these, are tracheae in abundance but not in quite the profusion possessed by the oviducts.

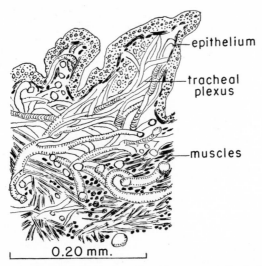

FIG. 88.—*Arixenia jacobsoni.* Section of oviduct near pedicel; the clear border of the epithelium is not evident in the empty and folded oviduct.

The follicular epithelium is a continuous lining of the ovariole with quite low cuboidal cells in the distal end. Its nuclei are small, ovate to round, and each has a clear nucleoplasm with peripheral chromioles and a single, central nucleolus. These cells lower down are not as tall as those of the oviduct but wider, and the nuclei are as large, or larger, depending on location and function as will be explained shortly. There is no longitudinal folding of the walls of the ovariole but there is a distinct constriction between the reflexed, distal portion and its larger basal section.

The basal end of the ovariole is very large compared to its distal part but the histological structure possesses the same distinguishing features. However, it is here that the oöcyte matures and embryonic development of the offspring is initiated. Its actual size fluctuates according to the nature of the reproductive products within its lumen: when empty, the tunica propria is folded but the epithelium is not. As the embryo leaves it, a brief interval elapses before the next oöcyte and nurse cell move into it. In the meantime it appears that at least some of the epithelial lining breaks down and forms debris in its lumen. Changes evident in the epithelium of this region will be discussed in connection with the embryology.

Development of the Embryo

As explained earlier, material is not available for providing more than a brief account of certain stages of embryonic growth. However, important comparisons can be made with *Hemimerus* to point out essential differences between the two groups in the nature of their adaptations to the viviparous condition. Embryonic development in this family seems to follow the general dermapteran pattern of oviparous species.

The Ovum.—At no place in the ovariole could undifferentiated germ cells be found. In tracing through the vitellarium into the attenuate tip region known as the germarium, small cells with large nuclei were discovered that differed only in size from those below. These are of two kinds: one with a very large, ovate nucleus containing several nucleoli and numerous coarse granular chromioles which cause it to appear almost as darkly stained as the cytoplasm. The other type of cell has a more rounded nucleus that contains a single large nucleolus and many fine, peripherally situated chromioles. The general cytoplasm is also somewhat lighter in color but this distinction is not very pronounced. One of each appears at the end of the ovariole and an epithelium loosely surrounds them. Lower down the ovariole the two types of cells increase in size and in number until, finally, in a cross section of the ovariole seven or eight nuclei may be seen in a single section. Approximately half of them are of each type of cell and it is possible, visually, to ascertain that, while they are closely crowded together within the flattened follicular epithelium, they are not all quite at the same elevation in the tubule. They are also much larger than the two first mentioned. None of those at the upper end are separated into pairs by an infiltration of the follicular epithelium. At the lower end of the reflexed portion of the vitellarium the increased size of the cells forces them, apparently, into a single row of cells, two to four in total

number depending upon the presence of an egg or an embryo
below them.

The follicular epithelium is taller around the bottom oöcyte
but remains rather flattened over the accompanying nurse cell
and a single layer of flat follicular cells intervenes between the
two. Definite constrictions of the ovariole and flat, transversely
arranged follicular cells separate each pair of oöcytes and nurse

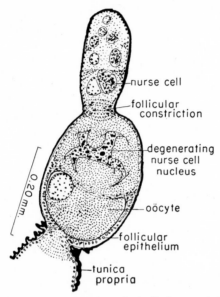

FIG. 89.—*Arixenia jacobsoni.* Portion of vitellarium containing older oöcytes,
the lowest almost ready to migrate into the empty follicular chamber. The
pycnotic condition of the nurse cell nucleus indicates its active role is over. Constrictions beginning to isolate two pairs of cells above.

cells from those above and below. It appears that the true oöcyte
is the anterior one in the migration of a pair of cells down the
ovariole and is the one possessing the clear nucleus, but this could
not be definitely determined. The following cell is, then, the
nutrient cell. The condition is shown in Figure 89, where a
portion of the ovariole is in cross section while the lower end is in
almost sagittal section as it bends to join the larger, lower part
of the ovariole. Growth in size seems to cease until the two adjacent cells are destined to move downward. In fact, the functional
activity of the nurse cell seems to be at an end as its nucleus is
becoming pycnotic, preparatory to final dissolution. In addition
to the complete absorption of the nurse cell, the oöcyte will
receive a further supply of yolk later from another source.

The lower, basal end could aptly be termed the follicular chamber of the vitellarium in this insect, for only one complete follicle occurs in it. It is separated by a fold and constriction of the follicular epithelium from the younger oöcytes just described as being above it. At the lower end, a very short pedicel joins it to the paired oviduct.

The follicular chamber of the mature insect seems to be continually active throughout reproductive life. When receptive, an oöcyte and its accompanying nurse cell promptly move in and the former continues its final growth which was previously interrupted for a time. Only rather mature oöcytes or eggs were discovered in the follicular chamber.

As the oöcyte nears maturity its first, or primary, enlargement is at the expense of the nutrient cell. As the former increases in size the latter, at the oöcyte's distal end, decreases in bulk, the nucleus becomes pycnotic and assumes odd, irregular shapes quite as described by Heymons for *Hemimerus*. All trace of it is lost by the time the oöcyte is ready for fertilization, or shortly thereafter (Fig. 90). The contribution from the nurse cell seems to be in the nature of small, fatlike droplets. This substance occupies the central portion of the oöcyte and is continuous up to the immediate vicinity of the nurse cell. Due to this activity, the nearly mature oöcyte, treated by the usual histological routine, shows a central core of a grayish, granular reticulum whose meshes are round or slightly ovate.

Sometime after the entrance of the fresh oöcyte into the follicular chamber the epithelium also contributes material to it. Here the follicular cells are low columnar with physiological activity evident within them. The basal half of the tissue is deeply staining and granular, and contains the nuclei. The half bordering the lumen of the ovariole is very light in color and is, apparently, filled with metabolic products. The adjacent peripheral areas of the oöcyte gradually acquire what are thought to be small yolk spheres typical of most insects and the amount increases until more than half the oöcyte contains yolk. Yolky areas are thickest, of course, at the lower portion of the oöcyte and the accretion evenly diminishes in amount nearest the remnant of the nutrient cell which is still discharging fatty substances into the oöcyte's anterior end. Thus, there are eventually two distinctly different oöcyte contents: a light grayish, finely vacuolar core of fatlike cytoplasm and a thick peripheral yolk. Between the two are several very large spheres, possibly fat, that are empty in the present material available for study (Fig. 90). The figure just referred to contains a nearly mature oöcyte with the surrounding follicular epithelium. It will be noticed that the two lie in direct contact. When viewed in this aspect the epithelium shows no cellular membranes but lateral borders between cells are readily visible in sections cut obliquely to the surface. The outer membranes adjacent to the lumen are so delicate as to escape observation to date.

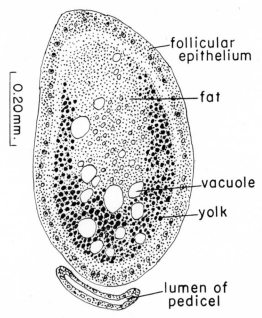

Fig. 90.—*Arixenia jacobsoni.* Maturing oöcyte in follicular chamber of vitellarium with a section of the pedicel below. The periplasmic membrane not yet present; light substance outside oöcyte probably secretion in distal end of follicle cells.

A mature oöcyte apparently does not possess a chorion but a thin, permanent periplasmic membrane serves eventually to intervene between egg and follicular epithelium. That the egg continues to obtain nutriment through the membrane seems to be beyond question, as will be discussed shortly. Fertilization of the egg and early embryonic development take place in the follicular chamber but how the sperms gain entrance to it has so far escaped observation.

The Germ Band, Amnion, and Serosa.—The earliest embryonic stage so far available is the germ band in an egg already possessed of the embryonic envelopes (Fig. 91.) This figure shows a columnar ectoderm and multilaminate lower layer of the usual type. It is very long in comparison to its width. The envelopes and periplasmic membrane are applied closely to the follicular epithelium. The former are typical and there seems to be no reason to believe they are formed unusually, as they are said to be in *Hemimerus*. At present they show no sign of having a trophic function and the serosal cells are quite different from their future aspect. An enlarged section of these structures appears in Figure 94.

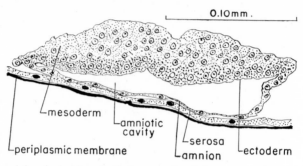

FIG. 91.—*Arixenia jacobsoni*. Early germ band in cross section.

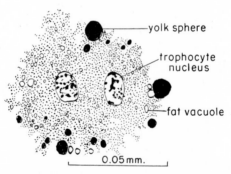

FIG. 92.—*Arixenia jacobsoni*. Trophocytes in egg at early germ band stage.

The nutriment of the egg in this stage supplies all of the requirements of the germ band. The trophocytes consist of cytoplasmic masses containing one or more huge nuclei with very clear nucleoplasm and scattered chromioles (Fig. 92). There are perhaps twelve or more present. It is quite possible their nuclei divide rapidly just prior to the rupture of the amnion and serosa later because, during blastokinesis, four to seven may be found

together in close clumps and their number has apparently increased because they are more numerous after revolution of the
embryo.

An older germ band shows antennal and thoracic rudiments of
appendages and it would seem that gnathal rudiments are slightly
behind them in appearance. The stomodaeal invagination has developed slightly and coelomic pouches are present in most of the
segments (Fig. 93). The embryo has grown around the ventral,
anterior, and posterior surfaces of the egg. The nutriment does
not entirely fill the center of the egg as it does in most insects, but
lies in an elongate mass between the two extremities.

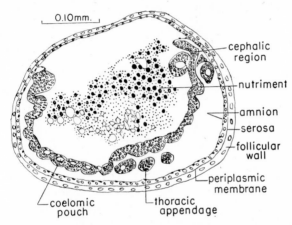

Fig. 93.—*Arixenia jacobsoni.* Late germ band in sagittal section.

The amnion is rather extensive over the ventral surface of the
embryo but is drawn away from it to lie closely against the serosa.
It never shows specific modification into a nutrient organ and
behaves in a fashion typical of the amnion of most insects. The
periplasmic membrane is clearly observable. It has undergone no
apparent change but the serosa and the follicular epithelium on
either side of it give evidence of approaching activity.

Figure 94 contains enlarged sections of the ovariole. At the top
are the follicular wall, the membrane, serosa, and amnion of the
germ band, the last seemingly wholly dependent upon the egg for
nourishment. The embryonic envelopes are typical but the serosa
is thicker than usual for most insects. Neither has reached its
final development. In the next sketch, however, we see the same
structures as before except that the musculature of the ovarial

wall has been largely omitted. The amnion is becoming the very attenuate membrane commonly observed but is adherent to the serosa. The latter shows considerable increase in thickness, the nuclei are much larger, more rounded, and the nucleolus and chromioles characteristically distributed and prominent. The

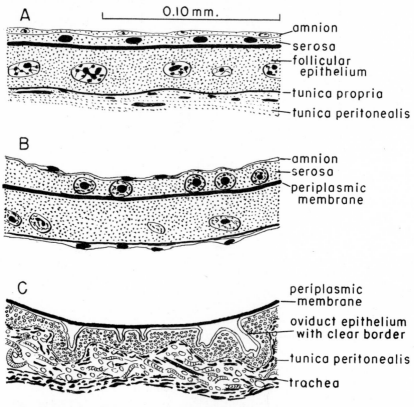

Fig. 94.—*Arixenia jacobsoni*. Sections of wall of maternal reproductive tract with adherent embryonic membranes. *A*, amnion, serosa and periplasmic membrane during early germ band stage shown in Fig. 91. *B*, in later germ band and succeeding stages. The tunica peritonealis is largely omitted. *C*, after revolution and the destruction of amnion and serosa. That the embryo now lies in a partially distended but still somewhat folded portion of the reproductive tract is quite evident from the altered appearance of the maternal wall. The typical follicular epithelium is absent. Same magnification throughout.

follicular epithelium of both figures also possesses greatly enlarged nuclei, which are more widely spaced and the cytoplasm still functions, presumably, as a center of transfer of nutrients as it did for the oöcyte. Different sections show that the nuclei are, in fact, flattened, ovate bodies when viewed parallel to the surface.

Embryo Prior to Revolution.—Older embryos with appendages, stomodaeum, proctodaeum, and nervous system near the
end of growth in length over the surface of the egg are shown in
Figure 95. Neither embryo is cut quite parallel to the body
length. The stomodaeum and proctodaeum are well developed
and their blind, inner ends abut against the almost complete

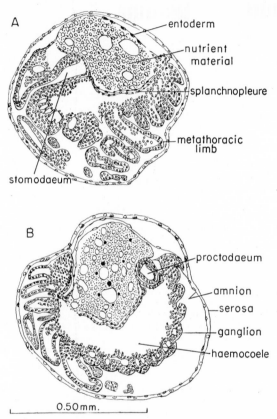

Fig. 95.—*Arixenia jacobsoni.* Embryos just prior to katatrepsis. Neither is
exactly sagittally sectioned but one shows the cephalic region, the other more of
the abdominal segments and the proctodaeum. Both of same age from adjacent
ovarioles.

enteron and its mesoderm. The amount of nutriment present is
about the same as in younger stages but the embryo is relatively
much larger in proportion to it. Another peculiarity is the
apparent scarcity, almost absence, of the true yolk formerly present in the egg. The serosa remains as described for the preceding
embryo. Both embryos lie in the same part of adjacent ovarioles.

Fate of the Embryonic Membranes.—If the dorsally curved superficial embryo at the height of its present growth in length should be said to be in anatrepsis, then the stage to be mentioned here would be at the close of katatrepsis. Actually the former is nothing but normal growth without shifting while the second consists of a shortening and straightening of the embryo and the ventral flexure of its posterior abdominal metameres. If any further revolution occurs it was not observed. Before this, the lateral body walls grew dorsally to unite in the mid-line except for a small area in the postcephalic region.

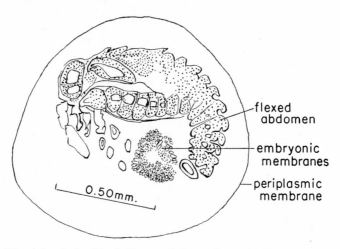

Fig. 96.—*Arixenia jacobsoni.* Postrevolution embryo with discarded amnion and serosa; definitive dorsal closure is not complete in mid-line. Parasagittal section.

Postrevolution Embryo.—The amnion and serosa are discarded during the dorsal overgrowth of the body wall, straightening, and posterior ventral flexure (Fig. 96). Three embryos in adjacent ovarioles and follicles show an early stage in this process. The envelopes are found to be entirely severed from the embryo and gathered into a spherical mass ventral to the metathorax and anterior abdominal segments. The center of this mass is occupied by the amnion where the cytoplasm is faintly stained. Scattered in it are the typical nuclei of this structure. The peripheral area is the rounded-up serosa with darkly staining cytoplasm, elongate cell outlines, now more clearly defined, and the characteristic nuclei of this envelope (Fig. 97). There are no other structures in the follicular chamber with which this mass could be confused. The question naturally arises as to the method employed to

recapture these envelopes by the embryo for their inclusion in the
mid-intestine.

That the amnion and serosa are eventually ingested is thought
to be beyond question (Fig. 98). Another series of three ovarioles
(of which only two are reproduced) represents a slightly older
embryonic stage. At the anterodorsal side of each embryo the
massed envelopes are drawn as they appear to be entering a

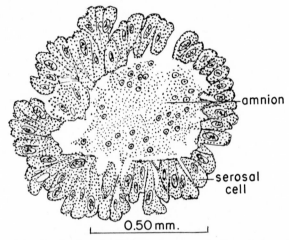

Fig. 97.—*Arixenia jacobsoni.* Enlarged view of discarded membranes of
embryo at age shown in preceding figure.

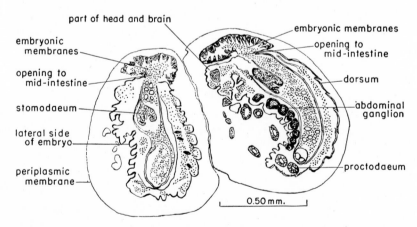

Fig. 98.—*Arixenia jacobsoni.* Two embryos enclosed in their periplasmic membranes with amnion and serosa of each entering the mid-intestine just before
definitive dorsal closure. Since no maternal wall separates them it is apparent
they are no longer within their respective ovarioles. Right figure in sagittal
section, left is frontal.

cephalically directed open extension of the mid-intestine. In each case traces of the well-developed fore-intestine are also visible in the section. The periplasmic membrane still surrounds the embryo and apparently remains intact throughout embryonic development. Within it there is, presumably, some sort of fluid supporting and, probably, supplying the embryo with nutriment. The volume of the cavity is considerably greater than the contained embryo so the latter is free from close adherence to its wall except as chance directs.

Two final points in connection with this stage of the embryo should be noted. First, the orientation of the embryo apparently bears no fixed relationship to the walls of the surrounding reproductive tract. This applies also to the embryos immediately preceding: each is viewed from a different aspect though all appear on the same section of the slide. Since all six of those that have been mentioned are directed alike in their anteroposterior axis, however, this observation may simply be due to their rotation around this axis at slightly different rates.

The second point is that the last three, after the destruction of the embryonic envelopes, seem to have moved down into another portion of the reproductive tract, probably into the paired oviduct. This becomes evident in two ways. A glance at the figure shows two with adjacent periplasmic membranes though both are completely enclosed on the other sides by commonly shared maternal tissues omitted from the sketch. This could not happen if they were in adjacent ovarioles. Second, the type of enclosing duct about them is different as is shown in Figures 88 and 94C. Comparison can readily be made with the wall of the ovariole surrounding the earlier embryos as drawn in Figure 94A, B. The epithelial wall at this location is much folded, nuclei are smaller and set close together in columnar cells with non-granular, free ends. The musculature of the wall is much heavier and infiltrated with great numbers of tracheae which completely disrupt the expected normal relationship between circular and longitudinal layers.

The remaining embryos are, with few exceptions, too old to provide data on organology. It is believed the embryo continues to receive nourishment from the mother by some osmotic route. Dense concentrations of granular precipitates in celloidin sections are commonly found between the adjacent fat body tissue and the outer wall of the paired oviduct. It is often especially condensed in the latter's folds. Careful examination of the older embryos sectioned fails to show any sign of a nutrient cephalic vesicle. From the dissections made it is concluded that six off-spring, three from each paired oviduct, compose the normal number born at any one time. Older embryos, some time before birth, lie with their heads directed anteriorly in the mother's body. The middle of the abdomen is flexed ventrally so that the posterior abdominal segments are pressed firmly against the ventral surface of those more anterior and against the thorax. The cerci extend forward to the head. The embryo lies on its side with its anterior ventral surface facing the mid-line of the maternal body. Only the eyes are dark, the rest of the body being very light yellowish, almost white, in color. Shortly after the follicular chamber is freed of an embryo another egg and nutrient cell appear to descend into it; therefore, the reproductive cycle is continuous.

Comparative Data.—From the data available certain interesting comparisons between *Hemimerus* and *Arixenia* in relation to viviparity can now be made. *Hemimerus* possesses ten or eleven long, tapering ovarioles uniserially extending dorsally and anteriorly from the paired oviduct, the distal one being attached to the end of the oviduct. A large proximal section of the vitellarium comprises a follicular chamber in which a single embryo develops. This chamber is separated from the rest of the ovariole above and from the tall pedicel below by follicular cells. This situation is largely duplicated in *Arixenia* except that the anterior portion of the ovariole is very short and is reflexed sharply on top of the follicular chamber. In the latter there are only three functional ovarioles on an oviduct and the distal one is not terminal in position. The pedicel is very short.

Hemimerus possesses several nonfunctional ovarioles in the ovary; *Arixenia* has only fully active ovarioles, the others, if formerly present, having been lost in evolutionary adaptation to viviparous reproduction, unless the bifurcate tip of the oviduct represents two of them.

Above the follicular chamber in *Hemimerus* the nurse and germ cells alternate; they do so for only one or two pairs at the most in *Arixenia*.

The nurse cell contributes apparently the same fatlike substance to embryos of both genera but *Arixenia* oöcytes also are found to acquire a peripheral layer of material from the follicular epithelium which is assumed to be typical yolk.

The nurse cell persists for an extended period, forming a corpus luteum surrounded by a maternal anterior pseudoplacental mass of follicular cells in *Hemimerus*. A posterior pseudoplacental body also is formed. In *Arixenia* no pseudoplacental masses can be found and the nurse cell disintegrates before actual embryonic development begins. No cellular septum partially segregates the nurse cell from the mature oöcyte in the latter case. The *Hemimerus* follicular epithelium seems to be multilaminate around the oöcyte but it is one-layered and quite comparable to that of other insects in *Arixenia*.

In both insects, the mature ovum is thought to be enclosed in a conspicuous periplasmic membrane. The ova of both lack the chorion usually present around the ova of other insects.

In *Hemimerus* the amnion appears first and secondarily gives rise to the serosa; the former, at least, possesses strongly developed pseudopodial processes linking it to the follicular wall for a time. In *Arixenia* the serosa appears earlier in relative embryonic developmental time and both envelopes apparently arise as in typical oviparous Dermaptera. Neither shows pseudopodia. The serosa becomes a thickened trophic organ, however, while the amnion does not. It remains very thin and relatively inconspicuous as in other insects and is closely applied to the former membrane.

The germ band stage of *Arixenia* is only gently curved dorsally over the egg before segmentation. In *Hemimerus* it is much longer in proportion to the rest of the egg contents and is sharply bent in the middle so both ends are closely parallel to each other throughout most of their length.

The embryonic envelopes are destroyed in *Arixenia* at a stage of development usually referred to as showing blastokinesis or embryonic migration, revolution, or reorientation within the egg of many insects. In *Hemimerus* they remain intact after katatrepsis and serve trophic functions, finally forming the fetal pseudoplacental masses.

The *Hemimerus* embryo, in later development, acquires a nuchal attachment to a mass of cells in the follicular cavity for purposes of nutrition. *Arixenia* embryos apparently form no such cephalic vesicle.

The old embryos belonging to both groups of insects are flexed ventrally in the same fashion, look much alike just prior to birth and are very large in relation to the parent bearing them. Apparently six is the usual number in any one litter in *Arixenia*.

Literature Cited

Burr (1912), Burr and Jordan (1912), Heymons (1912), Jordan (1909).

Chapter 12

PSEUDOPLACENTAL VIVIPARITY—BLATTODEA

Several roaches are said to be viviparous but the species discussed here seems to be the only one whose development has been followed in order to learn any of the details involved. It has been assumed that in all cases the ova possess sufficient yolk for complete nourishment of the embryo until hatching occurs. That this may not be true will be realized when it is recalled that many species retain within their uteri eggs that are rather small in proportion to the offspring derived from them. An examination of other species may reveal more remarkable digressions from the usual embryonic structures.

Order Blattodea   Family Blattidae

The embryological development of the roach, *Diploptera dytiscoides,* has not previously been investigated though it is widely distributed in subtropical regions, is extremely numerous in the Hawaiian Islands, and has long been known to be viviparous. It normally lives in, and beneath, fallen vegetation. Leaves, logs, boards, and grasslands, if disturbed with one's foot or a rake, will generally reveal several in erratic and hasty search for further concealment. Their habits in this regard so simulate those of certain Carabidae that they are known locally as "beetle roaches." Their explorations seldom lead them into homes, hence they appear to lack social and economic importance in this respect.

Hagan (1939) called attention to this species in briefly describing the very elongate pleuropodia possessed by the embryo. The present chapter seeks to trace the development of these organs in relation to embryonic growth, and to suggest some possible functions which would, perhaps, account for their size and persistence.

Since the embryological history of no viviparous roach has been published, this species cannot well be compared with related viviparous species. The history of *Diploptera* is not complete because several essential stages are lacking, but it can be said that from present data the general steps seem to vary little, and in

291

relatively minor aspects, from those of oviparous species. Should one wish to follow certain features connected with the development of one of the oviparous species in order to compensate, in part, for the gaps necessarily appearing here one could turn to papers by Bordas (1909), Heymons (1892), Ito (1924), Snodgrass (1933, 1937), and Vogel (1925) on the structure of the female reproductive tract—Ito's comparative histological treatment and the gross morphology as presented by Snodgrass being especially satisfactory; Kadyi (1879) and Pyror (1940) on oviposition and the structure of the oötheca; Brandt (1874), Morse (1909), and Wheeler (1893) on the sex cells; Blochmann (1888) and Gier (1936) on the symbionts; and Cholodkowsky (1891), Heymons (1895), and Wheeler (1889, 1893) on the development of the embryo.

Material, Methods, and Acknowledgments

Shortly before leaving the Hawaiian Islands the writer had an opportunity to collect and examine some of the more common roaches in his vicinity. Upon attempting to remove the chorion from an older embryo of *D. dytiscoides* it was discovered that the two were rather firmly united by a pair of slender threads which, under examination, proved to be extensions of the pleuropodia. A supply of specimens was collected, the body of each was opened and the insects were dropped into Bouin's picro-formal with the routine subsequent treatment.

During the following winter the eggs were removed and, so far as possible, a series of embryos was prepared. Whole mounts were stained in bulk in borax-carmine while sections were cut at 7 to 10 microns and stained either in Haidenhain's, Ehrlich's, or Harris' haematoxylin. The counterstain in sections was invariably alcohol-soluble eosin, except for a few instances where only a nuclear stain was employed.

Two or three subsequent lots of specimens were received through the courtesy of Francis Yap in Honolulu. The treatment was identical for all shipments of preserved specimens, but through the kindness of Lee A. Strong, Chief of the Bureau of Entomology and Plant Quarantine, one small lot was received alive for special treatment.

Despite the several lots of specimens collected, and the pains taken with them, it has been impossible to obtain a complete series of embryonic stages. A great gap will be apparent, for example, between the oöcyte and germ band with developing appendages. Several stages immediately following the germ band also are lacking. Apparently the early embryonic history in the egg is passed quickly, the older developmental stages progressing toward hatching in more leisurely fashion over a long period of time. The relative speed of development in the various stages would make a fascinating study.

Female Reproductive System

The major divisions of the reproductive tract are typical of blattids but their specific modifications in certain respects render them of considerable interest. Hagan (1941) has given a description of the system in greater detail than will be necessary here. The entire reproductive tract is rather concentrated in the ventral posterior portion of the body in the virgin female, but when eggs are developing in the brood sac, or uterus, the latter may extend well forward in the body and greatly disturb the normal position of the adjacent digestive tract. The uterus and ovaries lie against the posterior end of the mesenteron at its junction with the hind-intestine. Malpighian tubules in profusion, accumulations of fat body cells, tracheae, and the posterior nerve ganglia with their terminal plexuses make it somewhat difficult to obtain a perfect dissection without losing some of the accessory glands, or leaving them obscured by remnants of these organs.

The ovary is broad basally and tapers distally to a point consisting of the terminal filaments arising from the ovarioles. These fuse and a suspensory ligament continues anteriorly and upward in the haemocoele toward the mesocardium. There are six ovarioles in an ovary, each consisting of the usual parts. A germarium with from twenty to thirty oögonia is followed by the vitellarium extending posteriorly to the pedicel of the oviduct. Seven or eight oöcytes fill the vitellarium, the oldest and largest being, of course, at the lower end. The six pedicels connect the ovarioles of the ovary to the calyx of the oviduct which is the slightly dilated anterior end of the latter. The paired oviducts are short and unite in the median line of the abdomen to form an extremely short common oviduct. The latter opens into the genital chamber, which is the largest portion of the reproductive system (Fig. 99).

The genital chamber is divided into three regions: the genital pouch, which connects with the median oviduct, contains the ovipositor and also supports on its dorsal surface a number of glands; the brood sac which lies below the genital pouch and forms an enormous receptacle where the embryos complete their development in the eggs; and the vestibule, which is a short, wide

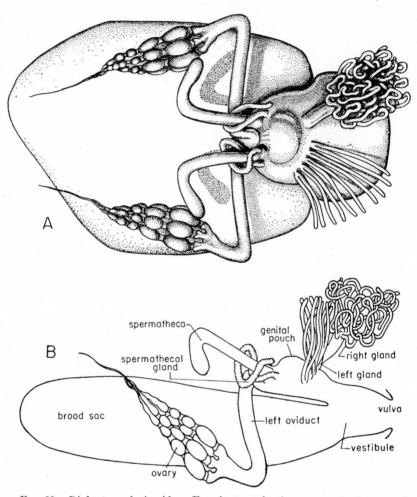

Fig. 99.—*Diploptera dytiscoides*. Female reproductive tract. *A*, dorsal and *B*, lateral aspects. The irregular dilation of the brood sac is caused by the diagonally placed ova containing developing embryos. Valvulae of the ovipositor lie within the genital pouch. (After Hagan, Psyche, **48**, 1.)

tube leading from the more anterior genital pouch and brood sac to the posterior vulva.

Two spermathecae arise anterodorsally from the genital pouch and beside each is a simple tubular spermathecal gland. Both

discharge their contents near the gonopore, or opening between
the median oviduct and the genital pouch. From the posterodorsal area of the pouch arise two glands on either side of the
median line (Figs. 100, 101, 102, 103). The left branches into ten
simple glandular tubes before leaving the genital pouch while the
other emerges as a stout tube with a slightly dilated distal end.

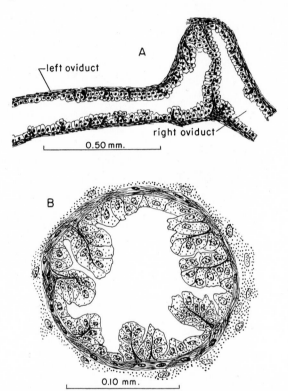

Fig. 100.—*Diploptera dytiscoïdes*. *A*, longitudinal section of most of left
oviduct and proximal portion of right. The internal epithelium appears to be
stratified in the relaxed state. *B*, cross section showing the folded epithelium,
basement membrane, muscularis and peritoneum.

From the latter approximately twenty unbranched glands take
their origin and at once become intertwined into a dense knot of
tubes. The functions of these two types of glands are not clear.
The left one always seems to contain a granular substance in the
lumen during gestation, while the other does not. It is quite
probable one supplies the oöthecal material, the second nutriment
for the developing embryos.

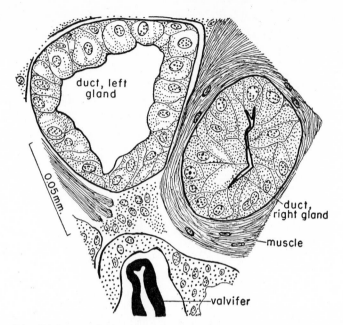

FIG. 101.—*Diploptera dytiscoides*. Cross section of both accessory gland ducts just prior to their opening into the genital chamber. From a young adult following the last molt but before the exoskeleton turned brown. Spermatozoa were already present in the spermathecae. Flemming's, Ehrlich's, and eosin.

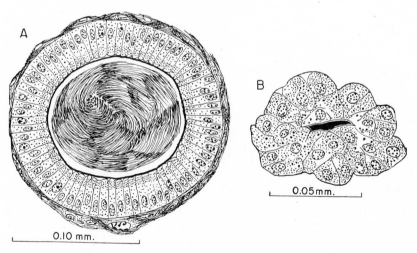

FIG. 102.—*Diploptera dytiscoides*. Cross sections of: *A*, spermatheca showing muscularis, columnar epithelium, intima and spirally twisted masses of spermatozoa; *B*, spermathecal gland with narrow, secretion-filled lumen and irregularly arranged epithelium.

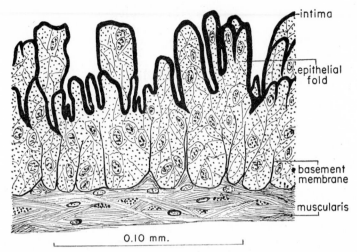

intima

epithelial
fold

basement
membrane

muscularis

0.10 mm.

FIG. 103.—*Diploptera dytiscoides*. Longitudinal section of the wall of the relaxed brood sac to show foldings of epithelium, basement membrane and chitinous intima. Four bent tips of adjacent papillae appear above in this section.

Development of the Embryo

The Egg.—Before describing the mature oöcyte it might be desirable to refer once more to the younger oöcytes and their formation. A germarium contains approximately twenty oögonia in the young adult female, for that is the estimated number found in nymphs of the last instar shortly before the final moult (Fig. 104). In addition to these, seven more are present which had passed into the vitellarium at this early date. After their discharge into the vitellarium they are called oöcytes. The three lowest in the vitellarium lie in complete follicles though they are not equally mature. Since no mitoses have been observed in the oögonia this is, presumably, the entire supply of functional cells. Older females which are mature and possess well-developed embryos within their uterine eggs seem to have eight oöcytes in each vitellarium so that, with the onset of reproduction, the number of complete ovarian follicles is increased from three to four in an ovariole.

While it is usually possible to distinguish between an oögonium and an oöcyte by the presence of yolk, at times this is difficult or impossible. A stage of development intermediate between the two is frequently found where the nucleus has become very large, more than twice the size of the oögonial nucleus, yet no observable yolk has entered the cytoplasm and the latter is still quite clear.

The youngest discernible oöcytes exhibit a finely granular cytoplasm which stains intensely while that of the oögonium scarcely stains at all with eosin. Quite early, too, the much larger oöcyte nucleus is filled with far more and finer chromioles than one sees in the oögonium. Finally, the follicular epithelium is more definitely a tissue around the sides of the oöcyte while it remains scantily and irregularly dispersed around the oögonial walls. Generally, one or two oögonia may be found beside the youngest oöcyte though all the lower oöcytes are disposed in a linear series.

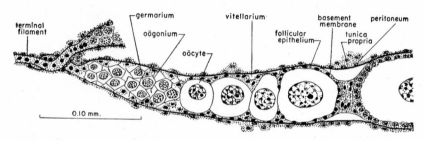

Fig. 104.—*Diploptera dytiscoides.* Upper part of an ovariole and the tip of another from specimen in the last nymphal instar. Five of the 7 oöcytes are shown. Oöcyte and oögonial cytoplasm is white but follicular and peritoneal cytoplasm is stippled.

In some respects the oöcytes of this species vary from the conditions given in the account of *Blatta* by Wheeler (1889). The mature chorionated oöcyte is little more than a third as large as that of *Blatta* though the adult diplopteran which is produced from it is longer, considerably wider, and much greater in bulk. The largest nucleus in the ovariole of *Blatta* is in the central oöcyte. It is in the lowest ovarian oöcyte of *Diploptera*. From the first, the oöcyte nucleus is very large and quickly becomes enormous as more yolk accumulates around it. The location of the nucleus is midway between the poles, but in the older oöcytes it usually moves peripherally. The first oöcyte nucleus is peripheral, the second from the lower end of the ovariole is very near the periphery and both are situated about one third the length of the oöcyte from its anterior end. The nuclei of the more anterior oöcytes are all centrally located when viewed either in longitudinal or cross section. The nucleus does not appear amoeboidal in its peripheral migration.

Oöcytes do not continue to enlarge while ova are undergoing development in the uterus; on the contrary, by the time blastoderm formation is completed in the uterine eggs the oldest oöcytes in the ovarioles have already attained a length of 0.78 mm. and a width of 0.26 mm. Further increase in all of them, irrespective of size, ceases until the offspring are born. Further acquirement of yolk is resumed in the oöcytes some time after birth of the off-spring. The oldest oöcytes quickly accumulate the remaining re-quired yolk and a chorion, then pass from the ovarioles through the pedicels of the paired oviducts and on down until they reach the lower end of the common oviduct. Here they are directed by the ovipositor from the genital chamber ventrally into the open end of the uterus. Since there are twelve ovarioles in the two ovaries, twelve oöcytes are normally deposited in the uterus in quick succession. It occasionally transpires that thirteen or four-teen oöcytes appear in a cluster but, so far, examination has gen-erally revealed the extra ones to be smaller than the others and the embryos, while often of the same developmental age, are half size, or smaller, and apparently fail to mature. One exception to this was found in an oötheca containing fourteen eggs with half grown apparently normal embryos. Unfortunately, the case was not discovered in time to ascertain whether the adult possessed ovaries with supernumerary ovarioles or the normal number.

It has been surmised that such accessory embryos develop in the second oöcytes, which have, somehow, been passed down with the mature ones through some functional disturbance. In another instance an oötheca with twelve eggs had embryos of the same age but one was considerably larger than the others. Perhaps it failed to pass into the oviduct to join an earlier brood. Again, it has been infrequently observed that an ovariole may become so twisted in the body that normal passage of the oöcyte to the pedicel has not followed its full development. This results in great lateral distention of the vitellarium as the lengthening oöcyte becomes lodged crosswise in the ovariole and pushes out the wall at right angles to the length of the lumen in which it lies. The eventual solution of this anomalous condition has not been learned.

The freshly deposited oöcyte in the uterus possesses a chorionic measurement of approximately 1.20 mm. in length, and the great-est dorsoventral dimension is 0.43 mm. near the posterior end though the sizes of various broods of eggs vary greatly, possibly because of food and climatic conditions. The anterior, micropylar end is slightly smaller, being about 0.39 mm. in dorsoventral measurement. The micropylar end is last in the passage of the oöcyte to the uterus and is directed anteriorly in the mother's body. The egg is cylindrical but when laid beside the others in the uterus it appears semihexagonal where it is compressed by adjacent ova. It is elongate and tapers toward the micropylar end where it is not so evenly rounded as the opposite pole but tends toward the shape of a narrowed parabola. The egg is not quite straight but slightly concave on the inner, ventral side and convex on the outer when arranged in the oötheca, the latter thus being its longest surface.

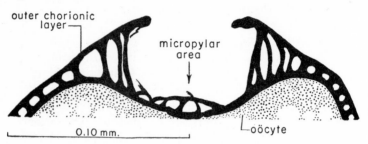

Fig. 105.—*Diploptera dytiscoides.* Sagittal section near center of the micropylar area of an oöcyte.

The structure of the chorion and its sculpturing corresponds closely to that given for *Blatta* by Wheeler (1889). The micropylar area is a rather large circular organ in the chorion (Fig. 105). It is elevated above the chorionic curved surface on its outer margin but the central portion is deeply depressed into the yolk. The cavity is very large, circular with nearly straight sides and lined, at least in part, with the superior layer of the bilaminate chorion. The trabeculae, which normally are rather short between the two chorionic layers elsewhere, are here very elongate where they separate to form the rim of the bowllike micropylar area. No perforations through this area could be definitely recognized, and no funnel-shaped structures such as Wheeler (1889) observed in *Blatta* under low power are distinguishable here. Instead, a perpendicular view under higher power of the microscope showed an enormous number of very minute, circular or slightly oval clear spots which are regarded as micropyles. They are very much smaller than the diameter of the trabeculae and appear to be simple tubes leading directly toward the yolk with no dilated distal end such as described for *Blatta.* They are somewhat less readily seen in their longitudinal sections through this area.

The cytoplasm of the mature oöcyte gives different optical appearances with various fixatives and stains. All of them agree however in showing the plasm in a very thin sheet covering the anterior end of the egg and continuing within the egg to surround enormous vacuoles of stored food, generally in the form of yolk. Mutual pressure of the vacuoles often causes the plasma sheets to assume polygonal cell-like shapes in forming partitions separating the vacuoles. A few fine granules are distributed in this meshwork. The yolk stains strongly and evenly in eosin following Bouin's picro-formal but with Helly-Zenker's and with Flemming's solution this homogeneous substance is removed, leaving either clear spaces or spaces partially filled with coarse, darkly stained granules. In addition, large spherical, black bodies peripherally situated in the oöcyte probably reveal the presence of fatty materials, not yet converted into yolk. Thus the egg of this species seems to contain the same substances that Wheeler (1889) has so well described for *Blatta*. The use of eosin stain must be carefully controlled when it follows Bouin's fixative; if the stain is too dense the cytoplasm often looks as if it entirely lacked polygonal separation into large globules by cytoplasmic membranes. It appears to consist almost wholly of yolk. Such an effect is similar to that described by Cholodkowsky (1891). But that this is not the true condition for *Diploptera* is revealed by lighter staining. The views obtained by using Flemming's fluid and Helly-Zenker's with post-chromation, with or without stains, seem to show beyond question polygonally arranged sheets of cytoplasm from whose meshes the yolk, but not the granules, have been dissolved.

The large nucleus is abundantly supplied with small chromatic granules and linin but these tend to coalesce into somewhat coarser masses after being treated with Bouin's fluid. A large nucleolus is usually present though one or two additional, of lesser size, may sometimes be found. With Flemming's fixation and no stain the nucleolus reveals minute vacuoles and one or two loosely aggregated masses of dark granules. Except for the presence of these structures, the nucleoplasm is clear though the nuclear and nucleolar membranes are visible.

As these mature oöcytes pass into the brood pouch, they are partially enclosed over their lower ends and sides by an extremely delicate oötheca, beside which either lamina of the chorion appears quite thick. Partitions likewise extend between the oöcytes as in blattids in general. The oötheca seems never to be complete, even over the parts of the oöcytes it is supposed to surround, nor does it cover more than half of the oöcytes, their micropylar ends remaining free from this investment. In order to exclude the necessity of mentioning this structure again later, it may at once be said that as embryonic growth proceeds and the egg elongates extensively during the process, the oöthecal membrane covers continually less and less of the egg and its contents. It is difficult, indeed, to see it at any time and it is rarely found around the older eggs.

The oöcytes are disposed in two parallel rows in the oötheca but those on the one side are offset sufficiently to permit them to fit opposite the intervals between those in the opposing row. At the two ends of the oötheca the first and last oöcytes do not lie in the rows to which they belong but rather in the mid-line, so each is alone without an opposing oöcyte. Supernumerary oöcytes of reduced size, if large enough to develop embryos, will be in their proper positions. Very small oöcytes, and those failing to continue development, will be much flattened and often completely hidden between the normal oöcytes. When the embryos begin their development, all those in one row face those opposite them; thus their future dorsal surfaces are invariably turned outward, away from the mid-line of the oötheca.

The eggs stand vertically, with the micropylar end pointed dorsally in the body as they tip over the edge of the genital pouch into the brood sac below. The oötheca seems to be laid flat from the start instead of vertical or else it rotates 90° to the left. As embryonic development proceeds, it will be found lying on its side with the free, micropylar ends of the eggs directed obliquely posteriorly toward the left wall of the brood sac. This fact is of considerable historic interest since it causes the embryos to develop with an orientation contrary to the principles of Hallez's law. According to Wheeler (1889) the oötheca of *Periplaneta* does not rotate while that of *Blatta* rotates to the right after protruding from the vulva. It is believed each diplopteran female produces more than one brood annually although the length of the gestation period and the span of her reproductive life have not been determined.

Symbionts.—Symbionts stained excellently in a slide of fat body tissue (Fig. 109C) taken from the surface of an adult ovary, but how and when they enter the oöcyte could not be determined, nor was any trace of them found in the blastoderm cells, the yolk, or the embryo. Those found in the mycetom cells of the fat body conform closely in shape and size with the bacterioids described by Gier (1936) in his excellent treatment of these organisms.

Following the present technique, their only apparent deviation which has been observed relates to their length and thickness, which in *Diploptera* are both somewhat greater than those in the blattids studied by Gier.

Tissue Differentiation.—The primary objective of this chapter is to trace the development of the pleuropodia, so far as possible, because their function is believed to be one of nutrition. This function has hitherto been ascribed with some degree of probability only to these organs in one other group, the Polyctenidae, whose species are likewise viviparous. In connection with this purpose, it will be necessary to identify and describe the developmental ages of the embryos which possess these organs in their various stages of growth. Thus, much of the embryogeny of the insect will be supplied and the history will be as complete as the material permits.

The Blastoderm.—Fertilization, cleavage, and blastoderm formation must occupy the same brief interval in this insect's embryonic history that Wheeler (1889) ascribed to *Blatta*, for only the blastoderm stage was found. However, the indications point to a similar series of events: the occasional appearance of rather deep cells at the surface, the formation of cell islands, and the gradual filling in of the whole surface by these cells and their descendants probably follow Wheeler's description. As the blastoderm nears completion the cells flatten until they become simply a thin superficial sheet, with the nuclei causing slight swellings as they depress the inner margin of the cell toward the yolk. Cell margins could not be noted in sagittal sections but surface views reveal them as polygonal cells with centrally placed, large circular nuclei whose diameter is not quite half that of the cell. The nuclei possess numerous coarse chromioles on linin fibers.

Serosal Membranes.—Slifer (1937) has called attention to accessory membranes which appear during the early embryonic history of certain Orthoptera subjected to experimental studies. This information has lead to the recognition of two such membranes in *Diploptera* which arise after the formation of the embryo. They might be homologized with the white and yellow cuticles of her terminology. There seem to be on the exterior surface of the white cuticle occasional traces of another limiting membrane, the yellow cuticle. The presence of the latter was not definitely determined everywhere for it was exceedingly thin. The white cuticle, however, is approximately as wide as the inner layer of the chorion. It is persistent in later stages of development and might, in reality, be the serosal cuticle mentioned by Wheeler. Both are products of the serosa and may be called here the cuticles. They generally stand away from the embryo or touch the ectoderm at intervals on the ventral surface. On the dorsal side, however, they adhere tightly to the chorion and when the latter is removed from the egg the yellow cuticle, at least, comes away with it. For this reason it is very difficult to free older embryos from these membranes without losing the pleuropodia which grow anteriorly between the cuticles and the chorion.

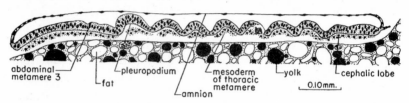

Fig. 106.—*Diploptera dytiscoides.* Parasagittal section of germ band showing rudiments of earlier appendages. Reconstructed from adjacent sections not exactly parallel to embryonic axis; serosa, chorion, and most yolk omitted.

The Young Embryo.—The youngest embryo or, perhaps as aptly termed, an early germ band stage (Figs. 106, 107*A*, *B*, *C*), is available only in sagittal section. It lies at the inner surface of the egg and extends from the posterior end of the latter approximately four fifths of the distance to the micropylar area. The cephalic end of the embryo is directed toward this pole. The length of this specimen is 0.97 mm. The embryo is depressed into the yolk sufficiently to enable the serosa above it to maintain a smooth contour in symmetrical harmony with its curvature elsewhere over the egg, and to reduce any undue pressure on the embryo which would ensue were it forced outward from the yolk. The amnion is completely formed and lies adjacent to the serosal membrane.

The ectoderm consists of a rather tall epithelium whose nuclei are so disposed at various depths as to give the impression of at least two layers of cells. Such, however, is not necessarily the case, for the cell membranes can often be readily traced to both surfaces. These nuclei are very small compared with those of the serosa or the yolk cell nuclei, the latter being several times as long. All of the ectodermal nuclei seen are oval to conform to the elongate shape of the cells, their chromioles are numerous, relatively large, and linin is present.

Transverse depressed areas delimit the primitive segments and are clearly visible as, for example, those marking the boundaries of the second and third abdominal metameres. The more posterior abdominal metameres have not yet differentiated. The anterior segments of the body possess evaginations which are the rudiments of various paired appendages. It will be noted that

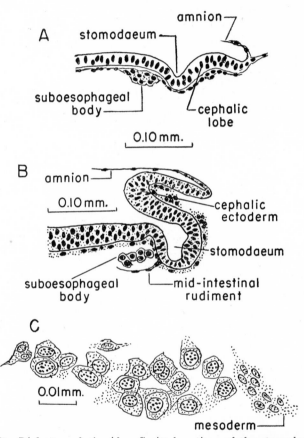

FIG. 107.—*Diploptera dytiscoides.* Sagittal sections of the stomodaeal region. *A*, embryo in Fig. 106; *B*, embryo in Fig. 108; *C*, suboesophageal body of embryo "A", much enlarged, lying adjacent to lower layer and stomodaeal invagination.

all are essentially alike at first in being simple local swellings of the embryonic ectoderm but of them all the appendage of the first abdominal segment appears most prominently even at this early stage. The ectodermal layer is fairly uniform in thickness throughout except for a slight thinning out along the anterior borders of the evaginations and at the intersegmental areas.

While there is evidence of the beginning of a provisional dorsal closure, this membrane could not be positively identified.

Beneath the ectoderm is a somewhat irregular sheet of cells about two thirds as thick as the outer layer. This is the inner, or lower layer. It is roughly two cells in thickness but thins out to a single cell beneath the intersegmental grooves. It invades all of the appendages, including the pleuropodium at this stage and will, eventually, give rise to internal structures. The nuclei are more rounded than those of the ectoderm and the cells are not of uniform shape.

Embryo with Appendages and Coelomic Cavities.—A still older embryo is shown in Figs. 107*B*, 108, 125. It is at once evident that the embryo has developed in many respects although its length has increased only slightly, this specimen measuring 1.12 mm. including the recurved telson. There has been a gain in breadth which has the visual effect of placing the appendages nearer the median line as expansion is confined to the lateral margins. Expansion and growth have not included the cephalic lobes for they appear relatively much narrower than formerly. The appendages are more limblike and are directed posteriorly in the case of the antennae, legs, and pleuropodia, or stand upright on the future gnathal metameres.

A most remarkable growth has occurred, however, in the pleuropodia. These are now bulbous at the base but distally are long, cylindrical, hollow tubes descending to the telson, thence laterally to pass dorsally on either side of it. They end, at present, on the dorsal side of the telson close to the proctodaeum. A sagittal section of an embryo of approximately the same age would show the anterior end lying a little distance from the micropylar end of the egg as before. The posterior end has sunk farther into the yolk to provide for the enlarged and ventrally flexed telson which no longer reaches the posterior pole of the egg. The cephalic end has tucked the most anterior margin down and backward into the yolk to enclose partly a space which will eventually be the cavity of the head. In cross sections of the insect the sides of the cephalic lobes will be found to have kept pace in upward growth with the most anterior margin so the head cavity is largely enclosed on all but the dorsal and dorsolateral aspects.

Along the inner margin the mesoderm has disappeared from the intersegmental spaces and has accumulated intrasegmentally in the form of a hollow mass of cells. The hollow spaces are coelomic cavities. Beginning with the antennae, each segment except the intercalary possesses a pair of such mesodermal rudiments, bilaterally arranged. While a few cells of the lower layer appear beneath the intercalary, no cavity could be distinguished. Where appendages are borne on the segments, the mesodermal rudiments and their enclosed spaces extend the length of these organs beneath the ectoderm. The mesoderm is not all confined to the coelomic areas for a few scattered cells are found elsewhere. Many of these, no doubt, will eventually be converted into blood cells and possibly other specialized mesodermal tissues. Exceptions to these statements are the last two abdominal segments, which have not been differentiated in this developmental stage. In the antennae and pleuropodia, too, mesodermal infiltration is limited to the basal portion as drawn in the figure. There are eight complete abdominal segments and the telson visible in an embryo of this age (Fig. 108).

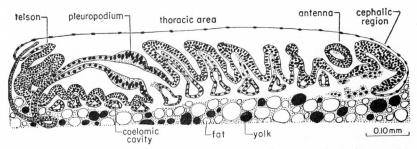

Fig. 108.—*Diploptera dytiscoides*. Parasagittal section of an embryo with about 8 abdominal metameres; it is slightly younger than shown in Fig. 125.

The labrum has been elevated from the surface as an unpaired median organ which lies over the opening of the stomodaeum. It, too, possesses a mesodermal core but no coelomic cavity. The first maxillae have broadened distally and each has had its distal end divide into three rounded protuberances. Practically the same modification is undergone by the rudiments of the labium, but in this case the appendage is cleft into only two branches, a distal longer one continues the straight line of the appendage away from the ventral surface of the embryo while the lesser branch arises from the posteromedian margin at a point only a little beyond the middle of the appendage. These diverticula will form the palpus, lacinia, galea and prementum, etc., of the two appendages.

In the median line of the cephalic area lies the stomodaeum of which an enlarged view is furnished in Figure 107*B*. This invagination penetrates inward and slightly forward, then bends dorsally and ends blindly against the yolk. Its inner boundary consists of mesentoderm continuous with the mesoderm which surrounds the base of the stomodaeal invagination and continues forward under the cephalic lobes. A small accumulation of similar cells at the posterior margin of the stomodaeum gives rise to a slight posterior extension of cells parallel with the main embryonic axis. This is the rudiment of the ventral strand of the enteron. Between it and the ventral embryonic body wall appears a single sheet of large cells which extends transversely across the embryo. The sections show the strand to be from five to seven cells in width. They are vacuolated, pale cells with definite borders to their abundant cytoplasm and with large rounded or oval nuclei whose chromioles are fewer in number and less intensely stained than the nuclei of the other embryonic tissues. They are present in the slides of this and later stages of development, but no function can be ascribed to them. They form the rudiment of the suboesophageal body, an evanescent organ (Fig. 107).

Blastokinesis.—Revolution or migration of the embryo in the egg does not occur. The only evidences of any shifting of the embryo over the yolk manifest themselves in its shortening so that the head retreats from its former position to about the center of the ventral side of the egg or, perhaps, two fifths the distance from the anterior end of it. The posterior end of the embryo is drawn slightly forward and the last recurved portion is no longer so strongly flexed along the ventral abdominal surface. Instead the terminal abdominal metameres tend to stand vertically, more or less at right angles to the longitudinal body axis. All this rearrangement seems to accompany, and be the result of, the widening of the embryo in its lateral spread over the yolk. It precedes the imminent dorsal growth of the body walls, and the more intimate concentration of the segments, particularly the most anterior. The embryo is now about two thirds the length of the egg, or a little less.

With definitive dorsal closure, the embryo will initiate a prolonged period of lengthening during the remainder of prenatal life. While the shortening and thickening of the embryo may be considered the anatreptic phase of blastokinesis, it would be difficult to distinguish the end of katatrepsis under the circumstances. Neither movement conforms to true migration as revealed by most insect embryos, and shortening of the diplopteran embryo occurs long after the amnion and metameres appear.

Fate of the Embryonic Membranes.—With the dorsal growth of the lateral walls of the embryo the amnion and serosa are ruptured, drawn dorsally, and invested by the developing mid-intestine. They occupy the anterior portion of the stomach while the remaining original yolk lies at the posterior half of this relatively large organ. The membranes immediately break down into a granular mass and are apparently utilized for nutriment while the yolk seems to persist for later conversion.

The Cuticularized Embryo.—This embryo is about four fifths the length of the egg, showing that a growth in length has attended completion of the body walls. The antennae and metathoracic legs are the longest of the usual appendages, reaching well down ventrally along the first few abdominal segments. The pleuropodia have passed dorsally on either side of the eighth and ninth abdominal metameres and, reaching the chorion, have grown anteriorly to the cephalic region. The gnathal appendages are elongate, fairly definitive, and closely concentrated. The entire ventral cephalic region still lies in the longitudinal axis but the head does not reach to the anterior pole of the egg. The optic lobes appear as slightly bulging vesicles on either side of the head beneath the chorion. A delicate but readily perceived cuticle, derived from the serosa, covers the body and appendages; apparently the pleuropodia have none.

Rudiments of nearly all the internal organs have made their appearance, yet no trace of salivary glands can be found and the gonads are very immature in appearance. The stomodaeum and proctodaeum are comparatively short and the oesophagus and crop are not distinctly differentiated as areas of the former. The mid-intestine is relatively enormous and extends from the thoracic region to about abdominal segment six or seven.

The Chitinized Embryo.—Between the formation of the dorsal body walls in the early cuticularized embryo and this stage, which is the last before hatching takes place, a comparatively long embryonic growth period ensues. This is attested by three observations from field collections of adult females: (1) few non-gravid specimens occur in a population, (2) stages between ovulation and the cuticularized embryo are infrequently found and older embryos are usually present in the brood sac, and (3) the embryo, after cuticularization, grows several times longer than its total length in preceding stages. To these three, a fourth may be added if the theory of the nutritional function of the pleuropodia, hereinafter presented, is acceptable; that is: (4) the embryo continues its growth at the expense of externally acquired pabulum elaborated by the mother. The abundance and consequent availability of additional nutriment may be dependent on environmental conditions and the metabolism of the parent insect. It is, however, pertinent to point out that collecting time for this study was limited and large numbers of insects were simply sorted from debris, fixed, and stored for future use. It may well have been true, in the absence of carefully controlled collecting, that gravid females were more sluggish or that visual aid selected more of the class with maturing embryos. Less distended and more agile females may have been permitted to escape.

Compared with a freshly laid egg lying in the newly formed oötheca, this egg with a fully developed embryo has enlarged a little over five times to accommodate the embryo within. The chorion is tightly stretched into a thin membrane whose original bilaminate and trabeculate structure is largely obliterated. The exochorion surrounding the micropyle is ruptured and hangs in loosely attached strands, and is often not discernible elsewhere.

The embryo everywhere presses tightly against the chorion. Its head is flexed ventrally so that the vertex is the most anterior end of the body. The micropyle of the chorion is over the front of the head for the vertex protrudes just dorsal to it. The body is cylindrical but tapers toward both ends and it is slightly curved with a convex dorsal outline. The mouth parts are condensed into the nymphal position, the antennae lie beside the ventral mid-line and run to the seventh abdominal segment where each recurves and returns a short distance lateral to the limbs. Eleven abdominal metameres are present; the tenth is narrow, short, and most obscure. The last one (the telson) is subspherical and points ventrally; cerci and styli protrude ventrally also (Fig. 126).

Chitin with rather fine, delicate setae in abundance covers the body, though here and there very stout, long setae appear. The mandibles show at least four long, very dark dentations. The eye bears a vertical, narrow, elongate pigmented area. The pleuropodia are relatively very thin structures which extend over the occiput, passing beneath the margin of the micropyle before coming to an end. They are by far the longest organs of the body.

Organology.—In following the development of organs there is little need to discuss the early germ band stage of the embryo beyond the description already given. For this reason reliance will be placed mainly upon the last of the embryonic stages just described for the material in this section. The easily recognized characteristics of each of them will bear brief recapitulation. We shall designate as embryo number one the germ band stage possessing the rudiments of most of the appendages and seven to nine abdominal metameres. Embryo number two has ten abdominal segments, is preparing for dorsal growth of the body walls and circumscription of the yolk. Embryo number three possesses a cuticle and has invested the embryonic membranes and the yolk. Embryo number four is chitinized and almost ready to hatch. Intermediate stages will be interpolated when advantageous to describe the gradual evolution of certain structures. External appendages, except the pleuropodia and a pair of glands apparently associated with them, have been ignored for nothing differing materially from the oviparous type of development was discovered and they follow the usual orthopteroid pattern.

The Body Wall and the Mesoderm.—In a young germ band the mesodermal segments conform to the metameres being established in the ectoderm. The embryo in Figure 106 shows the condition at the stage of development represented. At this time there is, in each metamere, simply a mass of mesodermal tissue. After the establishment of a few more segments in the retarded posterior region of the embryo, these mesodermal segmental masses reorient themselves into paired, more or less globular, hollow spheres in each metamere. These are the somites and their cavities represent the coelome (Fig. 108). This reshuffling of the mesoderm cells occurs very rapidly when such activity is once initiated and the posterior abdominal segments seem to possess them in succession shortly after each segment is formed. In longitudinal view the coelomic cavities are elongate, but round in cross sections. The dorsal wall is considerably thinner than the ventral, and the median wall in the abdominal somites, at least, is thick in older germ bands. The fugitive intercalary coelomic cavities were not seen but the antennal, gnathal, thoracic, and ten abdominal cavities were clearly shown. Wheeler (1893) declares Cholodkowsky incorrectly mentioned eleven pairs of abdominal coelomic cavities. Another pair of cavities appears in some preparations of *Diploptera* but they do not conform in structure to true coelomic cavities. Rather, they are artifacts in sectioning or, most probably, cavities in lateral swellings beside the proctodaeum near the tip of the telson. Perhaps the latter author also found them in *Blatta*.

As the fundaments of appendages grow larger the somite is altered in shape: the ventral part contributes elements which invade the limbs as rudiments of future muscles. The dorso-lateral portion gives rise to musculature of the body wall and much of the fat body. The median wall forms adipose tissue, the heart and aorta, the musculature of the digestive tract and surrounds the germ cells to form the gonads and paired oviducts.

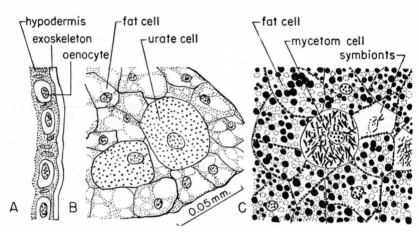

Fig. 109.—*Diploptera dytiscoides. A,* oenocytes forming in hypodermis of young cuticularized embryo. *B,* urate cells in fat body tissue of late embryo. *C,* mycetocyte cells with bacterioids in fat body of adult. Champy-Kull, post-chromation, Haidenhain's.

The beginning of mesodermal differentiation into the tissues just mentioned starts when the embryo has acquired ten abdominal somites. Prior to this the somites undergo some alteration of shape. Portions of them have protruded deeply into the lumens of the appendages where these have evaginated, including the pleuropodia. It may be said here for clarity that all traces of mesoderm are later withdrawn from the lumen of each pleuropodium. The abdominal coelomic cavities, conforming to the activity of anterior somites, elongate in anteroposterior direction until their walls almost meet. Before they do meet, however, the cavities come to open dorsally through the thinning out and final rupture of this portion of the somite. Mesodermal cells lying beneath each coelomic cavity first begin to space themselves medianly in a reticulation, the earliest appearance of fat body tissue. The whole somite, more or less, is soon involved in the process when the embryo shortens and widens by lateral ectodermal growth and the extension of the body wall to circumscribe the yolk.

The fat body accompanies the lateral and dorsal wall upward, apparently limited to the peripheral portion of the body. It later becomes more widely distributed, enclosing the fore-intestine, gonads, tracheae, etc., and occupies a very large part of the haemocoelar space including extensions into the occipital region.

Three types of cells may be found in the fat body of the embryo: the typical, vacuolated fat cell or trophocyte, the urate cell, and oenocytes. The first two are mesodermal derivatives while the last is ectodermal in origin. Urate cells and oenocytes seem to be confined to the abdomen. These cell types are shown in Figure 109, where a section of fat body, fixed to demonstrate the vacuolar pattern, has been prepared from an adult insect for comparison with the shape and size of similar tissue from the embryo.

Suboesophageal Body.—This organ arises in *Diploptera* as a small mass of cells beneath the ectoderm of the intercalary and the anterior portion of the mandibular segments. It appears to originate from the mesodermal cells of this area and not from cells adjacent to the stomodaeum. It was present in the youngest embryo sectioned, an early germ band with but three differentiated metameres in the abdomen (Figs. 106, 107).

The cells are loosely aggregated, showing clear spaces between some of them. Even at this stage their nuclei are twice the size of the mesodermal cells. The chromatin is scattered in a few coarse granules distributed rather uniformly within the nucleus. The cytoplasm is scanty, finely granular and the cell membrane is distinct. After an embryo has acquired eight or nine abdominal segments, the stomodaeum has lengthened and projects posteriorly beneath the yolk. The suboesophageal body has left its former position and migrated closer to the stomodaeum. It forms a flat sheet varying from one to three cells in depth; it is a trifle longer and wider than the stomodaeum, hence two or three of its cells project a little posterior and to either side of this structure. A very few fine vacuoles may be seen in the cytoplasm.

The organ shows little change until after the mid-intestine is formed when it will be found lying against the ventral wall of the oesophagus in a position directly vertical to the suboesophageal ganglion. This position is maintained as long as it continues as a distinctly organized unit in the embryo. At first it is simply a flat sheet of cells, one cell in thickness except for the marginal cells which may be displaced somewhat ventrally to the adjacent cells. At this time, it is approximately nine cells long and twelve wide but specimens vary slightly in these numbers. As embryonic growth continues and the crop is differentiated, the organ will be discovered beneath the latter, about one fourth the crop length from the oesophagus-crop junction. As just observed, it is still dorsal to the ganglion. Enclosed in fine meshes of the fat body, it is drawn up tightly against the crop, curving its margins to conform to the contour of this part of the alimentary tract. At first it may extend from half to two thirds the circumference of the crop but as this portion differentiates and enlarges it is finally confined to the crop's ventral surface. The cytoplasm has accumulated a very large number of small vacuoles.

The chitinized embryo showed no sign of the suboesophageal body though occasional, isolated cells were found that closely resembled its cells. The organ is reported to persist into the nymphal stage of certain insects, and to be broken into isolated cells in the vicinity of the salivary glands in other embryos before hatching. The cytoplasm is also said to be slightly yellow in color in some instances and in late stages large vacuoles more or less fill the cytoplasmic portion of the cell. In the present slides of *Diploptera,* the cytoplasm is always pale and never shows a yellowish tinge. Apparently individual cells occasionally contain a huge vacuole any time after the organ approaches the oesophagus. The organ appears to arise from a single rudiment and the cells vary from angular to round in different specimens. It is definitely a much smaller organ than is generally described for insects and, while occupying much the same location as given for *Xiphidium* by Wheeler (1893), it differs distinctly in both size and location from the lepidopteran, *Diacrisia* (Johannsen, 1929) and *Locusta,* as shown by Johannsen and Butt (1941, p. 231). Finally, it seems to arise much earlier than reported for most Orthoptera, appearing prior to complete metamerism and the formation of coelomic cavities.

Oenocytes.—Certain hypodermal cells of the abdomen enlarge to form oenocytes along the dorsal and dorsolateral body wall. They are most numerous where the morphological dorsal and lateral boundaries merge and do not seem to arise necessarily in proximity to tracheal invaginations.

As the oenocyte cell grows larger it does so parallel to the body surface and at the expense of adjacent hypodermal cells which appear to be much crowded thereby (Fig. 109). Eventually it ruptures the basement membrane and becomes detached from the hypodermis. Such a cell may frequently be detected lying free in the haemocoelar space beneath the hypodermis, but this location is transitory for it will later be found among the cells of the fat body.

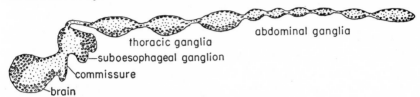

FIG. 110.—*Diploptera dytiscoides*. Lateral view of nervous system of cuticulated embryo, reconstructed from adjacent serial sections.

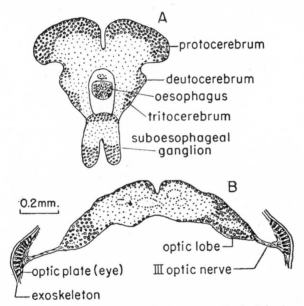

FIG. 111.—*Diploptera dytiscoides*. A, frontal section of brain, cuticulated embryo, composite drawing. B, cross section of optic lobes of protocerebrum in embryo almost ready for birth. Magnification indicated applies only to this figure.

The Nervous System.—For one interested in a critical analysis of the embryonic nervous system of orthopteroids, reference might be made to recent papers by Baden (1936), Roonwal (1939), and others. No attempt will be made to trace such development in *Diploptera* at the present time.

When the telson is starting to flex ventrally, or at about the time seven abdominal segments have segregated, the neuroblasts appear in typical fashion and subsequent processes follow the steps outlined by others, with no essential deviations. An embryo which is approximately half grown contains the brain, suboesophageal ganglion, three thoracic and six abdominal ganglia. Of course, all ganglia referred to are paired (Fig. 110). The brain and suboesophageal ganglia are shown in frontal section in Figure 111A, since their relations to each other and to the oesophagus may be observed best in such an illustration; few authors provide this aspect of these parts. The diagram, unfortunately, does not make fully clear the shape and size of the optic lobes from this angle, but Figure 111B will serve to do so.

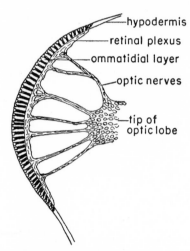

FIG. 112.—*Diploptera dytiscoides*. Section of compound eye and optic nerves of a cuticulated embryo; composite drawing from adjacent serial sections.

Only one other matter need concern us in relation to the brain here and that is the morphology of the optic nerve of this insect in its present stage of embryonic development. Most illustrations of the insect compound eye, the optic nerve, and the optic lobe are drawn from adult insects or specimens that possess a single nerve leading from the eye to the brain. In early embryos it was observed that more than one nerve was present. The number of such nerves increased with further growth until a specimen of the age discussed here revealed six nerves. These lead from different positions in the retinal nerve plexus of the eye and some are even branched at the point of origin. Although Figure 112 fails to give the correct junction of these nerves to the brain the chief error lies in the lack of depth in the diagram, not all of them entering the optic lobe in a simple row, as shown.

Reproductive System.—Germ cells are first clearly identifiable in the first six abdominal segments when this part of the body has acquired nine metameres. At first, they are rather scattered in the median and ventral mesoderm of the coelomic cavities (Fig. 113), but a little later they seem to be aggregated into more definite, ovate masses without visible cell membranes (Fig. 130). The cytoplasm is evenly granular and readily distinguishable from that of somatic cells. At this time they lie near the posterior margin of the somite rather than directly opposite the center of the cavity.

With the appearance of the fat body, dorsal closure, and investment of the embryonic membranes the first rudiment of the gonad is present as an oblong, cylindrical body near the lateral

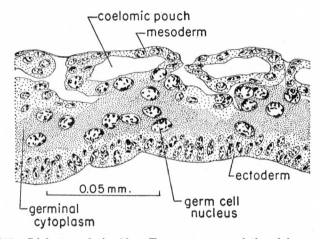

FIG. 113.—*Diploptera dytiscoides.* Two metameres of the abdomen in parasagittal section to show the germ cells in relation to splanchnopleure. Embryonic development approximates that shown in Fig. 124.

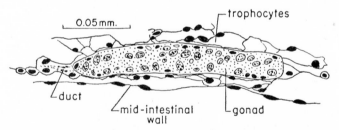

FIG. 114.—*Diploptera dytiscoides.* Gonad from fat body of embryo shortly after formation of dorsal body wall.

wall of the mid-intestine. It extends through parts of three segments (Fig. 114). One is inclined to designate this stage a gonad for, at this time, there is insufficient evidence for differentiation of the sex. It may well be the typical rudiment of the ovary or of the testis or the general appearance assumed by both at this stage. Too few were found to attempt comparisons. The gonad is much shorter than the area formerly occupied by the germ cells when they were segmentally arranged. Mesodermal cells have formed a limiting membrane around the gonad and although a duct appears to lead from it, this could not be traced through the fat body.

The gonad lies embedded on three sides by the fat body but it is particularly noteworthy that most of the investing cells are urate cells. This was found to be true in all cases and, from a physiological viewpoint, may be quite significant. Even where testes and ovaries are readily distinguishable in later stages, up to the time of hatching, urate cells are the most numerous of all cells surrounding them. For the sake of clarity, however, these cells have been omitted from the drawings.

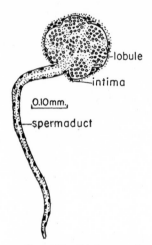

A slightly older embryo shows either testes or ovaries. The testis has been derived from the indifferent gonadal stage by shortening and rounding up into a sphere with very slight bulges around it revealing the presence of the lobules into which it is divided internally (Fig. 115). In no section could evidence of more than eight such lobules be detected, so they are few in number. Descending posteriorly from the testis, the spermaduct passes to segment eight, where it turns abruptly and reaches the ventral body wall. In this testis the germ cells are very small, their nuclei comparing in size with the nuclei of the mesodermal investment.

Fig. 115.—*Diploptera dytiscoides*. Testis with primary germ cells in lobules and the spermaduct with lumen from an embryo with chitinous exoskeleton forming.

The youngest distinguishable ovary, about the same age as the testis just described, shows that the gonad has divided into six elongate portions, each of which will be a germarium (Fig. 116). The terminal filaments have formed but are thicker in diameter than they will be eventually. On the other hand, the vitellarium has not arisen and the oviduct abuts the germaria.

The germ cell nuclei of the cells in the germarium have not diminished in size from those in the gonad but they are more widely spaced due to the accumulation of considerably more cytoplasm about them. Their cell membranes are quite indistinct, therefore the germ cell limits cannot usually be definitely determined. The ovary lies in segment six and the oviduct curves gradually as it turns ventrally to the body wall of segment seven.

The ovary of a chitinized embryo reveals five large primary oöcytes in each ovariole (Fig. 117). The space they occupy is presumably the beginning of the future vitellarium and the

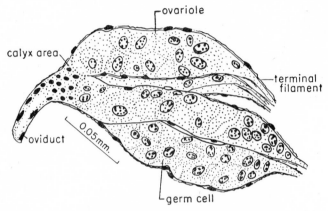

FIG. 116.—*Diploptera dytiscoides*. Ovary with five immature ovarioles from an embryo corresponding in age to Fig. 115.

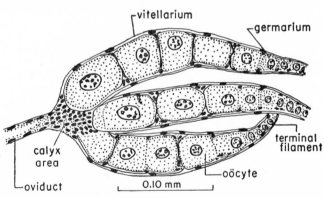

FIG. 117.—*Diploptera dytiscoides*. Ovary of chitinized embryo; parts of germaria, terminal filaments, and oviduct omitted but location indicated.

remaining germ cells lie, very compressed, at the upper end near the base of the terminal filament. There is no follicle as yet around each oöcyte but a few cells are to be seen lying against them in the spaces between contiguous oöcytes. Wheeler (1893) observed a multiplication of germ cells when they first became evident in the germ ridges of the somites. No such discovery was made in the case of *Diploptera,* nor has mitosis been seen at later stages. Nevertheless, the number of germ cells in an ovariole seems to be smaller than one perceives in it during the reproductive period of the adult, so somewhere multiplication is thought to occur but has not been encountered.

From the beginning, the oviduct is more robust than the spermaduct. The nuclei of its cells are very elongate and widely spaced. In the spermaduct the cells are short and the nuclei, in consequence, are broadly ovate and closer together. Both ducts, where seen, were old enough to possess a lumen.

Sexual maturity usually lags behind physical maturity in insects though this is by no means invariably true, as known instances of paedogenesis and neoteny among them will attest. In *Diploptera* it is evident that sexual maturity follows physical maturity rather promptly, if the presence of well developed follicles in the last nymphal instar is any criterion. Figure 104 shows the condition of the ovarioles in an ovary of such a nymph, though the lowest follicles were omitted from the drawing. Seven immature oöcytes are present, the lowest three being quite large and surrounded by definitive follicular epithelium. Earlier mention of ovarioles of this age was made in the discussion of the egg.

The Alimentary Tract.—The digestive system will not be followed in detail in its development in the embryo for it appears to contribute nothing additional to the usual sequence of events in roaches. Nevertheless, some idea of its extent and size in the embryo is important for other reasons.

An embryo with but three abdominal segments already shows the beginning of the stomodaeal invagination as a deep pit (Figs. 106, 107*A*) before the telson is reflexed. Its inner surface is covered by a single layer of mesoderm which is quite thin in comparison with the ectodermal layer. Just posterior to the rudiment of the stomodaeum a loose mass of cells marks the origin of the suboesophageal body.

About the time eight abdominal metameres have appeared, the proctodaeum may be seen for the first time in the recurved telson. The stomodaeum at this stage has definitely invaginated toward the yolk and the cephalic area is raised anterior to it (Figs. 107*B*, 108, 124). The mesoderm still separates it from the yolk, as before, but this tissue is very attenuated over the deepest point of invagination. At the posterior, inner border, a thin entodermal rudiment extends a short distance posteriorly but no theory of its antecedents, differing from those of previous investigators, will be offered to interpret its origin.

With the upward growth of the body walls and the destruction and enclosure of the membranes within the newly formed mid-intestine, the digestive tract consists of a very long cylindrical tube. The fore part of it, the oesophageal portion, is arched inward and back to form a fairly thick-walled tube, gradually enlarging as it approaches the stomach. It penetrates into the mid-intestine slightly where its walls are reflexed to become continuous with the very thin, squamous cells of the latter organ. The merging of the walls of the two is not abrupt for the taller, narrow stomodaeal cells grade gradually into the flat type. The posterior end of the stomodaeum is just sufficiently dilated to indicate the imminent emergence of the crop portion of the fore-intestine. The part of the fore-intestine projecting into the stomach will give rise to the valve typical of this junction but at present their union is widely open.

The hind-intestine originates near the ventral, posterior end of the embryo and, as a very short, thick-walled tube, passes dorsally and anteriorly, bending slightly just prior to its contact with the wall of the mid-intestine. Both mid-intestine and hind-intestine are closed off from one another at this junction. Yolk fills slightly more than half of the mid-intestine and is located posteriorly; the anterior part contains the embryonic envelopes but is not, apparently, completely filled with them.

A chitinized embryo, almost ready for hatching, presents a functionally differentiated digestive tract. The fore-intestine possesses a muscular thick-walled oesophagus in which the lumen is star-shaped and nearly closed due to the internal folds present there. The posterior portion of this organ has become a large distensible crop which is much folded, but these folds involve the entire wall as well as the internal epithelium. It also stains lighter than the anterior portion and, even folded, is much larger in diameter.

The stomach or mid-intestine is still large in diameter and long with walls containing both circular and longitudinal muscles in thin layers supporting a tall, or columnar, digestive epithelium. It no longer runs straight in the haemocoele but is folded upon itself at the anterior and posterior ends. The embryonic membranes within it have been digested or at least broken down into a granular consistency with no nuclei or semblance of cellular structure. The original yolk is largely present with yolk nuclei in various stages of disintegration, although occasionally one seems normal. Whether the yolk is partly digested or is relatively intact cannot be visually determined, for this is subject to chemical and physiological investigation. It appears to be yolk reserve for future needs, perhaps for early postnatal requirements.

The proctodaeum has also formed two clearly differentiated areas of hind-intestine. The anterior part of the intestine is thin-walled, voluminous in extent and apparently filled with two sorts of waste product. The first part of the waste product is granular and vacuolated while the lower third of it seems to be a homogeneous coagulum following fixation and staining. The more posterior portion of the hind-intestine is thick walled, internally folded, and dilated in the lower rectal region just before the anus. The entire proctodaeal tract contains a thick chitinous membrane between the epithelium and the lumen.

The salivary glands seem to be simple, branched, tubular glands which lie on either side of the anterior end of the crop. Extending forward from each is an exit duct, the pair lying on the outside margins of the ventral nervous system. As these pass anteriorly they fuse into a common duct dorsal to the nerve trunk.

The use of an ocular micrometer to ascertain roughly the approximate proportionate lengths of various parts of the digestive tract revealed some very interesting differentials in growth when this system in an embryo with mid-intestine just formed is compared with an embryo about ready to hatch. In the first embryo (Emb. 54) the lengths expressed as percentages of total length of the digestive system are: stomodaeum 19%, mesenteron, 67%, proctodaeum 14%. In the second embryo (Emb. 132) the proportions are: oesophagus 18%, crop 29% (stomodaeum 47%), mid-intestine 28%, proctodaeum 25%. It will at once be realized that, regardless of the probable error involved in establishing these proportions, the stomodaeal portion is the longest part of the system though proportionate increases of fore- and hind-intestines are not very far apart. The mid-intestine, on the contrary, has diminished, relatively, from about two thirds of the digestive tract to little more than one fourth of it in the older embryo.

The Yolk in Relation to Viviparity.—In the discussion of the alimentary tract, it was pointed out that yolk in considerable amount was present in the stomach at the time of hatching or just prior to that event. Some implications may be drawn from this fact after further comments are recorded as to the condition and relative amount of the yolk remaining in the digestive system at birth.

The quality of the yolk certainly varies from that of the egg prior to its investment by the mid-intestine epithelium. Before enclosure it consisted of a granular meshwork whose interstices were filled by spheres or vacuoles of fats, etc., typical of such yolky insect eggs. As the yolk lies in the enteron one can follow the visual changes that occur in it. The meshwork gradually disappears and yolk masses due to secondary cleavage are all that remain. In the oldest embryos yolk masses are no longer visually separable and the yolk spheres occur as individual polyhedral bodies in which no details are to be seen. When they appear thus, they are no longer confined or restricted and float freely about in the mid-intestine though most densely compacted in the posterior part of the stomach. Though many may be found anteriorly, they are more closely aggregated medianly and most densely packed together posteriorly. When search is made with considerable magnification, an individual yolk body occasionally will appear to be undergoing further dissolution, for one edge will be ragged as if small particles had broken away. Fine lines or breaks generally penetrate the border of this rough edge to indicate that more pieces are in process of leaving as fine granules. Finally, it may be remarked that this situation may be traced in either paraffin or celloidin-paraffin sections. Although isolated particles or organs may be lost from paraffin slides in staining, nothing is lost from slides with the latter procedure. These polyhedral bodies of yolky material stain yellowish-pink or pink with eosin much as in the yolk of early embryos, and they differ somewhat in individual, adjacent bodies in the amount of stain each retains.

The quantity of yolk in the form of polyhedral bodies to be found in an embryo almost ready for hatching is of more interest here than its quality, provided it is truly nutritive material. It is also difficult to determine without precise measurement, but all that appears to be necessary here is to show that an appreciable amount of material remains in the mid-intestine at hatching or just prior thereto. If it can be even roughly shown that much of it remains, the query would naturally follow as to what the embryo used in lieu of it in order to complete development.

It was earlier pointed out that the embryo in its development stretched the egg to about five and one-half times its original length at deposition in the brood sac. Such an egg (Oötheca 89) measures 9×28 ocular divisions over the yolk as seen in surface view. The embryo that has just completed mid-intestine formation (Emb. 54) has a mid-intestine with yolk content 7×14 ocular divisions in one section of the slide. An embryo almost ready to hatch (Emb. 108) was stained, embedded in celloidin and hemisected. One half the embryo contained a portion of the stomach with a mass of yolk measuring 6×22 while the other half contained a similar mass 10×33 ocular divisions. The total yolk mass for this embryo might roughly average 8×27 ocular divisions, and one could assume the yolk is not compacted.

There is no intention of treating the above measurements as absolute figures but due allowance has probably been made for density of yolk and shape of the egg compared with the cylindrical intestine, etc., to allow for unusual error. We may, therefore, focus our attention on the point at issue: the embryo in its development seems to lose little of its store of nutriment from egg or mid-intestine. If anything, the embryo appears to add to this reserve as it approaches the hatching period. The embryo readily used the yolk in early development so that when the mid-intestine was formed approximately half of the supply had disappeared. However, the alimentary tract was then essentially completed and during the course of further growth and differentiation the nutrient material in it increased in quantity. Attention should be drawn to the embryonic envelopes which have so far been ignored. They were formed, of course, at the expense of the yolk but, except for metabolic by-products, were later utilized again as nutrient material. How does the embryo grow and develop with an augmented reserve of nutriment in its alimentary tract at hatching unless it is getting more than it requires from another source?

The Adenopodium.—Glands are numerous and variously located in the insects, particularly the blattids, as the contributions of Bordas (1901, 1909), Dimmock (1882), Gerstäcker (1861), Haase (1889a, 1889b), Harrison (1906), Minchin (1889), Oettinger (1906), and others have shown. At the posterior end of the diplopteran embryo, a mass of ectodermal cells on the lateral border of the ninth abdominal metamere forms another gland which seems to be peculiar to this insect and hitherto undescribed.

When first formed, in an early germ band stage, the margin of the ninth segment bears a large number of cells which cause it to swell out considerably. Shortly after all of the ventral abdominal segments are delimited, the pleuropodium grows posteriorly to the telson where it is deflected laterally to pass dorsally toward the yolk. At the same time the massed cells of the ninth segment, beside which the pleuropodium passes, become rearranged to form a cuplike organ distinctly separable in appearance from adjacent cells (Fig. 118). It is purely ectodermal in origin and its margins merge into the rest of the ectoderm surrounding it. Originally it is almost globular with its cells very elongate but with indistinct cellular membranes. The nuclei are staggered so as to make it appear at least four cells in thickness.

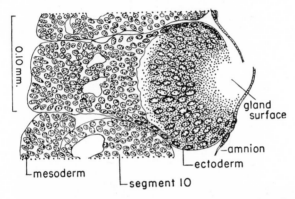

FIG. 118.—*Diploptera dytiscoides.* Longitudinal frontal section through half of abdominal metamere 9 from an embryo whose telson has almost straightened. The adenopodium is subglobular with the cup-shaped, free margin beneath the amnion. Its base consists of a unilaminar ectoderm which here merges into the inner ends of the embryonic ventral ectoderm.

They are also markedly larger than those of nearby cellular components. The free surface of the incipient gland presses the amnion outward, away from the embryo. The gland has not yet established contact with the pleuropodium with which it will later continue in close association. The center of the gland's outer surface is concave with the cells becoming very pale and attenuate at their distal borders.

An older embryo almost ready for dorsal overgrowth of the yolk shows this gland as much greater in diameter, with a convex base and a shallow concave free surface. It not only covers the marginal surface of its own segment but also encroaches on abdominal metameres eight and ten. The nuclei, too, are being oriented in a single layer (Figs. 119, 120). In both figures the gland closely resembles early stages of the pleuropodium of the

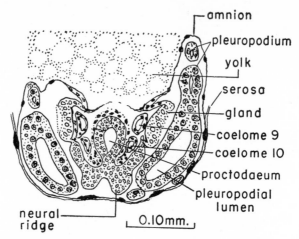

Fig. 119.—*Diploptera dytiscoides.* Posterior end of embryo lying beneath the yolk just prior to rupture of the envelopes and dorsal growth of lateral body walls, showing glands of the ninth abdominal metamere and the pleuropodia pressing the amnion upward.

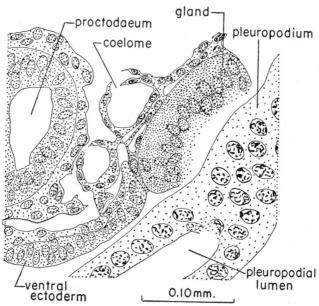

Fig. 120.—*Diploptera dytiscoides.* Enlarged portion of Fig. 119 showing the right adenopodium in detail.

invaginate type on the first abdominal segment of several species and continues to show even closer similarity in later growth.

The embryo that has recently completed investment of the yolk possesses an invaginate adenopodium whose cell tips, approximately equal to half the bulk of the gland, protrude externally from the body. The internal portion of the gland is distinctly subglobular with its flatter outline against the body wall.

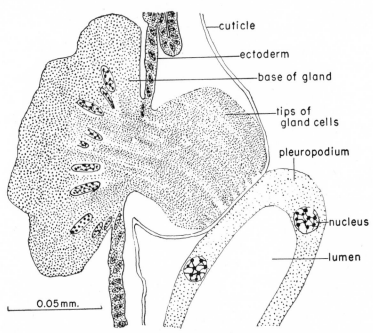

FIG. 121.—*Diploptera dytiscoides*. Adenopodium in its greatest growth and invagination from an embryo that has just completed dorsal overgrowth. The invaginated portion varies from subglobular to mushroom shape, extended portion is evenly granular but extreme tips may be serrate.

Its nuclei become very elongate and lie as a single, arched layer in the center of the basal part of the gland. The cytoplasm is finely granular and from the level of the nuclei toward the protruding cell tips, narrow marginal clefts or lighter areas between cells seem to indicate that each cell is separable from those adjacent though no cellular membranes are visible within the organ (Fig. 121).

The distal, protruding part of the gland is shaped quite like the invaginated portion but at its very end all cytoplasm is so closely pressed together, or so filled with material, that spaces between cells are obliterated. In most cases the inner end of the gland, between the nuclei and the proximal border, is likewise uniformly and evenly granular.

An older embryo between the stage of development just mentioned and the chitinized embryo, reveals alterations in shape of the adenopodium (Fig. 122). The basal portion of the gland has retreated from the hypodermis and extends deeper into the haemocoelar space. The distance is relatively greater from the

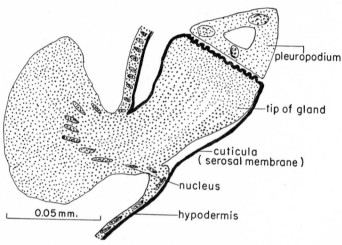

FIG. 122.—*Diploptera dytiscoides.* Adenopodium of embryo before the appearance of chitin, the nuclei are beginning to migrate distally. The pleuropodium is in cross section.

row of nuclei to the inner margin of the gland. The protruding portion is elongate and, in becoming narrower, has caused the cuticula to be thrown into folds over its distal end. Cell tips plainly show clefts or lighter areas with greater clarity than formerly although their distal ends still remain a dense mass of cytoplasm.

The chitinized embryo possesses this gland in its late, or final, stage of activity (Fig. 123). The invaginate portion is very irregular in shape and the nuclei are displaced in position, some of them even slipping out into the protruded portion of the gland. In the distal portion, too, the cytoplasm is spreading apart so large clefts show in it although an even homogeneous terminal border persists. The embryo has secreted chitin and setae over the hypodermis and part of the border of the cell tips also possesses chitin.

The origin, growth, and behavior of the adenopodium seem to warrant its classification as a homologue of similar organs appearing on the first abdominal segment of many insect embryos. In fact, the arguments of earlier writers seeking to establish the homologous relationship between such organs and the polypod stage of the embryo, supported also by Berlese's (1913, Imms,

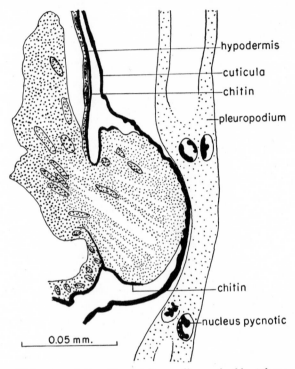

Fig. 123.—*Diploptera dytiscoides*. Adenopodium of old embryo some time prior to hatching, cytoplasm is disintegrating and nuclei are migrating distally. The function of the pleuropodium likewise is waning for the nuclei are pycnotic.

1931) theory of metamorphosis, are equally pertinent to this organ on the ninth abdominal segment. Such fugitive organs of the first abdominal segment have long been known as pleuropodia, a quite inadequate term to discriminate between the various types of such structures, but one which is so deeply imbedded in embryological literature as to resist efforts to substitute a more precise term. To distinguish this organ in its location on the ninth abdominal segment from the pleuropodium seems justified. Since its structure and possible function suggest a glandular activity of some kind the term *adenopodium* is offered to identify it. This term was originally offered by Wheeler (1890) as an alternative to pleuropodium, but it remains unused. Quite recently Snodgrass suggested the revival of this term and its application to the gland-like homologue on the ninth abdominal segment.

The function, or functions, of the adenopodium may only be surmised at present. Wheeler (1890) presents plausible reasons for considering certain types of pleuropodia as glandular in nature and all may be used for the adenopodium. Hussey (1926) has summarized the literature on the pleuropodia and adds, as her own contribution, two examples of the invaginate type which closely duplicate the diplopteran adenopodium in structure.

The adenopodium exhibits certain peculiarities that should be mentioned. It is always in contact, or practically in contact, with the pleuropodium. The pleuropodium penetrates the white cuticle while the rest of the embryo does not; this membrane therefore lies between the adenopodium and the pleuropodial extension. This association is not, apparently, due exclusively to the fact that the pleuropodial extension passes by the adenopodium and is thus purely due to position. In three of the figures of the adenopodium this proximity is illustrated, but in one of them the adenopodium is obviously adherent to, or has bent to come in contact with, the pleuropodium. This view is duplicated in too many other embryos cut sagittally, transversely, and frontally to rule this figure an artifact. There must be some interdependence with the pleuropodium and contact occurs even when the latter is not directly opposite this organ.

Three hypotheses may be suggested to account for the invariably intimate association of these two organs in the same embryo: (1) contact is established early in the embryonic history of the adenopodium and pleuropodium and simple adherence of the two may deform the former, if necessary, and keep them together, (2) the adenopodium may be metabolically active in passing secretions or excretions into the pleuropodium, and (3) the adenopodium may be physiologically active in acquiring something from the pleuropodium.

Of these three hypotheses, the last two have a definite appeal to plausibility. The first fails entirely to account for the adenopodium except as a mechanical anchor to retain the bending pleuropodium in position at the narrowest part of the embryonic abdomen and to avoid pressures against it if shifted elsewhere. But this postulates teleological connotations beyond the scope of this consideration. Besides, the cuticula already serves this function quite incidentally for most of the length of the pleuropodium, but fails to prevent pressure being exerted against the latter, apparently without deleterious effects.

The second suggestion, that the adenopodium discharges waste liquids or gases to the pleuropodium is more probable. Carbon dioxide and other metabolites could readily be thus disposed of conveniently, especially since the embryo stretches the chorion so extensively during growth that space is at a premium. The principal objection to this is the very evident accumulation of waste products in the hind-intestine of the embryo which, in appearance, seems not to vary in amount from similar deposits of other insect embryos.

The final hypothesis, that the adenopodium may derive substances from the pleuropodial extension, seems most probable but, like the second theory just discussed, is wholly dependent on an interpretation of the function of the pleuropodium itself. There seems to be a nutrient increase for the embryo from some outside source but through which medium it is acquired is problematical. The thesis offered in these pages assigns a nutritional function to both the adenopodium and the pleuropodium.

One other contingency in this category should be specifically mentioned briefly. Slifer (1938) has assigned to the pleuropodium of *Melanoplus differentialis* the glandular function of secreting enzymes to dissolve part of the cuticle to assist the embryo in hatching. The pleuropodium of *Diploptera* is definitely glandular although perhaps its functions and that of the adenopodium are quite different; in such an event, their association need not exist. In Slifer's investigations only the white cuticle is found to be affected by the hatching enzyme while in *Diploptera* the pleuropodial extension at a very early period lies external to this membrane, beyond its contact with the adenopodium. The activity of the adenopodium quite obviously begins long before a hatching enzyme is necessary and this seems also to be true of the pleuropodium.

The cuticle surrounds the adenopodium as well as the basal part of the pleuropodium. This membrane is soft, flexible, and very loosely adherent to the outer surface of the body. It interposes a barrier between the body and any space or structure outside of it. For any solution to pass through the cuticle it must be freely permeable or at least semipermeable. This assumption appears to be justified when it is recalled that various fluids, including those with large molecules such as celloidin and paraffin, have successfully passed throughout the embryo and yolk without previously puncturing many of the eggs used in this study. Several additional eggs have suffered only a slight rupture of the chorion although this operation may well have involved the cuticle. The two are often strongly adherent, particularly along the dorsal surface of the egg. Contrary evidence is supplied by the fact that infiltration is much slower with the cuticle intact. Also, Jahn (1935) finds the outer layer of the cuticle (yellow cuticle) relatively impermeable in the eggs of grasshoppers.

Finally, with regard to peculiarities of the adenopodium, the presence of granules along the internal border of this organ should be mentioned. The inner half of the structure lies, as already stated, free in the haemocoele except for its broad attachment to its protruding cell tips and its junction with adjacent hypodermal cells. Along the free, inner border of this organ in doubly embedded specimens, the granules, common to the haemocoele, are so numerous as to obscure the actual inner margin of the adenopodium. They have been omitted from the illustrations for clarity and the organ is shown with this margin as it appears in most sections embedded only in paraffin. These granules may or may not be actual granules in life; they might be vacuoles or nutrient substances that have coagulated due to treatment. However, they are present elsewhere both within and without the embryo or even outside the chorion of the egg, as will be mentioned later. It is assumed they are composed of nutriment acquired by the embryo through the pleuropodium or the adenopodium, or both.

The fate of the adenopodium is unknown; it appears in all embryos sectioned up to the time of hatching. Eventually it is probably covered by the hypodermis and resorbed in the body, as Hussey (1926) suggests for the invaginate pleuropodia of specimens she studied in the Hemiptera.

Pleuropodia.—These organs are strictly evanescent embryonic structures appearing in the history of many insects. They appear on the first abdominal segment of *Diploptera* about the time the thoracic appendages arise, or shortly thereafter (Fig. 106). At first they are indistinguishable from leg evaginations, but become broader and more prominent by reason of their vigorous development. As they elongate in an early embryo they turn posteriorly and tend to cover succeeding abdominal segments almost as fast as the latter differentiate (Figs. 124, 125). When they reach the eighth or ninth segment they are deflected laterally on either side of the flexed telson and pass dorsally toward the yolk. Eventually their permanent dorsal flexure is opposite segment eight.

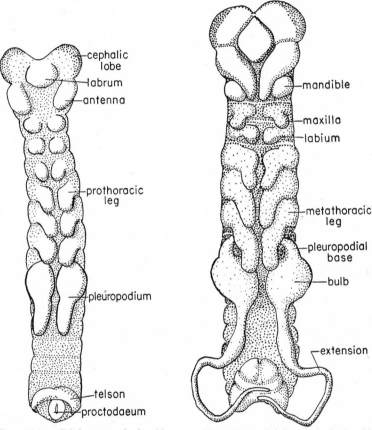

FIG. 124. — *Diploptera dytiscoides.* Young germ band with eight abdominal segments, pleuropodia becoming bulbous and projecting posteriorly. Additional labelling in Fig. 125.

FIG. 125. — *Diploptera dytiscoides.* Embryo just prior to dorsal growth of the lateral body walls. Additional labelling in Fig. 124.

As the young embryo approaches the stage just preceding the rupture of the membranes and their withdrawal, the pleuropodia almost equal the body length. In this case, they apparently do not supply an enzyme to dissolve the amnion nor do they force their way through it as Hagan (1939) stated for they lie in a loose coiled mass posteriorly. They turn dorsally, then ventrally again and finally return to the dorsal side pushing the lateral margins of the amnion far above the embryo at that point (Fig. 119).

With the dorsal withdrawal of the amnion and serosa, the pleuropodia reach the dorsal chorion, where they penetrate the white and yellow serosal cuticles and turn anteriorly beneath them. They continue forward uniformly enclosed by the yellow

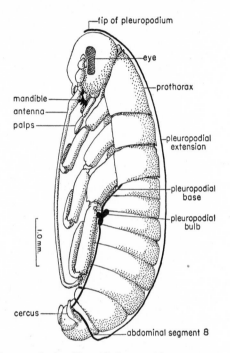

Fig. 126.—*Diploptera dytiscoides.* Embryo with setae, removed from chorion some time before hatching. Pleuropodium consists of three distinct parts, the tip ending beneath the rim of the micropylar area. Freehand.

cuticle, which binds them so firmly to the chorion that they will tear away from the embryo rather than part from it. Anterior dorsal growth is very rapid. Their course along the dorsal chorion is approximately parallel and fairly close together although they converge slightly toward one another anteriorly. When the pleuropodia reach the micropyle each separates from the other somewhat to pass beneath its edges. After continuing over the anterior end of the egg, growth in length ceases (Fig. 126). The path of each shows considerable waviness as if elongation must at once provide for future stretching when the embryo attains full size. Pleuropodial growth and development are complete shortly after definitive dorsal closure of the embryo.

The shape and thickness of the pleuropodium are not uniform throughout its length. At first arising quite like the limb rudiment with a coelomic cavity beneath it and mesoderm penetrating its basal lumen, it outstrips mesodermal growth. When the coelomic cavities open to the epineural sinus, the mesoderm recedes from the pleuropodium to the haemocoele. As soon as the pleuropodium covers two or three abdominal metameres its tip narrows. With continued growth three distinct portions are distinguishable: (1) a basal section, (2) a bulbous area, and (3) an extension. Figure 126 is a freehand sketch designed to illustrate approximately the relative positions of these parts in relation to an older embryo. For most of the following discussion reference will be made to Figures 119, 124–130.

The Base of the Pleuropodium.—This arises as part of the general appendicular swelling of the first abdominal segment and is quite typical of similar evaginations that presage the limbs of the thoracic metameres. From its first appearance, however, its growth is more rapid and it is more bulky than the leg rudiments though slightly later in developmental sequence. The cells are typically ectodermal, one layer in thickness and closely pressed together. The evagination is simple, no evidence of distal differentiation becoming visible until later (Fig. 106).

As the pleuropodium elongates, it turns posteriorly quite limblike and its tip extends tailwards. At this stage, terminal modifications in growth become visible and the basal portion of the pleuropodium is distinctly separable from them. The growth of the base is slow from now on and terminal differentiation and elongation are accelerated (Fig. 124).

The base is broadly connected to the embryonic ectoderm and merges directly with it. Distally it becomes a thin-walled tube whose cells gradually enlarge in width so that the nuclei appear to be more widely spaced along its walls. The nuclei begin to vary in relative size, too, those next to the body wall much resembling ordinary ectodermal nuclei, while distally they become gradually larger with more nucleoplasm and more diffuse distribution of the chromioles. The nuclei, however, never attain the size of those in the rest of the pleuropodium.

About the time the lateral dorsal walls of the embryo are to develop, the base is a long, round, thin-walled tube that is slightly curved so a whole section of it in one plane is, from now on, impossible to obtain. It is of uniform diameter throughout its length except for a slightly flaring attachment to the hypodermis. Its cells and their nuclei are the largest they will become in actual size although the former will later cover more area by flattening still further. This condition continues until the embryo completes the dorsal body wall (Figs. 127, 128).

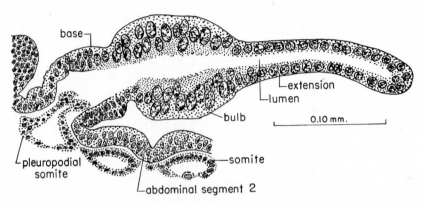

Fig. 127.—*Diploptera dytiscoides*. Base, bulb and part of the pleuropodial extension, longitudinal section, from an embryo a little younger than shown in Fig. 125. The mesoderm occludes the lumen proximally; not all of the extension shown because of its distal curvature.

When the embryo begins to elongate and assume its final form and proportions, the metathoracic limb tends to broaden so the trochanter would lie over and press upon the bulbous portion of the pleuropodium were it not for a compensating elongation of the pleuropodial base. The cells of the base greatly stretch in length and become correspondingly thinner in an older embryo. When chitin appears the base has doubled in length over the preceding cuticular stage and becomes very thin walled. The nuclei of these cells are again small and the chromatin is condensed. The basal attachment to the hypodermis of the embryo is still broad in one view, more narrow in the other, showing that the junction is now ovate in place of round, as formerly. After leaving the embryo, the base is somewhat narrowed but assumes a greater diameter again in its distal half. There seems to be no doubt that continued basal constriction causes abscission of the pleuropodium at hatching (Fig. 126).

In their flattened condition the cytoplasm of the cells becomes quite vacuolate due to the accumulation of considerable fluid in each cell. This vacuolization is not definite in the sense of numerous, small storage vacuoles of accumulated specific products. Whatever is present is rather a diffuse accretion with the cytoplasm rather sparsely scattered in strands in the center and around the periphery. The cells of the base of the pleuropodium give evidence of no other activity than the passive one of forming a simple tube connecting the haemocoele with the bulbous portion of the pleuropodium.

When it first appears, the mesodermal somite of the first abdominal segment is indistinguishable from those of other metameres in the abdomen. Its posteromedian border contains a number of germ cells which are gradually lost to the body cavity when the fat body makes its early appearance in this area. However, an arm of the somite extends well up into the pleuropodial base and its distal end consists of a few irregularly arranged cells almost suggesting their preliminary distribution to form a primitive musculature. Actual formation of muscles within the pleuropodial base never is realized. The development of rudiments of fat body tissue and internal haemocoelar muscles causes the complete withdrawal of all mesoderm from the base. From this stage on, no tissues block the lumen of the base or its free communication with the haemocoelar space of the embryo.

The Bulb.—This part of the pleuropodium has its origin in the posteriorly directed, leglike pleuropodium before the latter has extended over more than two abdominal metameres. While the extreme tip continues to extend posteriorly, the section immediately behind it begins to dilate into a simple, ovate organ. The size is apparently attained by a lengthening of the constituent cells and their enlargement. This operation involves so much of the pleuropodium that the base is relatively very short and tends to be hidden from view beneath it (Fig. 124). The proximal end of the bulb, beside its junction with the base, also reveals separate centers of enlargement. On the dorsal side at this point, the bulb produces a large, local swelling which is subglobular, being too round distally to be called ovate. Its attachment to the original bulbous portion is slightly constricted. Simultaneously, a truly globular dilation evaginates on the ventral part of the bulb. This is the smallest of the enlargements of the bulb while the dorsal and median, or original, swellings are of approximately equal bulk.

The shape of the bulb has just been given for its frontal aspect as it lies against the abdomen of the embryo (Fig. 128). In edge view, that is when sectioned in a plane at right angles to the dorsoventral axis of the embryo, it looks quite different. In this case it is an elongate, oval structure without any evidence of more than a single, flattened enlargement of the pleuropodium (Fig. 129). Now the junction of the base with the bulb can be seen to lie on the inner surface of the latter. It is evident the differentiation of the bulb is directed away from the embryo and toward the margin of the egg.

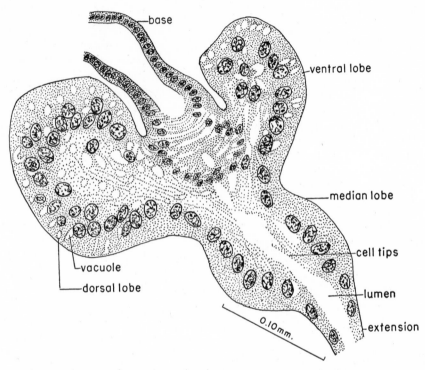

Fig. 128.—*Diploptera dytiscoides.* Sagittal section of base and lobes of the bulb of the pleuropodium; base is curved so junction with bulb is obscured. Embryo with lateral body walls almost complete.

The bulb becomes trilobate shortly before the beginning of fat body formation and prior to the actual dorsal growth of the lateral body wall of the embryo. Contrary to the general squamous arrangement of the cells of the base in their continued history, the cells of the bulb become constantly more like the cells in the invaginate, glandlike pleuropodium of other insects. There is one exception to this similarity, which will be referred to later when calling attention to the polarity of these cells.

Before the dorsal growth of the lateral body wall of the embryo and during the early stages of that activity, the trilobate bulb is larger in comparison with the size of the embryo than at any subsequent time (Figs. 128, 130). Its actual size is maintained through embryonic life until the embryo has become almost full grown. During the last of the embryonic period before birth it decreases slightly just prior to hatching.

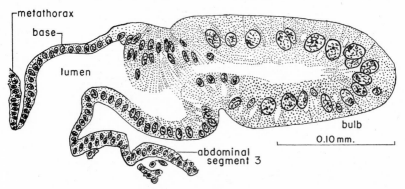

Fig. 129.—*Diploptera dytiscoides.* Sagittal section, edge view, of base and median bulb of pleuropodium shown in Fig. 128.

When the bulb is fully formed its cells are very large, elongate and taper to small, free tips. These tips extend into the lumen, those of the dorsal and ventral lobes being curved toward the median bulb while those in the latter enlargement are directed backward toward the base of the pleuropodium. The attenuate tips of the cells almost occlude the lumen of the pleuropodium but spaces are visible between them although cell membranes are invisible in the present preparations. The cytoplasm is most densely granular at the bases of the cells while the free tips in the lumen are slightly lighter in staining reaction.

The nucleus of a cell in the mature bulb is very large and may be compared with a serosal nucleus or even a yolk nucleus in this respect. It is situated a little above the fixed end of the cell and is oval in shape. A large perinuclear vacuole surrounds each nucleus. When the cells of a bulb are sectioned transversely near their tips each contains numerous minute vacuoles which, of course, may be related to the granules occurring in such abundance elsewhere in the cytoplasm. Long before the embryo secretes an exoskeleton the bulbous portion has shifted from the ventral surface of the embryo and taken a position along its lateral wall. Cross sections of the embryo at this elevation show that the enormous base of the metathoracic leg and the distended lateral body wall above it leave between them a free space to be occupied by the bulb. Whatever the reason for the migration of the bulb into this area, there is no doubt that here it feels no pressure from the chorion, from adjacent embryos, or from the uterine wall which might influence or curtail its activity.

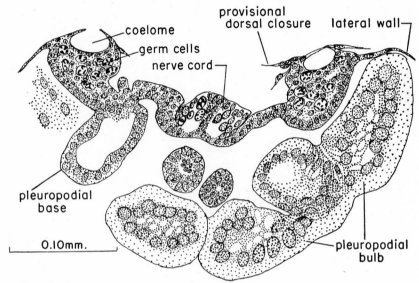

FIG. 130.—*Diploptera dytiscoides.* Slightly diagonal cross section of an embryo showing posterior margin of pleuropodial base and the first abdominal segment at left. The anterior margin of the second abdominal segment and the pleuropodial bulb appear at right, partly diagrammatic. The lateral body wall is continuous with the amnion. A slightly older embryo than shown in Fig. 125.

Just before hatching, the nuclei of the bulb slip forward toward the lumen, where they may be seen at the end of the perinuclear vacuoles. The vacuoles become larger, the cell tips tend to separate from one another and the nuclei become pycnotic. The activity of the bulb is over.

The Pleuropodial Extension.—The third part of the pleuropodium, which shall be called the extension, is at first a thick, elongate conical section projecting beyond the median bulb. The extension now enters upon an extraordinary and rapid growth in length, which appears in successive stages as follows (Figs. 124, 125, 126). At first the end of the conical part lengthens its narrowed cylindrical tip. Curiously, the new terminal growth of the extension is slightly greater in diameter than its more proximal, adjacent portion. However, as the tip of the extension continues to lengthen, its basal sections, just mentioned as being differentiated by their diameter, lose this distinguishing feature and the entire extension becomes almost equally slender throughout its length. Only the proximal connection to the median bulb retains a conical shape, and this is very much reduced from its original size.

The extension is the thinnest part of the pleuropodium but is by far the greatest in length. It forms a cylindrical, hollow filament, one cell layer in thickness. After the embryo fills the egg and begins to stretch the chorion with continued development, the extension along the back of the embryo is compressed into a tube which is ovate in cross section. Its distal end is not open but closed by terminal cells. Throughout its length it appears as if no more than two cells form the circumference of the entire wall at any level so, although it is long, few cells are involved. It extends from the bulb to, and slightly beyond, the micropyle. Just before hatching the cells flatten still more so the wall of the extension becomes exceedingly thin.

The nuclei of the cells in the wall of the extension are very large, second only in size to those in the bulb of the pleuropodium. They are of flattened, oval shape and are almost as thick as the cells in which they lie. The lumen is uninterrupted by any structure within the extension, but the presence of the adenopodium against it already was mentioned. When the embryo nears the hatching time the nuclei of the extension are the first to become pycnotic.

Discussion.—Mitosis was never seen in the bulb or extension of the pleuropodium and very seldom in the lower proximal portion of the base when the organ was comparatively short. After the trilobate bulb is fully formed, or later when the extension reaches the chorion, mitoses were never discovered in its base. This observation agrees with that of Slifer (1938) as do, in general, her remarks regarding the rate of growth of the trilobate bulb in relation to embryonic development in *Melanoplus*. One's observations would lead to the conclusion that the great length of the pleuropodium in *Diploptera* is due to the lengthening and enlargement of the cells involved rather than to their increase in number. While the pleuropodium is attaining its enormous length, the paucity of mitoses in it is surprising; search elsewhere finds karyokinetic figures in great abundance in the ectoderm of other appendages, the segmental ectoderm, and in the mesoderm. This is particularly true in the germ band stage when the pleuropodium is also actively engaged in its early steps toward differentiation and elongation.

Polarity is noteworthy only in the bulb. Elsewhere in the pleuropodium the cells, derived originally from embryonic ectoderm, offer no change in polarity. The cells of the base remain like ectoderm cells even though those in its more distal portion become larger. Throughout the extension the cells are flattened to become the thin wall of a cylindrical capillary tube. The lumen throughout the pleuropodium is only an extension of the body cavity into this organ. It is thought to be filled with liquid.

The condition of the cells of the bulb offers a marked contrast to those of base and extension. In this section of the pleuropodium, the outer ends of the cells (the free or surface ends in the histological sense) remain apparently unchanged in relation to the environment though they are the largest cells of the embryo. Internally, however, they have become very long and the cell tips (corresponding to the internal, fixed bases of ectoderm cells) are attenuated, free and project so far into the lumen as almost to occlude the latter. It would seem that these cell tips are the seat of functional activity of some kind.

The situation just outlined has been mentioned by others in describing evaginate pleuropodia. Williams (1916) believes such cells in the lampyrid, genus *Photuris*, secrete materials outside the pleuropodium which have been taken up from its lumen. But in the genus *Photinus*, with the same type of cell, he thinks the secretion passes inward and is discharged into the lumen. Slifer (1937, 1938) illustrates the same type of cell again in *Melanoplus* and concludes that a secretion is extruded from the outer surface of the pleuropodium.

Several species of insect embryos possess an invaginate type of pleuropodium. In these cases the attenuated cell tips are invariably the outer (free) margins of the cells. Nearly all observers agree that where secretions were seen they were discharges from the cell tips to the outside of the body. Of such authors we may mention, by way of illustration, Blunk (1914), Carrière (1891), Hussey (1926), Korschelt (1912), and Wheeler (1890). The Polyctenidae have been omitted because their pleuropodia are so extreme as to constitute, perhaps, an exceptional case.

It would appear then that both invaginate and evaginate pleuropodia may possess elongate cells with one fixed end and an opposite free pole. The invaginate type always has the fixed, basal end of the cell correspond in position with other cells of the embryonic ectoderm, and the attenuated cell tips from which secretions have been observed to come correspond to the outer surface of embryonic ectoderm cells. In the evaginate type of pleuropodium the physical conditions of the cells are identical but reversed in position as regards the two (basal vs. outer) poles of the cells. Again the general opinion prevails that such cells discharge secretions outside the body, but this time the cells transfer material in the opposite direction in relation to cell modification in structure. In other words, secretions are said to pass outside the body without regard to the orientation of the obviously modified poles of the cells involved.

Perhaps this condition is unique for insect pleuropodia, as the writer cannot recall any case where ectoderm cells (or their derivatives) that have maintained a distinct polarity have failed to show a functional activity in relation to such polarity. Salivary, repugnatorial, accessory sexual, and other glands correlate polarity with function. Perhaps one of the best examples to be cited as an exception to this statement is the type of cell present in the ampulla of the Malpighian tubule of *Rhodinus,* as illustrated by Wigglesworth (1931). The tubule consists of a very long, fine capillary portion and a basal ampulla adjacent to the alimentary tract. The ampulla contains large, elongate cells with attenuate tips extending toward the lumen of the intestine, cells which resemble those in the invaginate pleuropodium. Since the tubule is an evagination from the intestine the potentially free surfaces are the attenuate tips of the cells. These cells, he says, resorb secretions descending the tubule and, presumably, pass them through their bases back into the haemocoele. Slifer's excellent introduction to the physiological aspects of the whole question should be a stimulus to investigate the problem further with the idea of function foremost in mind.

The possible function of the diplopteran pleuropodium is a puzzling and interesting problem. The base and the bulb are similar to the entire pleuropodium of some orthopteroids but the extension is unlike any previously described. Relative to the size of the embryo it is not so voluminous as this organ in the viviparous Polyctenidae (Hagan, 1931), but it is a more distinctly organized structure with definitely differentiated parts. In actual size it surpasses others in length and extends to a predetermined locality, the micropylar area. To do this it grows posteriorly from the first to the ninth abdominal segment where it passes dorsally between segments seven to nine and grows anteriorly to the cephalic region. Segment eight is the narrowest and most constricted of the abdominal metameres so it is not appressed. On the dorsal side of the embryo it is pressed into an oval shape but the lumen seems never to be obliterated.

Essentially, the pleuropodium is an extremely long, fluid-filled tube. Near its origin, however, the bulb is present with its very large cells and their attenuated ends directed toward the lumen from the dorsal and ventral lobes, those of the median lobe extending down the lumen toward the base. Because this bulb is the terminal part of other pleuropodia, the question arises as to why a very long extension continues so far around the embryo. Some have advanced theories that the pleuropodium serves to soften and lubricate the surface of the embryo and its enveloping membranes; to supply an enzyme to dissolve the membranes and assist in hatching; to function as a respiratory organ; to get rid of wastes, etc.

The diplopteran embryo stores quantities of waste in its hind-intestine, as do other species of embryos which seem to possess no pleuropodia. To secrete a hatching enzyme the bulb should correspond to the effective organ in Orthoptera, for example, and the extension appears to be unnecessary for embryos of this order in general. Further, the embryo stretches the chorion and cuticles so greatly during late embryonic development that the exochorion is largely lost and the white cuticle can be seen in isolated fragments distributed along the inner face of the yellow cuticle. If destruction of the cuticle occurred only locally, beside the extension, this evidence would be a contribution toward a solution of the problem. Finally, the bulb is quite evidently the focus of whatever metabolic reorganization is possible in the pleuropodium. If it provided a lubricant its products could be efficiently dispersed into the periembryonic fluid from a short pleuropodium as well as from a long one. This leaves, apparently, only two suggestive hypotheses if a function is ascribed to the pleuropodium: it may be a respiratory organ or a trophic organ.

The following observations may support the supposition that the pleuropodium serves as a respiratory organ. The embryo is very much larger than the original space occupied by the egg, hence a fresh supply of oxygen and a means of eliminating excess gases may be more pressing than in cases where the embryonic mass does not so greatly exceed the yolk mass. The pleuropodial extension lies against the chorion for most of its length. The chorion, especially, at the micropyle, may be sufficiently permeable to permit the diffusion of gases in both directions between the liquids in the pleuropodium and the brood pouch. The reader will recall that the oötheca does not cover the anterior portion of the egg. Pleuropodial respiration would appear to be a simpler operation than that performed by the vertebrate allantois.

If the pleuropodial function is thought to be one of nutrition we might substitute simple diffusion, or transfer of liquids instead of gases—or of both liquids and gases simultaneously. It was noticed when studying sections of chorionated embryos embedded in celloidin that granular secretions were present in the brood pouch, between eggs undergoing development, and in the micropyle of the egg. These, or similar granules, were present in great abundance in the haemocoele of older embryos. The maternal accessory glands might be the source of such granules, in the brood sac at least. If small enough, or as is more probable, if they are soluble, they might be assumed to be passing into the egg, perhaps transported by the pleuropodial extension although no such granules have been discovered in the organ as a precipitate.

Attention has previously been directed to the original quantity of yolk and the bulk of the material remaining in the midintestine about the time of hatching. Certainly the original mass of yolk seems to be disproportionate to the final bulk of the embryo and its stored material in the stomach at birth.

Another problem which confronts us is the probable necessity for the persistence of the pleuropodial bulb. That the bulb is not simply a degenerate organ may be tentatively assumed for it has developed into a very large and complex structure when compared with any evaginate pleuropodium known. The bulb varies somewhat in proportions and a trifle in shape, and its pleuropodial base migrates during the growth of the embryo, just as Wheeler (1890) has already pointed out in other insects. The idea that the bulb might be a pumping organ is untenable if one considers it structurally for no mesoderm or other contractile elements are present; the ectodermal cells of which the bulb is composed are obviously unsuited for contraction. But, physiologically, this result may be achieved through the bulb's possible metabolic activity. Should the extension acquire gases or food the glandlike cells of the bulb could conceivably extract such material, pass it along, and thus create a deficit in the extension. This deficit would presumably be repaired in the extension by accretion through osmosis or simple diffusion from the fluid in the brood sac. Of course, in disposing of waste gases the reverse operation could be assumed.

One should consider, too, the reduction that has occurred in the number of offspring produced at one time and their complete retention within the reproductive tract. Most roaches release larger numbers of eggs simultaneously, whether they are stored in an external oötheca or retained for a time within the body. A low reproductive potential is often correlated with viviparity and is a necessity in relation to uterine nutrition. In this connection, the possible function of the accessory glands might be mentioned. There are three sets of these glands; one pair is typical of spermathecal glands, another gland probably furnishes oöthecal secretion, while the function of the third may be nutritional. All were described earlier.

The final problem is to account for the intimate association between the adenopodium and the pleuropodial extension. As an organ, the former bears so close a resemblance to the invaginate pleuropodium of the insects in origin, structure, size, and fate as to afford little doubt of its homology with these oft-described glands. That the adenopodium early attaches its fine cell tips to the pleuropodium and adheres to the latter throughout its existence is significant, but at present one is quite at a loss for an explanation of its behavior. Certainly there appears to be no more intriguing field for an insect physiologist than an attempt to discover the physiological activities of this structure and the pleuropodium. The observations enumerated here are far from being proof of the function or functions these organs may possess, but they are suggestive. They are tentatively offered in the present belief that nutritional or respiratory functions, or both, are the most plausible of the hypotheses offered to account for their development. The problem should be most alluring and profitable to anyone able to treat living specimens with radioactive tracers.

LITERATURE CITED

Baden (1936), Berlese (1913), Blochmann (1888), Blunk (1914), Bordas (1901, 1909), Brandt (1874), Carrière (1891), Cholodkowsky (1891), Dimmock (1882), Gerstäcker (1861), Gier (1936), Haase (1889a, 1889b), Hagan (1931, 1939, 1941), Harrison (1906), Heymons (1892, 1895), Hussey (1926), Imms (1931), Ito (1924), Jahn (1935), Johannsen (1929), Johannsen and Butt (1941), Kadyi (1879), Korschelt (1912), Minchin (1889), Morse (1909), Oettinger (1906), Pyror (1940), Roonwal (1939), Slifer (1937, 1938), Snodgrass (1933, 1937), Vogel (1925), Wheeler (1889, 1890, 1893), Wigglesworth (1931), Williams (1916).

Chapter 13

PSEUDOPLACENTAL VIVIPARITY—CORRODENTIA, HEMIPTERA (APHIDIDAE)

The two examples of this type of viviparity to be discussed in this chapter offer several similarities in the employment of the extraembryonic envelopes as trophic membranes. The first is a new addition to the list of viviparous species while the species of aphids have long been known for their cyclic alterations of generations, parthenogenetic reproduction, and great economic importance. Neither has succeeded in developing specific nutrient organs to the extent shown by other insects having this type of viviparity.

Order Corrodentia   Family Psocidae

The first example of viviparity in the Psocidae was quite recently discovered by Fernando (1934) whose interests are primarily concerned with the formation of germ layers in the embryos of this family. The species, hitherto unknown, has been described as *Archipsocus fernandi* Pearman. General embryological details are few and the descriptive text adheres strictly to the problem of germ layer formation and the peculiar nutrient organs. The latter are especially significant in classifying the type of viviparity exhibited by the species and also because of their development and function in comparison with other pseudoplacental insects. Another species, in the genus *Hypertes,* has also been reported as viviparous but Jentsch (1936) says it is oviparous.*

Development of the Embryo

The Egg.—The ova, to the number of twelve or more, pass through their embryological history within the thin-walled ovaries in which they lie. They are liberated at intervals, so various stages of development appear in any gravid female. The mature

* This summary appears through the courtesy of the Quarterly Journal of Microscopical Science and The Clarendon Press.

ovum lacks both yolk and a chorion; it is 57.6 microns in length and 37.2 microns in diameter with a relatively thick periplasm enclosing a central, vacuolated cytoplasmic meshwork which contains nutrient material. The cleavage nucleus of the fertilized egg is relatively enormous (Fig. 131).

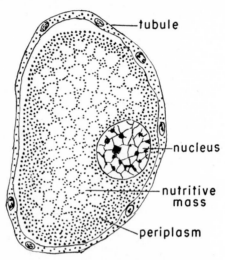

Fig. 131.—*Archipsocus fernandi*. Ovum in ovarian tubule. (After Fernando, Quarterly Journal of Microscopical Science, 77:99–119. 1934.)

Cleavage and the Formation of the Blastoderm.—After the first cleavage the daughter nuclei lie in the central cytoplasm, but when eight nuclei are formed six of them migrate to the periplasm while two remain behind as trophocytes surrounded by the typical stellate cytoplasm. The two eventually increase in number until about twelve may be found in the central portion of the egg. Superficial nuclei are very much smaller than the original cleavage nucleus and, as they increase in number, they continue to space themselves at intervals throughout the periplasm. Finally, the periplasm aggregates into dense masses around each nucleus, thus producing a simple cellular layer of blastomeres at the surface. Subsequent cleavages cause a lengthening of the egg. At the posterior end a few more deeply stained nuclei in a common periplasmic area are the primordia of the germ cells.

The Ventral Plate and the Germ Band.—The sequence of events summarized in this section are of special interest to all students of hexapod embryology, for the origin and formation of the entoderm in this insect are clearly revealed. Moreover, the evidence offered by this psocid strongly supports the theoretical interpretation of entoderm formation recently given by Snodgrass (1935). The blastomeres which were formerly slightly spaced from one another now lie closely appressed in a continuous blastodermic layer. The ventral portion extending the entire length of the ovum becomes four or five cell layers thick, with the germ cell nuclei at the posterior pole in a cytoplasmic mass projecting toward the center of the egg above this area. Centrally situated trophocytes with large nuclei also are visible. The ventral blastoderm is the embryonic rudiment or ventral plate (Fig. 132).

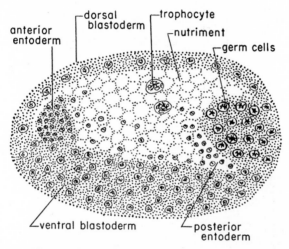

FIG. 132.—*Archipsocus fernandi*. Sagittal section of embryonic rudiment with germ cell mass. The formative entoderm cells are migrating entally from the anterior and posterior entodermal rudiments to form the middle entodermal mass. (After Fernando, Quarterly Journal of Microscopical Science, 77:99–119. 1934.)

The first step in the differentiation of the germ band from the ventral plate occurs when many small nuclei are separated from the inner anterior and posterior ends of the ventral plate. Some migrate into the vacuolated center of the egg while a few others take median positions directly above the ventral plate; the remainder rest at the poles. These are formative entoderm cells and their origin obviously is the ventral embryonic blastoderm of the polar areas. They will be referred to shortly as the anterior and posterior polar masses. Fortunately, the small size of these cells, together with their faintly staining small nuclei, clearly distinguishes them from blastodermal and germinal cells so that their migration and future history are readily followed.

The ectoderm is now clearly differentiated and, simultaneously with the migration of the entodermal rudiments, the mesoderm is separated from it by proliferation. No gastrular groove is evident during the process (Fig. 133). The laterally thickened ventral blastoderm increases its height by continued multiplication of its nuclei and cytoplasmic area. At the same time the median ventral portion becomes compressed by the lateral areas.

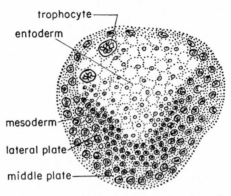

FIG. 133.—*Archipsocus fernandi*. Transverse section through middle of an egg showing lateral and middle plates of the embryonic rudiment, the mesoderm and entoderm. (After Fernando, Quarterly Journal of Microscopical Science, **77**:99–119. 1934.)

As its cells multiply most of the new cells are displaced to a dorsal position, where they spread over the inner surfaces of the superficial layers. The latter form the middle and lateral ectodermal plates of the embryo while the former comprise the mesodermal rudiment. The mesodermal layer possesses nuclei which are intermediate in size between the large nuclei of the germ cells, trophocytes, and ectoderm on the one hand, and the small entodermal nuclei on the other.

The Amnion and Serosa.—As the germ band elongates in its continued growth, its procephalic portion becomes flexed dorsally while the region of the telson bends ventrally, causing the embryo to resemble a similar stage in the Hemipteran embryo. This is not, apparently, an invaginated type of germ band for at both anterior and posterior ends evaginating folds arise which include cells from the lateral plates on its proximal surface and extra-embryonic blastodermal cells on its exterior surface. These two folds grow over the ventral part of the embryo, fuse, and enclose it in a typical amnion and a serosa. The embryonic membranes, it may be recalled, are not formed quite in this manner by invaginating embryos.

Segmentation and the Appearance of the Appendages.— Transverse constrictions mark off the primary segments, with ten of them finally visible in the abdomen. Antennal, mandibular, and thoracic appendicular evaginations arise in the usual fashion and are later followed by the remaining buccal appendages. None of these, however, offers anything unusual in its behavior.

The Alimentary Tract.—The stomodaeal and proctodaeal invaginations are multilaminar and arise as in most insects, but the mid-intestine is organized in a more intricate manner. As the stomodaeum elongates its inner end thins out to a single layer of cells which at first comes directly in contact with the central nutrient portion of the egg. It has, however, pushed before it

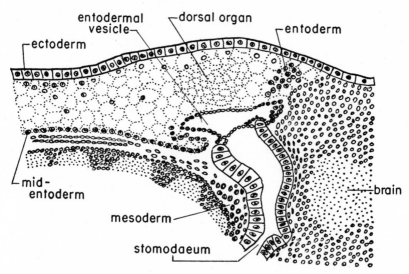

FIG. 134.—*Archipsocus fernandi.* Sagittal section of stomodaeum, entodermal vesicle and formative mid-intestine. (After Fernando, Quarterly Journal of Microscopical Science, **77**:99–119. 1934.)

some of the entodermal cells from the anterior polar mass already mentioned. The rest of the entodermal polar cells are not carried in with it but are pressed dorsally above the brain. The transported entodermal cells soon arrange themselves into a hollow vesicle, a portion of whose wall is formed by the blind inner end of the stomodaeum (Fig. 134). Shortly afterward, the cells at the blind end of the stomodaeum disintegrate and its lumen is then continuous with that of the vesicle. The wall of the vesicle elongates and, forcing itself into the nutrient portion of the egg, absorbs the nutriment as it grows toward the proctodaeal region. The stomodaeum follows somewhat more slowly but always maintains its contact with the entodermal vesicle (Fig. 135). The anterior vesicle eventually meets and fuses with a posterior vesicle

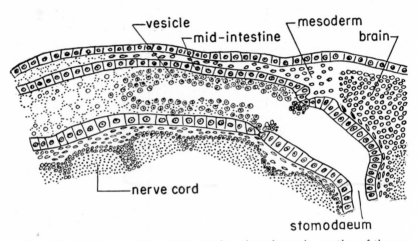

Fig. 135.—*Archipsocus fernandi.* Sagittal section of anterior portion of the egg with fully formed mid-intestine enclosing the entodermal vesicle. (After Fernando, *Quarterly Journal of Microscopical Science,* 77:99–119. 1934.)

which formed in a similar manner at the inner end of the proctodaeum. This ends a transitory phase of entoderm formation with the stomodaeal and proctodaeal invaginations united by a tube comprised of entodermal cells and with a common lumen throughout. Formation of the permanent mid-intestine follows in this summary but in point of time is contemporary with the formation and fusion of the vesicles.

As the anterior and posterior vesicles first arise at the inner ends of the stomodaeum and proctodaeum, the entodermal cells lying just above the embryonic mesoderm migrate to form an anteriorly and posteriorly directed strand between the latter and nutriment in the egg. The scattered entodermal cells within the nutriment probably join these, in part, but most of them wander dorsally to form a similar band of cells above the nutriment, although the dorsal reorganization is slower than the ventral.

The entodermal cells above the brain, and at the posterior end of the body as well, were left behind by the invaginating fore- and hind-intestines. They now participate in mid-intestine for-

mation by joining with the ectodermal proctodaeal and stomodaeal invaginations and with the dorsal and ventral strands of
entoderm covering the nutrient mass. The ventral strand, followed by the still lagging dorsal strand, now spreads laterally
to enclose the nutriment entirely. In this way the mid-intestine
is developed and surrounds not only the remains of the egg
nutriment with its trophocytes but also the entodermal tube that
was formed by the fusion of the anterior and posterior vesicles.
In fact, since the two phases are concurrent, the developing
vesicles are digesting the nutriment and advancing as rapidly as
the mid-intestine is forming around them, so that at the completion of mid-intestine formation there remains in its lumen only
the tube formed by the entodermal vesicles. In the meantime the
nutriment, including a dorsal organ to be mentioned later, has
been used up. The cells comprising the fused vesicles, are, in turn,
digested and utilized by the entoderm before the embryo is born.

Pseudoplacental Organs.—Upon completion of the amnion
and serosa the latter becomes distinctly trophic. Wherever it
comes closely in contact with the wall of the ovarian tubule it

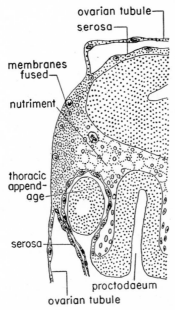

Fig. 136.—*Archipsocus fernandi.* Proctodaeal region of embryo in sagittal
section showing the posterior fusion of the serosa with the tubule to form a
nutrient organ. (After Fernando, Quarterly Journal of Microscopical Science,
77:99–119. 1934.)

sends out delicate cytoplasmic processes which fuse with the latter, much as the membranes of *Hemimerus* adhere to the follicular cells surrounding them. Adhesion to the ovariole is more pronounced in the posterior and anterior polar regions of the egg. Immediately behind the proctodaeum the wall of the ovariole, the serosa and the posterior nutrient portion of the egg fuse so firmly that they appear as a common vacuolated, granular, protoplasmic mass into which embryonic entodermal cells freely migrate (Fig. 136). A similar condition obtains in front of the brain where the attachment involves the ovariole and the serosa but the amnion, which is also present, retains its typical thin aspect. In spite of this a stainable substance believed to be nutrient in nature, accumulates within the amniotic cavity directly beneath this point. With the destruction of the embryonic membranes the serosa no longer functions as a nutrient organ.

Katatrepsis.—About the time the anterior and posterior entodermal vesicles form, the embryonic membranes are ruptured as the embryo undergoes revolution. Before the mid-intestine is completely developed the lateral walls of the ectoderm have grown dorsally and fused, completing the body form.

The Dorsal Organ.—After revolution, the embryo lies in the oviduct unprotected by an egg chorion or other covering. At this time a dorsal organ appears whose function is unknown but it recalls to mind a somewhat similar structure that develops in the embryo of *Isotoma* (Philiptschenko, 1912).

It first presents a reticular cytoplasmic appearance with deeply staining material in its vacuoles and a few scattered trophocytes, while entodermal cells may be present in peripheral positions. It occupies the space adjoining the brain and extends from the anterior entodermal vesicle to the dorsal ectoderm. A little later the constituent nuclei become more numerous and there is an increase in the number of trophocytes and entodermal cells, the latter congregating in the dorsal and ventral peripheries. A local area of ectodermal cells over the central portion of the dorsal organ then invaginates as a fold into the organ, while the adjacent cells of the reticular area arrange themselves in a uniform layer along its inner margins. All cells in the dorsal organ now look very much alike so that entoderm cells and trophocytes can no longer be traced in their migrations.

Invagination is followed by a complete degeneration of the ectodermal cells concerned and the regularly arranged cells of the

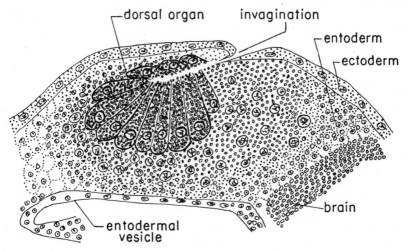

Fig. 137.—*Archipsocus fernandi*. Ectodermal invagination forming the dorsal organ, sagittal section. (After Fernando, Quarterly Journal of Microscopical Science, 77:99–119. 1934.)

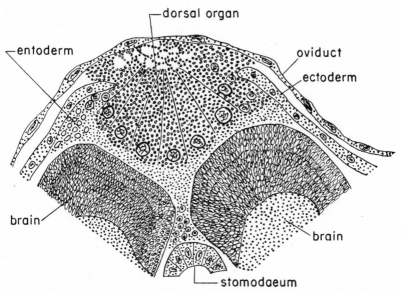

Fig. 138.—*Archipsocus fernandi*. Transverse section of dorsal organ with the contents passing outward through the aperture to lie in contact with the wall of the oviduct. (After Fernando, Quarterly Journal of Microscopical Science, 77:99–119. 1934.)

dorsal organ beneath are thereby exposed to the lumen of the invagination along their upper surfaces. Such cells elongate and become very large and columnar in shape, with basally situated nuclei (Fig. 137). These changes are followed by a partial evagination of the dorsal organ so that the everted tips of the columnar cells come in contact with the wall of the oviduct. The tall columnar cells are densely granular and their external ends highly vacuolated where they touch the oviduct (Fig. 138). Shortly after this stage is attained the ectoderm becomes a hypodermis and secretes a cuticula which severs all connection between the embryonic tissues and the maternal, including the area over the dorsal organ. The latter is finally enclosed within the mid-intestine and digested. The embryo meanwhile passes down the oviduct and, in due time, is born.

LITERATURE CITED

Fernando (1934), Jentsch (1936), Philiptschenko (1912), Snodgrass (1935).

Pseudoplacental Hemiptera

Order Hemiptera   Family Aphididae

Investigators certainly have worked longer over the embryology of the aphids than over that of any other viviparous insect. Nevertheless, the desired details of any one species are not yet available, nor do they equal the data accumulated for the oviparous honeybee and, perhaps, one or two other species. Some of the investigations made, however, are doubly valuable in that they are largely comparative.

It is possible that the serosa is mildly trophic throughout its existence, although no one has mentioned this function. The serosa eventually becomes a thin membrane intervening between the embryo and the follicular epithelium of the ovariole. The present evidence seems to point toward an initial supply of yolk in the young oöcyte, further increase with symbiont invasion, and the probable trophic function of the serosa. There is no chorion. The follicular epithelium encompasses the embryo throughout its development in the ovariole and is discarded in the posterior end of the genital duct at birth.

When Leeuwenhoek (1695), with his catholic taste in microscopic observation, decided to view the reproductive system of aphids through a lens he suddenly and unexpectedly opened a field of investigation, speculation, and controversy entirely new to entomologists. Instead of the eggs he sought, he found about fifty or sixty embryos in various stages of development. Rearing young aphids, he observed that they molted three or four times and, within less than two weeks from birth, began producing offspring without previously mating with males. At least he could find none of this sex in his colonies and concluded that the viviparous females must be hermaphroditic.

Some time elapsed before entomologists returned to this subject when Réaumur (1737) began experimenting with the agamic form. He dissected specimens, found developing embryos, and obtained offspring from viviparous females, thus confirming Leeuwenhoek's earlier observations. For some time he, too, thought the insect must be hermaphroditic.

Other matters then claimed Réaumur's attention and his student, Bonnet (1743, 1745, 1779), was encouraged to continue the work. The information most sought at this stage was whether the insect actually produced young without prior mating with a male. To ascertain this point Bonnet carefully isolated several young offspring at birth and, when they reached the reproductive period, observed and recorded the members of the new generation as they appeared. From one individual thus tabulated 95 descendants were counted. Bonnet conducted further tests and followed isolated females through several successive generations. In the fall he observed the presence of males and females, their mating, and the deposition of eggs.

Bonnet never definitely accepted Leeuwenhoek's view regarding the possible hermaphroditic condition of the female aphid. Trembly (1776) also had suggested to him the concept that the stimulus given to the fertilized winter egg of the aphid might prolong its influence throughout the summer generations, but to this suggestion Bonnet seems not to have committed himself. He saw no real difference between the agamic and the amphigonous egg. To account for their different products he assumed that in the former the embryo was supplied with ample food by the mother which enabled the offspring to complete its entire development at once. The oviparous form, on the contrary, he thought lacked sufficient food and depended upon the increment received through the process of fertilization to make up the deficiency. Bonnet's work received its wide acclaim and acceptance largely through the kindly support of Réaumur (1741). Bonnet, however, is clearly entitled to the position he held in biology during his life by virtue of his labors in both the applied and theoretical fields of biology. While we are interested in him primarily as the discoverer of parthenogenesis it is quite probable that his observations on the production of successive generations of aphids added materially to his preformation, or incapsulation, theory.

Since Bonnet's tests others also have attempted to rear parthenogenetic series of aphids. Some simply wished to confirm his results, others with different objectives used the subsequent generations for material in their studies. It will be sufficient to mention only a few such examples. Reyger (1754) reared two generations in order to observe molting and similar data; de Geer (1771) tried to discover whether viviparous females occasionally became oviparous; Kyber (1815) wanted to test the influence of temperature and the host plant on viviparous reproduction; Duvau (1825) obtained eleven successive generations in one summer to confirm preceding work; Comstock (1925, p. 417) reported 98 successive agamic generations; Baker and Turner (1916a, 1916b), Ewing (1916), and Uichanco (1921) reared them in the progress of other experiments. Ewing, incidentally, succeeded in obtaining 87 such generations in his interesting statistical study of the influence of heredity and environment in pure lines.

It will be quite impossible to evaluate justly and fully the numerous contributors to new speculations on agamic reproduction, for the literature is voluminous. Reference to such details may be had by consulting Duvau (1825), Burnett (1853), Huxley (1859), Lubbock (1859, 1867), Balbiani (1869), Leuckart (1874), Buckton (1876), Brass (1882), Will (1883, 1888), Uichanco (1924), although this list is only partially complete. Shorter reviews are to be found in other papers, some of which are to be cited in the following discussion.

Leeuwenhoek's discovery, followed a few years later by Bonnet's verification of it and evidence of the occurrence of reproduction in agamic aphids without the intervention of males, aroused endless discussion at first as to the accuracy of the observations and, later, speculations as to the exact scientific significance of the reproductive act in these insects. Mating and fertilization of the eggs were not understood at the time but these events were recognized as essential parts of sexual reproduction and the eggs of insects were believed to require the stimulus of a "spermatic force" in all cases. At this time, too, students in other zoological fields were just beginning to recognize asexual forms of reproduction in aquatic invertebrates and to appreciate the remarkable powers some of them possess in the regeneration of lost parts. Metagenesis was a new and little explored concept. Steenstrup (1842) had no hesitation to include at once the aphids among his examples of species exhibiting an alternation of generations. Thus, unfortunately and erroneously, this term was introduced into entomological literature, where its replacement by the more accurate "heterogeny" has been discouragingly slow.

To understand anything at all about aphid reproduction from a study of the internal factors involved it has been essential to employ various optical instruments and technical histological processes. These things were largely lacking when aphid reproduction was injected into scientific thought during the years following Bonnet's time. Only simple lenses, used singly or in rude combination, plus infinite patience and considerable skill in dissection brought any answers to the applicability of the theories of metagenesis, parthenogenesis, and embryological sequence to the aphids. The aphid problem appeared on the scientific horizon long before the implements of science were ready to assist in its solution.

The ensuing work on aphids evolved along several divergent lines of thought. These we may well consider in turn without special reference to their chronological order. Some sought to discover whether either the viviparous or oviparous forms could revert to the other method of reproduction. Experimental tests and observations were conducted to determine this fact by de Geer (1771, Vol. 3) who, incidentally, correctly predicted that tropical species would be found with no oviparous forms. Other investigators were Kyber (1815), Bouché (1844), Kaltenbach (1844), Ratzeburg (1844), Morren (1836), Newport (1846), Von Heyden (1857), and Johnson (1900), who found viviparous reproduction to be prolonged into winter. Intermediates have more recently been studied by Turner and Baker (1915), Baker and Turner (1916a, 1916b), and Shull (1933).

Since it was assumed by earlier workers on aphids, in harmony with contemporary opinion, that fertilization was a necessary preliminary to the production of offspring various suppositions attempted to account for the fertility of the agamic female. One assumption was the hermaphroditic condition of this form. Among those who supported this view were Leeuwenhoek (1695), Réaumur, who for a time believed this to be true but eventually abandoned the idea, and Sales-Girons (1875). Balbiani (1866, 1869) was the strongest advocate of the hermaphroditic condition of agamic aphids and made much of his work emphasize and support this view. He had a strong opponent in Claparède (1867).

Upon the appearance of Steenstrup's (1842) work on the alternation of generations, with the inclusion of the aphids as one example of this phenomenon, many seized this explanation eagerly and avidly engaged in controversies with opponents. Steenstrup found the young of viviparous females developing in organs which he admitted might be regarded as parts of a reproductive system. In spite of this he assigned to the agamic form the asexual or budding method of reproduction in which the mother became only a nurse or protector of the offspring. Those who took this viewpoint were Kyber (1815), Dufour (1833), who held the opinion that offspring arose spontaneously, which might be classed as a form of asexual reproduction, Morren (1836), who also accepted Dufour's belief in modified form, Carus (1849), Burnett (1853), Radlkofer (1858), and Lichtenstein (1878).

Long before the controversy sustained by the authors just mentioned was found to be useless in solving the problem of aphid reproduction, certain observed anatomical facts had already shown the necessity of breaking away from the idea of metagenesis in aphids. It became apparent that no males were instrumental in fecundating certain reproductive elements. Further, an increasingly large number of reputable anatomists were convinced that the eggs of agamic forms were entirely comparable to the ova of the gamic generation except for the relative amount of yolk present and the absence of fertilization. The belief arose, then, in the influence of a spermatic force which resulted from the fertilization of the winter egg and which persisted in the females of the viviparous summer generations. Some claimed this activating influence was passed on for a limited number of generations, when fertilization again became necessary; others felt the number of generations so influenced was quite indefinite and that cold weather was the primary agency in the reappearance of the males and females of the oviparous generation. Adherents to this hypothesis were Kirby and Spence (1828), Dutrochet (1833), Plieninger (1849), and Burnett (1850, 1853).

Owen (1849, 1854) thought fertilization of the egg caused it to split into germinative elements. From a portion of them the embryo is developed while the remaining elements were retained in its reproductive system. The unused elements were later active in forming the offspring of each succeeding generation. This has been termed a restricted form of the preformation theory.

Still others, with more foresight, realized the necessity for detailed anatomical studies of the reproductive organs and the early steps in the formation of offspring if some of these arguments and conflicting views were to be based on fact. This class of investigator included all those who earnestly sought some knowledge from direct observation with the aid of the best available technique and accessories. They include Von Siebold (1839), who first recorded the absence of colleterial glands and functional spermathecae, Newport (1846), whose careful dissection disproved the statement that the overwintering egg contained an encapsulated, agamic insect, Von Baer (1828), Leuckart (1858), Leydig (1848, 1850), Claus (1858, 1864), Metschnikoff (1866a, 1866b), Balbiani (1869 *et seq.*), and Lemoine (1892, 1893).

Even after several accounts of the reproductive system and its germinal elements had appeared, not everyone believed that the development was truly sexual. With this reservation in mind, yet recognizing the similarities between gamic and agamic elements, Huxley (1859) refused to consider the ova of viviparous forms as true eggs and applied the term "pseudovum" to indicate the distinction he thought existed. Of course, he recognized the parthenogenetic condition of the egg. Lubbock (1859, 1867), Metschnikoff (1866), Buckton (1876), and Zacharias (1884), among others, agreed with him.

In the meantime the discriminating work of Leydig (1850), Von Siebold (1839, 1856, 1862, 1871), and Leuckart (1851, 1858, 1859, 1874, etc.) convinced the embryologists that another type of egg may exist in insects, one requiring no fertilization. Owen (1849) had already coined the term parthenogenesis with somewhat different meaning but Von Siebold (1856) gave it a new connotation by using it to designate the development of the unfertilized egg. Many examples of parthenogenetic development were found in insects and other animals within a short time, and the phenomenon was universally accepted on this basis. Henneguy (1899) summarized the methods of reproduction in insects shortly afterwards. For further elaboration of the historical side of parthenogenesis one may consult Lankester (1872, 1919), Phillips (1903), and Taschenberg (1892).

Yet another concept entered into the problems of aphid agamic reproduction in more recent years. This was the paedogenetic development of offspring. Even the first investigators had observed well formed offspring in females only a few days old and Leuckart (1858) made special efforts to distinguish gamic from agamic females by seeking differences in the reproductive elements of very young individuals. He found that the viviparous members, while still immature, possessed offspring in various stages of formation, while the gamic individuals contained only eggs. Later, the agamic females came to be referred to as paedogenetic, a term that had come into entomological literature through a consideration of reproduction in other species. Here again Steenstrup's (1842) views served to have an important but unfortunate influence. Following his publication the idea arose that embryologists did not consider the agamic form mature and occasionally in recent literature are found opinions differing on this question. Frequently the oviparous form only is referred to as sexual, thus inferring that viviparous reproduction is asexual. But the physical maturity or immaturity of the viviparous reproductive female is not the point emphasized by the embryologist. He merely asserts that the earliest formed offspring of an agamic female begin their development long before the mother is mature; in fact a number of her own offspring commence development before she is born. In this sense she is paedogenetic as well as viviparous, although her later offspring may not be derived from paedogenetic products at all. Thus Korschelt and Heider (1899, p. 388) and others speak of paedogenesis in aphids. Uichanco (1924) has very clearly and fully developed this fact.

These investigators heretofore mentioned, whose interests and activities in the study of aphids have been the cause of most of the wider application of the numerous theories and speculations just outlined are, in the main, not those to whom we look as the contributors to a knowledge of the aphid embryo and its prenatal development. However, some of the broader aspects of their influence along various lines seemed necessary and pertinent here, as an introduction to the work of those yet to be considered. Reference may now be made to those who have contributed most directly to an understanding of the embryogeny of the viviparously formed aphid.

Metschnikoff (1866a, 1866b) published brief accounts of the primary and secondary yolk and their fate in aphid embryology. The first paper appeared just before Balbiani's (1866) article. The two men differed fundamentally in two essential details: the significance of the secondary vitellus, and the hermaphroditic or parthenogenetic nature of the egg. Metschnikoff's second paper gives a more detailed account of the embryology of the aphid.

Balbiani (1869) began a series of excellent papers on aphid embryology which was more comprehensive in its treatment than that of any predecessor. In it he treated the oviparous and viviparous forms separately. Faulty interpretations of the nature and significance of some of the structures observed have led him to such erroneous conclusions that much of his work cannot be classed as an entirely constructive contribution to the subject. Brass (1882) reviewed the work of his predecessors and studied the early embryology of the agamic aphid, in which he mentioned for the first time the revolution of the embryo.

Will (1883, 1887, 1888) enlarged our knowledge of aphid embryology, especially in his last paper primarily on *Aphis pelargonii,* because he was then able to employ the paraffin section method, an advantage denied earlier workers. Witlaczil (1882, 1884) with observations chiefly on *Aphis platanoides,* Hirschler (1911, 1912) working with *Rhopalosiphum,* Uichanco (1924), and Tóth (1933, 1935) are other workers in this field. Uichanco's paper on *Macrosiphum tanaceti,* with supplementary observations of more than fifteen other species, contains an excellent historical and developmental account of the mycetom in relation to embryonic and postnatal growth. Tóth, the most recent contributor, in his studies on almost thirty species discusses especially the structure of the ovary, maturation, and the embryogeny of the embryo, including the blastoderm stage. About half of this paper treats in detail the morphology of the symbionts and their invasion of the mycetoblasts. His valuable contribution is intermediate in scope between the morphological embryologists on the one hand and cytologists on the other. Among these latter investigators may be mentioned Schleip (1909), Stschelkanovzew (1904), Stevens (1905), Tannreuther (1907), and de Baehr (1910, 1920, etc.).

More theoretical controversy and unsound arguments have centered about the method of reproduction in the viviparous aphids and the development of their progeny than have been directed toward any other insect embryology. Yet it is a peculiar fact that in spite of the intense interest aroused in the subject the various contributors have far from completely described the embryogeny, and no comprehensive work has appeared which provides an adequate account of any one species of viviparous aphid embryo, and clarifies the points over which the earlier investigators have so thoroughly disagreed. Extensive comparative studies of different species would be of great value to both the taxonomist and the morphologist.

Before entering upon a description of the structures and functions of the viviparous female aphid it might be well to digress for a moment in order to make clear the limitations of the subject pertinent to our interests here. All of the aphids, whose embryology will be summarized presently, offer the same general type of life history, containing oviparous as well as viviparous generations. It will be recalled, from accounts of the life histories of aphids, that the overwintering eggs from the oviparous generation give rise in the spring to viviparous females which produce living offspring, not eggs similar to those from which they developed. As a rule, viviparous generations of females succeed one another throughout the summer. In the fall, however, a generation appears from viviparous mothers that contains both males and oviparous females. These mate and the females deposit the overwintering eggs. Only the first spring generation has developed from fertilized eggs and all of its embryogeny occurs outside of the mother from which it was derived. The members of this generation, therefore, are oviparously produced but they may be referred to as viviparous females because their offspring will be retained within the body until after the egg stage of their ontogeny is passed and they appear as nymphs. So far as is known, all viviparous females produce their offspring from parthenogenetic eggs. The last fall generation produced from viviparous females with parthenogenetic ova are not viviparous, but oviparous, since they deposit the fertilized overwintering eggs. This point has been stressed here because much confusion has arisen in the literature by speaking of viviparous offspring when the viviparous condition of the mother is really meant. The offspring, born viviparously, sometimes are oviparous in functional behavior and certainly are not to be classified as viviparous offspring in such cases.

Since the overwintering fertilized egg develops its product outside the maternal body while the viviparous female gives birth only to nymphs whose early ontogeny occurred within the mother, one should not be surprised to find considerable differences in the conditions surrounding the two embryogenies. The following description will be confined to the viviparous female and her reproductive element, the parthenogenetic egg.

Female Reproductive System

The Ovary.—The ovaries are paired and each consists of a few ovarioles (often six) grouped at the end of one of the paired oviducts. The paired oviducts are short and connect posteriorly with the vagina, or common oviduct. The ovarioles are peculiar and Uichanco (1924) describes them as consisting essentially of thin, noncellular investing membranes to be mentioned in the following paragraph. Each ovariole consists of the typical subdivisions: terminal filament, germarium, and vitellarium. The first is a thin, threadlike extension of the membrane which serves to attach the ovariole to the dorsal diaphragm near the posterior margin of the metathorax. Its base is thickened and abruptly widened to surround the large pyriform or globular area known as the germarium. At the posterior termination of the germarium the ovariole becomes a narrow tube of considerable length, the vitellarium, which finally joins the paired oviduct in the immediate vicinity of its neighboring ovarioles.

The terminal filament contains a central mass of minute granules of unknown origin. A single layer of very thin epithelium in the germarium, probably of maternal mesodermal origin, intervenes anteriorly and laterally between the external membrane and a central mass consisting of a few large cells whose appearance and functions will be described later. The epithelium is many-layered posteriorly, and entirely occludes the passage into the vitellarium. The cells are larger than elsewhere in the epithelium of the ovariole and, according to Uichanco, constitute the formative egg follicle, for from them the egg follicle is derived. The vitellarium has no epithelium of its own but its lumen contains ova and their attendant follicular cells at a very early stage in its history.

The Paired Oviducts and Vagina.—The short paired oviducts have a sparse external musculature which surrounds the internal epithelium. The latter is formed of flat subpolygonal cells with highly vacuolated cytoplasm. The nuclei are large and spherical in shape. The muscles of the vagina are much more numerous than those of the paired oviducts and are particularly abundant near its external opening. Immediately beneath this layer is the basement membrane. The next layer is epithelial in nature and presents an irregular internal surface due to the varying heights of its constituent cells. The latter tend to be columnar in shape and their cytoplasm, like that of the paired oviducts, is highly vacuolated. The nuclei are large, spherical or ellipsoidal and contain distinct nucleoli. This layer also is much thicker in the posterior portion of the vagina. The cells of the vagina secrete a thin but distinct cuticula which is absent from other portions of the system.

Paedogenesis.—The viviparous aphid is extremely precocious in the process of ovulation, one or two eggs being liberated from each germarium of its ovaries before it is born, as Metschnikoff (1866b), and Witlaczil (1884) observed. Ovulation continues throughout the nymphal stages and for some time after physical maturity is attained. In fact Uichanco (1924), who has so carefully worked out this schedule for *M. tanaceti,* asserts that approximately 75 per cent of all the ova liberated by the viviparous female are discharged from the germarium during the course of her embryonic and nymphal stages. Thus, about 81 ova, varying from freshly extruded eggs through a series showing different stages of embryonic development to fully formed embryos, may be found in the vitellaria before the mother is a physically mature individual. Presumably 27 or 28 ova are liberated during her adult life, making a possible total of approximately 108 offspring.

Shortly after the adult stage is reached by a female her own young begin to appear. Because many of these offspring initiate their embryonic development before their mother reaches maturity, Uichanco insists she is a paedogenetic insect, irrespective of her ontogenetic stage when the young are born. His work certainly clarifies the position of the embryologist who speaks of paedogenesis in aphids, as previously mentioned in the introductory historical section of the aphid discussion.

Development of the Embryo

Ovulation.—In describing the structure of the ovariole, attention was called to a few large cells which filled the center of the germarium, but discussion of them was deferred since they are more intimately concerned with reproduction than with the structural composition of this organ. It is now necessary to consider the structure and function of these large cells. Each of them in a very young ovariole is large, polygonal in shape, with finely granular unvacuolated cytoplasm. The nucleus is almost spheri-

cal and a nuclear membrane is clearly discernible. A poorly staining nucleolus and a few chromatin granules are distributed in the
nucleoplasm. No one seems to dissent from the view that these
cells are germ cells, alike in size, shape, and structure. However,
with the further enlargement of the cells some differences between them are discernible. Those in the anterior portion of the

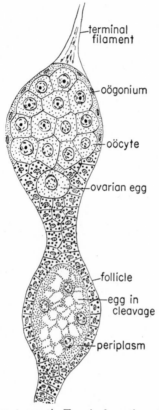

FIG. 139.—*Macrosiphum tanaceti*. Terminal portion of an ovariole from first
instar nymph showing germarium, an extruded egg and a developing embryo in a
follicle. (Modified from Uichanco, 1924. Courtesy of the Institute of Science,
formerly Bureau of Science.)

germarium now show a more distinct nucleolus, and a large
amount of highly vacuolated cytoplasm surrounds each nucleus.
According to Uichanco (1924), those situated most posteriorly
possess little cytoplasm and this shows only slight vacuolization.
In addition, the nucleolus does not appear and the chromatic
material has migrated centrally, where it lies as an irregularly
shaped mass of darkly staining, elongate objects (Figs. 139, 140*B*).

The nucleoplasm between the chromatin and the nuclear membrane is clear.

According to this author, these changes in the cells seem to have come about largely as a result of their chance position within the germarium rather than from any alteration of their functional potentiality. All are oögonia and capable of becoming parthenogenetic ova if given the opportunity. It is thought the posterior cells look different simply because they are in an early stage of nuclear division. This explanation merely confirms the views earlier expressed by Witlaczil (1884), Stevens (1905), and Mordwilko (1907). According to this concept, nurse cells would be lacking although Uichanco believes the unused and undifferentiated oögonia at the anterior end of the germarium may assist in passing nutriment to the lower oöcytes and young ova.

Others, as Will (1883, 1888b), Tannreuther (1907), Hirschler (1924), Tóth (1933), and de Baehr (1910, 1920) assert that the anterior cells have lost all developmental potentiality and are nurse cells assigned exclusively to the elaboration of nutriment for the most posterior, and less numerous, oöcytes. Tóth is unable to discover cellular boundaries between these anterior cells. Also, contrary to those who perceive no functional differences between the cells, these writers describe a nutrient cord which extends from the nurse cells down to the young oöcyte which has just been expelled from the germarium into the vitellarium (Fig. 140). Paspaleff (1929) shows the same structure in two of his figures. This structure supplies nutriment to the ripening reproductive cell from the nurse cells and would account for the rapid growth in size of the young egg as it is being expelled from the germarium. Its presence is generally accepted for the ovaries of amphigonous aphids but, apparently, has not always been demonstrated in parthenogenetic forms. One is at a loss, at present, to account for the persistence of two conflicting views on this subject, and it remains a problem for future students to settle. Whatever the facts may be, only the posterior cells function as ova.

During ovulation it is assumed that each ovariole liberates an oöcyte in turn. Thus, if there are twelve ovarioles in the individual, one ovariole would extrude oöcytes 1, 13, etc., another would discharge oöcytes 2, 14, etc., and so on. As each oöcyte migrates out of the germarium into the vitellarium of its ovariole it becomes surrounded by an investment of follicular cells subtracted from those already described as forming a large mass between these two divisions of the ovariole. A number of follicular cells also follow after each oöcyte which causes a distinct spacing of the young ova from one another. This process proceeds sufficiently slowly for the oöcyte to accumulate a supply of nutriment so that when finally discharged it is several times as large as it was in the germarium. All embryonic development takes place in the vitellarium of the ovariole.

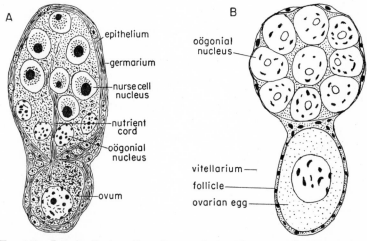

FIG. 140.—Longitudinal section of germarium with nurse cells, germ cells and ovarian egg. A, *Byrscrypta gallarum.* Nutrient cord supplies material to ovum. (After Tóth, 1933.) B, *Macrosiphum tanaceti.* Same figure from second instar nymph. (After Uichanco, 1924. Courtesy of the Institute of Science, formerly Bureau of Science.)

Cleavage.—The oöcyte, or young egg, requires no fertilization since it is parthenogenetic. The first step necessary is the completion of the single maturation division which Blochmann (1887) discovered. According to Tóth (1933) the spindle may be formed anywhere in the egg but always arises in a position perpendicular to the surface and extends into the superficial periplasmic layer. There are no visible centrioles or astral rays in the mitotic figure. The polar body is difficult to demonstrate and deteriorates within a short time. After maturation, the egg nucleus migrates to a more central position, where it is surrounded by a small amount of cytoplasm with its reticular extensions reaching to the periplasm, the latter being very irregular in thickness over the egg. The reticulations enclose most of the nutrient substance stored in the egg, but attention should here be directed to its relative scarcity; the egg is yolk poor. After maturation the oöcyte is a mature ovum. The follicular epithelium secretes no chorion and the ovum remains without this structure throughout embryonic development.

After a short interphase, during which added increments of nutrient substances cause the egg to enlarge still further, the first nuclear cleavage occurs. The cleavage spindle is much larger than in the maturation division and astral rays are present although the centrioles are not evident. The spindle lies in an

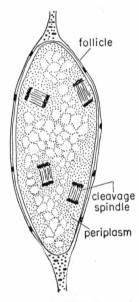

Fig. 141.—*Macrosiphum tanaceti*. Metaphase of the third cleavage stage in blastoderm formation. One nucleus was subcentrally situated at interphase. Vestiges of matrix of egg follicles anteriorly and posteriorly to follicle shown. (After Uichanco, 1924. Courtesy of the Institute of Science, formerly Bureau of Science.)

anteroposterior direction, according to Uichanco, but Hirschler (1912) and Tóth find it bears no relation to the egg poles or the polar body in their species. The daughter nuclei, on opposite sides of the egg, form close to, or in contact with, the periplasm and are quickly drawn well within this superficial layer of cytoplasm, leaving the reticulated portion with its enmeshed nutriment occupying the entire central portion of the egg.

The nuclear divisions immediately following are synchronous, but not all observers agree as to the length of time this harmony lasts, nor as to the positions taken by the daughter nuclei. Tóth insists that simultaneous cleavage occurs at least till the end of the fifth or sixth division. As to the position taken by the earlier cleavage spindles, Hirschler (1912) and Uichanco (1924) noticed occasional spindles that were not parallel to the surface, hence one daughter nucleus in such cases was to be found nearer the inner portion of the egg (Figs. 139, 141). According to the former, yolk nuclei may be derived in part from these lagging nuclei in some eggs. Will (1888) and Tóth (1933) are positive that all the cleavage nuclei migrate into the periplasm, where the spindles lie parallel to the surface until later divisions. Uichanco takes the position that all cleavage nuclei are potential blastomeres and only chance placement or migration within the egg causes some to become yolk nuclei. Most writers seem to agree that the yolk nuclei arise from the ental migration of nuclei from the periplasm and that they do not originate from nuclei which lag behind in the yolk during cleavage. This point seems unessential except in so far as it may have a bearing on the origin of the vitellophags.

The yolk nuclei whose origin has just been described, while presumably homologous to the vitellophags of other insect eggs, have a different future before them. Uichanco has applied the term *mycetoblasts* to them, for he believes they ultimately become the elements of the mycetom. Tóth's viewpoint is presented later.

The Mycetoblasts and Symbiont Invasion.—After the second cleavage stage, the follicular epithelium separates slightly from the egg except at the posterior pole. Here the periplasm of the egg becomes progressively thinner as cleavage continues until it finally disappears completely and reserve nutrient material reaches the surface of the egg, where the latter comes in contact with the adjacent follicular mass of cells (Figs. 142, 143). Thus the egg is open at this point and forms the blastopore, though it should be emphasized that this structure is not to be confused with a true blastopore. The symbiotic organisms, apparently already present in the follicular cells, immediately commence to migrate into the end of the egg in the vicinity of the mycetoblasts, which are now found near the posterior pole. Their migration ceases after they have entered the reticulated yolk. The adjacent follicular cells have become very large and swollen at this time, probably because of great influx and multiplication of the symbionts. Perhaps the mass of follicular epithelium which forms a plug of cells spacing each egg from its predecessor is the reservoir supplying the symbionts to the egg follicle cells at the posterior end of the egg in the vicinity of the blastopore (Uichanco).

Tóth disagrees with the preceding outline of the origin of the mycetoblasts. Infection by symbionts apparently comes later than Uichanco believes. After the seventh cleavage has occurred he has found from six to eight very large nuclei in the periplasm

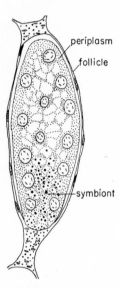

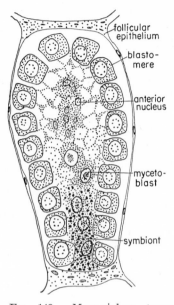

Fig. 142. — *Macrosiphum tanaceti.* Early stage of blastoderm formation with cleavage nuclei entering periplasm. Symbionts represented by coarse stippling at posterior pole of egg. Longitudinal section. (After Uichanco, 1924.)

Fig. 143. — *Macrosiphum tanaceti.* Differentiation of the blastomeres in the egg. Invading symbionts represented within the blastopore by coarse stippling. Longitudinal section. (Modified from Uichanco, 1924.)

(Courtesy of the Institute of Science, formerly Bureau of Science.)

near the posterior egg pole (Fig. 144). These are distinctly different from other nuclei not only in size but also because of their dense plasm and the presence of plasmatic chromatin derived from a diminution of this material in the nuclei. These large, characteristic cells are primitive mycetoblasts. The blastoporal opening may already be present, or blastomeric nuclei and periplasm may extend entirely over the egg surface; thus, either an open or a closed blastoderm may be formed [Hirschler (1912), Tóth (1933)]. In the latter case a secondary shifting of these nuclei and thinning of the periplasm eventually enable the mycetoblasts to reach the surface at the posterior pole. Symbiont invasion occurs through a similar opening which has meanwhile developed in the egg follicle opposite the blastopore, hence symbionts are not obtained from the follicle cells but directly by free, active migration from the maternal mycetocytes. Just how this takes place is not known, but several hypotheses have been offered by different investigators. Eventually, successive mitoses fill the periplasm with nuclei and the few large mycetoblast nuclei migrate to the center of the egg to form the mycetoblast cells of the future mycetom.

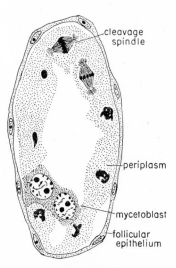

FIG. 144. — *Aphis sambuci.* Seventh cleavage in blastoderm formation with mycetoblasts and degenerating polar body. Compare with Fig. 143. (After Tóth, 1933.)

Uichanco has observed the further derivation of a few smaller nuclei at the anterior end of the egg which migrate into the anterior central part (Fig. 145). These, he surmises, finally invest the mycetoblasts to form an epithelial sheath over the mycetom, a view subsequently confirmed by Tóth.

The Blastoderm. — Blastomeres are formed by the simultaneous contraction of the periplasm in the immediate vicinity of each nucleus and thus nucleated cells suddenly cover the egg except at the posterior pole, where approximately one fourth of the surface remains open (Fig. 146a).

Cell multiplication causes the blastoderm to become multilaminar in the anterior region but posteriorly it results in blastoderm extension toward the tip of the egg (Figs. 143, 145). At the same time the mycetoblasts, with their reticulate syncytial cytoplasm, enmeshed yolk, and symbionts aggregate into an ovate mass—the formative mycetom which is gradually enclosed laterally by the posterior extension of the blastoderm. In this way the blastopore is very much constricted in diameter and only a comparatively narrow opening now permits further contact between the formative mycetom and the follicular epithelium.

Considerable space has been devoted to the early embryonic activity within the egg because of the differences of opinion which have prevailed regarding the points presented. Yet several opinions were omitted which, however valuable in themselves, must reluctantly be left for those who are especially interested in the details of aphid embryology to seek in the litera-ture. Perhaps much of the contradictory evidence in the early embryogeny is the result of the selection of different species of aphids by the various investigators. There is need for much more exhaustive work on any single species in this group as well as a very wide field in painstaking comparative studies.

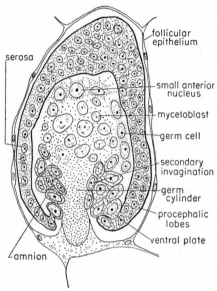

Fig. 145.—*Macrosiphum tanaceti.* Egg showing differentiation of the ventral plate, procephalic lobes and the segregation of germ cells. Symbionts represented by coarse stippling except in syncytial cytoplasm around the three anterior nuclei. The thickened blastoderm at anterior end will be part of the serosa. Longitudinal section. (Modified from Uichanco, 1924. Courtesy of the Institute of Science, formerly Bureau of Science.)

Formation of the Germ Cylinder and the Embryonic Rudiment.—The egg is now covered with a blastoderm except for the blastopore at the posterior end. The next process is the formation of the definitive rudiment of the embryo and the organization of the embryonic envelopes (Figs. 143, 145). The constriction of the blastoporal opening presumably came about through a multiplication of cells posteriorly, together with some redistribution of those already in the blastoderm. The cephalic lobes arise by a thickening of the blastodermal cells on one side of the egg in a narrow region extending forward a little ways from the lip of the blastopore (Fig. 145). The thoracic and abdominal areas have not yet formed but appear later in posterior sequence in a manner somewhat modified from the more familiar insectan type, because of the presence of the blastopore and the formative mycetom.

As cell multiplication continues around the lip of the blastopore the new cells turn in toward the center of the egg, thus forming a cylinder of cells around the yolk mass with the enclosed symbionts constituting the posterior part of the formative mycetom (Fig. 146b). Continued anterior growth of the germ cylinder pushes before it the mycetoblasts and the major part of the associated yolk with its symbionts, though the central cavity of the cylinder is at all times filled with the posterior end of this structure (Fig. 145).

Upon reaching a point in the interior about one fourth or one third of the total length of the egg the open interior, or anterior, margin of proliferating cells of the germ cylinder no longer extends the cylinder forward. Instead, they turn in toward the lumen of the cylinder between its unilaminar wall and the contained yolk of the mycetom. Further extension of the tube is now in a reflexed posterior direction until the inner layer of cells reaches approximately the posterior end of the egg. The cylinder now consists of two layers of cells, confluent at their inner fold. The outermost is the original cylinder wall projecting inwards one third or less of the length of the egg, where it folds over and forms an inner second layer extending to the posterior end of the egg. Figure 146c shows this in schematic form. When the innermost layer of cells lining the cylinder reaches the posterior end of the egg this posterior, distal margin of the tube fuses and closes the end of the egg. Thus, no further invasion of the yolk by maternal symbionts can take place (Fig. 146d).

As the procephalic lobes appear, organization of the more posterior portion of the embryo, the ventral plate, proceeds in a portion of the germ cylinder immediately behind them. This is a continuous process and the independent origin of two separate embryonic centers which later fuse, as described by Will (1888), does not take place. The ventral plate extends from the procephalic lobes as a thickened portion of one side of the germ cylinder to its inner, or anterior end (Fig. 146c-g). The rest of the cells in the cylinder, including the reflexed portion, probably undergo no more mitoses, but the cells in the ventral plate do, especially near the inner end. The elongation of the posterior end of the plate thus steadily proceeds and the formative myceton

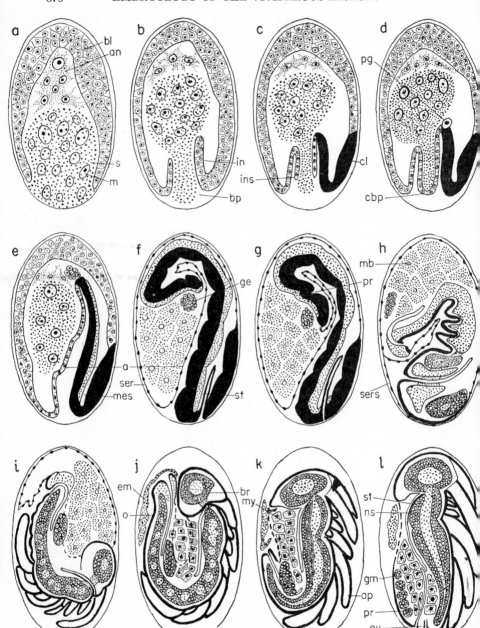

FIG. 146.—Diagrammatic representation of germ band formation and blastokinesis in aphids, based primarily on descriptions and illustrations by Will, Witlaczil, and Uichanco. Sagittal sections with anterior end of the egg uppermost, ventral side to the right; inner follicular cell membranes shown as the outer oval

is pushed aside in the process. The walls of the cylinder are pulled along with the further growth of the ventral plate since it remains attached where it formerly folded over the inner rim of the anterior end of the cylinder. The latter's reflexed portion is thereby gradually pulled into the interior of the egg.

As the ventral plate continues to grow in length, it reaches the thickened anterior blastoderm, thence bends posteriorly as shown in Figure 146*f*, *g*, and finally flexes entally at right angles to elongate slightly and form the telson. The telson is often crowded laterally in the egg by the mycetom so that it does not lie in a median plane. Tóth has recorded some departure from this outline of the formation of the embryonic rudiment and the invasion of the symbionts in certain species of aphids. In this he agrees with the observations of Klevenhusen (1927) if not in the latter's interpretation of them. The details are not considered essential here since the end result is the same, with the formative mycetom and the embryo eventually found as described. For those who wish more detailed information regarding the nature of the symbionts, the source and methods of infection, and their functions attention may be called to the excellent treatment of this subject afforded by Buchner (1912, 1930) and the more recent comments of Tóth (1933) and Klevenhusen (1927).

Origin of the Mesentoderm.—Hirschler's (1912) description of the origin of the inner layer during the formation of the ventral plate varies slightly from Will's (1888) account. The latter ob-

---

Fig. 146—*Continued.*

line. Processes are shown, the tissues not necessarily in correct proportion. *a,* blastoderm stage; *b,* primary invagination of germ cylinder, mycetoblasts crowded centrally; *c,* secondary invagination of germ cylinder with embryonic rudiment; *d,* closure of blastopore, appearance of primordial germ cells; *e,* mycetoblasts pushed dorsally, amnion and mesoderm appear and germ cells multiply; *f,* mycetocytes formed and germ band flexed with early metameres visible, stomodaeum appears; *g,* later than preceding figure with a definite proctodaeum; *h,* hypodermis formed, nervous system in part, rudiments of some appendages, secondary serosa covers blastopore, mycetocytes forced anteriorly; *i,* katatrepsis initiated and the gonads migrate. Broken lines show approximate lateral overgrowth; *j,* head at anterior pole, appendages prominent, mycetom forming; *k,* straightening of the embryo and early stage in formation of germaria; *l,* revolution completed, germaria formed and common oviduct invaginates. Stomodaeum and proctodaeum await mesenteron formation. Contrary to other insects, the scanty yolk is not enclosed in the digestive tract.

a, amnion; *an,* anterior nuclei; *ap,* appendage; *bl,* blastoderm; *bp,* blastopore; *br,* brain; *cbp,* closed blastopore; *cl,* cephalic lobe; *em,* ruptured embryonic membranes; *ge,* primary germ cells; *gm,* germaria; *in,* primary invagination of germ cylinder; *ins,* secondary invagination of germ cylinder; *m,* mycetoblast; *mb,* mycetocyte; *mes,* mesoderm; *my,* mycetom; *ns,* nervous system; *o,* lateral overgrowth; *ov,* common oviduct; *pg,* primordial germ cell; *pr,* proctodaeum; *s,* symbionts; *ser,* serosa; *sers,* secondary serosa; *st,* stomodaeum.

served the invagination as a median longitudinal groove, growing posteriorly. This groove represents an infolding of some of the ectodermal cells which are subsequently enclosed by a fusion of the superficial ectoderm along the margins of this depression. After being thus cut off, the inner layer flattens out and becomes the mesodermal layer. Hirschler, however, working with *Rhopalosiphum,* found the inner layer arising by delamination in a very young ventral plate. A narrow median row of columnar ectodermal cells suffered transverse mitosis whereby a wedge-shaped column of cells arose in the median line. This strip of cells lies within the ectoderm, which surrounds it on three sides, while its broader expanse faces dorsally. This median longitudinal column of cells is eventually forced above the ectoderm to form the inner layer or mesentoderm. Only at the posterior end of the ventral plate is there any sign of an invaginated portion such as Will described, and this is represented by a very shallow groove.

The derivation of the inner layer begins just anterior to the future stomodaeal invagination and extends to the proctodaeal region. When pushed dorsally the mesentoderm forms a flat median band of cells that quickly splits to give rise to two median strands which migrate to lateral positions under the ectoderm. Between the two bands of a slightly later stage, from the stomodaeal invagination to the first thoracic segment, and also in the last three abdominal segments, a few cells are detached medianly from the two strands and remain lying between the latter. These form the entoderm layer while the remainder of the original mesentoderm is wholly mesodermal in nature. No presumptive entoderm is to be seen from the first thoracic segment to the fourth from the last abdominal metamere. Mesodermal invasion of the procephalic region takes place later, for at present the two lateral strands of mesoderm end in their fusion just anterior to the future stomodaeum. Following these steps the mesodermal strands undergo segmentation corresponding to the future metameres of the embryonic rudiment and coelomic pouches appear in them. Also, two extensions of the fused mesoderm before the stomodaeum eventually invade the procephalic region to furnish the musculature there.

Primordial Germ Cells.—As the organization of the germ cylinder begins, one finds the primitive germ cells for the first time. These consist of a very few syncytial nuclei arranged in a flat layer of cytoplasm slightly anterior to the germ cylinder between the mycetoblasts and the blastoderm lying immediately anterior to the procephalic lobes (Fig. 145). These primitive germ cells quickly form a subspherical mass which is pushed before the elongating germ band until it finally occupies a dorsal position between the end of the latter and the formative mycetom (Fig. 146d-l). According to Paspaleff (1929) and Tóth (1933), evidences of the germ track, or the sex cells, may be detected even earlier than has just been shown. The former has observed in *A. rosae* and in *A. rosarum* a vacuolated, restricted, cytoplasmic area near the posterior end of the egg soon after the polar body is given off in maturation. This is the germ track cytoplasm. Its complete history has not been determined. Hirschler (1912) had described this area but ascribed other probable functions to it. Witlaczil (1884) and Tóth have found a single primordial germ cell at the end of the ventral plate in the early formation of the germ cylinder, at about the same developmental stage as has been given in Uichanco's account at the beginning of this paragraph. The primordial cell gives rise to several primary germ cells which thereafter behave as already described.

Formation of the Embryonic Membranes.—The cells comprising the germ cylinder, except those involved in ventral plate formation, are now to be recognized as amniotic in nature. All of the original surface blastoderm, except the cells composing the procephalic lobes, becomes the serosa. The amnion and serosa become rather thin membranes due to the increase in the size of the egg and the resultant enlarged areas to be covered by them. The serosa covers the egg except at its posterior end and over the procephalic lobes. The amnion is, of course, attached laterally and caudally to the ventral plate of the embryo as it was originally in the germ cylinder. In median section it can be followed from its caudal union with the germ band in its extension forward over the ventral surface of the embryo to a point opposite the posterior portion of the formative mycetom. Here it turns away from the germ band and passes around the formative mycetom to join the serosa. Later, after the embryo has shifted to a position indicated in Figure 146g, h, the serosa initiates a secondary extension at the margin of its union with the amnion. This sheet of tissue gradually encloses the posterior end of the egg, but still leaves the procephalic lobes uncovered. Will (1888) maintains this secondary serosa is unilaminar and has no counterpart in other insect embryos.

Polarity of the Egg.—Much of the developmental sequence given in the discussion of the invagination of the ventral plate into the central portion of the egg, the later extension of the embryonic envelopes, and so on, overlap in time some other changes in the embryo. The sequence followed here, however, permits more concentration on the transformation of the embryonic rudiment, with only casual references to these points as occasion requires. For example, attention could have been directed some time ago to the general topography of the egg as made evident by the appearance of the embryo. From the early formation of the blastoderm there was no doubt as to the anterior and posterior ends of the egg, the latter preceding the former down the ovariole and lacking the blastodermic cells in most cases (Fig. 143). With the development of the germ band the procephalic lobes are to be found on the posterior ventral third of the egg and, of course, the side of the egg opposite must be dorsal. Since the original egg had no chorion, micropyle, or definite shape to indicate these regions before embryonic development began, they must be determined by the position of the early embryo and by analogy with other insects' eggs and embryos.

Segmentation.—When the ventral plate has assumed the position shown in Figure 146f it has almost reached its greatest length in relation to the size of the egg. About this time deep transverse constrictions of the ectodermal surface indicate the segmental boundaries. These segmental areas, in general, appear in serial order posteriorly, after the cephalic metameres are marked, and involve the mesodermal rudiment as well. The ectoderm seems to elevate into slightly projecting rounded areas with the deep depressions between them which have just been mentioned. It also becomes a more definitely defined layer with elongate cells and nuclei. The mesoderm beneath the ectoderm thins out or even disappears at the intersegmental boundaries and forms large elliptical or oval masses within the segments. Inspection reveals the presence of the procephalic portion of the germ band on the posterior ventral surface of the egg. The buccal and thoracic areas occupy all of the anteriorly recurved part of the ventral plate, while the abdominal region comprises the remainder of the embryo to the telson. Witlaczil (1884) states there are visible three cephalic, three thoracic, seven abdominal segments, and the telson. Other authors have been rather reticent in mentioning the number of primitive segments.

The stomodaeum also becomes evident, before the mesentoderm is completely cut off, as a deep, narrow invagination which projects dorsally and appears to be wholly ectodermal in constitution. Later differentiation will invest it with ental mesoderm. The proctodaeum is somewhat delayed and can be seen only after the former has been well established.

The Early Nervous System.—The nervous system first originates by delamination in the procephalic region and thereafter, apparently quite independently of the former, in the buccal, thoracic, and abdominal portions of the germ band. Regarding the preceding statement, one should remember that in Will's (1888) view the procephalic lobes develop from the thickened anterior part of the blastoderm (Scheitelplatte) which, of course, arises very early in the embryological history, long before there is any evidence of the embryonic rudiment as later investigators describe it. For this reason he may have been somewhat emphatic on this point.

Wheeler (1893) has shown that the "Scheitelplatte" lacks the prospective significance Will assigned to it, and later students of aphid embryology are agreed that the procephalic lobes arise more posteriorly in the blastoderm, as has already been outlined. None, however, has contributed further information as to the details of the origin of the nervous system in this group of insects. Will fixes the time of the differentiation of the brain as being prior to the development of the stomodaeum, while the ventral longitudinal nervous system is delimited posteriorly, not only after the rudiment of the fore-intestine is evident, but also after the emergence of the appendages.

The earliest trace of the ventral nerve is shown by mitotic activity in the more deeply situated cells of the ectoderm on either side of the median line of the embryo which give rise to the neuroblasts of the paired ventral chain. The neuroblasts, as shown by Will's figures, seem to be similar to those described by Wheeler (1891) for *Xiphidium*, although he has not discovered the same regularity in number or arrangement of the cells. The two lateral strands are gradually forced dorsally until they come to lie immediately beneath the ectoderm.

A median cord now appears between the lateral cords which consists of a narrow wedge-shaped row of cells in the ectodermal layer of the germ band. The latter is still multilaminar at the time, and the median cord lies adjacent to its surface in the embryo. It slowly migrates deeper into the ectoderm and eventually reaches its internal, or dorsal, surface. The lateral and median cords form the paired ventral nervous system with its ganglia, intersegmental, and transverse connectives. In the pro-cephalic lobes the definitive brain never severs its intimate connection with the ectoderm in the areas representing the potential visual centers. Subsequent to the formation of the ganglia, rotation occurs and embryonic development continues. During these changes the ganglia undergo progressive coalescence in order to reach their definitive number and position in the body.

Katatrepsis.—The embryo began its development near the posterior pole of the egg by posterior growth of the ventral plate rudiment into its interior. Anatrepsis has not been mentioned by the different authors, but the embryo conforms to the invaginate type of germ band, a type which is always associated with ana-trepsis. However, when the embryo has attained the fundaments of its organs, as just described, it is necessary for rotation to take place so that further structural differentiation, especially of the lateral and dorsal body walls, may ensue. The amnion is freed from its intimate contact with the mycetom and is drawn dorsally upward, together with the secondary serosa (the serosal extension over the posterior pole) by the contraction of the serosal envelope present over the dorsal, lateral, and anterior egg surfaces. These areas of the egg are now covered with a common amnio-serosal membrane. At the same time, the embryonic cephalic region moves anteriorly along the ventral surface of the egg until it arrives at the anterior pole (Fig. 146*i*, *j*, *k*). In this migration it is, of course, followed by the invaginated portion of the embryo which gradually reverses itself from its former sharply ventral flexure to a slightly dorsal curvature with the distal abdominal portion strongly curved upward, for the embryo is still much longer than the length of the space it occupies. Naturally, growth has continued throughout this entire structure and involves the whole egg as well as the contained embryo. The egg of *M. tana-ceti*, just before rotation, measures 230 to 280 microns in length and 130 to 165 microns in diameter (Uichanco, 1924).

The Formation of Germaria.—Early in the process of kata-trepsis the mass of germ cells, hitherto in a fold of the anal plate, elongates and breaks up into several smaller groups corresponding to the number of germaria peculiar to the particular species of aphid considered. This number, for example, is 12 in *M. tanaceti* and 10 in *A. platanoides*. Half of them take new positions on one lateroposterior side of the mycetom, half on the other, where they are clearly seen after rotation. Each separate group is surrounded by a definite mesothelial layer, the prospective ovariole. Later, the individual units, or primitive germaria, will grow terminal filament extensions anterodorsally, and posteriorly they will complete the vitellaria of their respective ovarioles. Directed posteriorly downward, a common cord or strand of cells will differentiate into one of the paired oviducts from the right and left sides respectively, each united distally to the ovarioles. Most of this development will occur during the embryonic period, to be discussed in the following pages.

Postrevolution Development.—After blastokinesis, the further development of the embryo proceeds rather rapidly without interruptions due to symbiont invasion, rotation, or other factors which intruded earlier with the first differentiation of tissues, organs, and systems. Most of the essential, specialized, and more complicated parts are now represented by rudiments which have only to grow toward physical and functional utility. Nevertheless, postrevolutionary development may be conveniently divided into two stages to which reference will occasionally be necessary. The first of these stages covers the growth of the embryo after rotation while its posterior abdominal region is curved dorsally on account of its length, which is greater than that of the space wherein it lies. The second postrevolution stage begins when the embryo has contracted, straightened out, and is no longer than the egg. This stage ends at the birth of the individual.

The Body Wall.—The ectoderm originally was multilaminar, but after the splitting off of the mesentoderm beneath it the cells become very tall, columnar in shape, and appear to be more nearly one cell layer in thickness. The elongate oval nuclei are irregularly distributed at various depths beneath the external surface. Upon the separation of the nervous system and the erection of the appendages from its surface, the ectoderm rapidly resolves itself into a thinner layer which becomes a hypodermis shortly after revolution. Since the embryonic envelopes have been drawn dorsally by the contraction of the serosa, the ectodermal walls, whose borders are still fused to these membranes, are caused to bend dorsally at the edges. Rapid upward growth of the lateral walls eventually provides the external surface of the embryo with its characteristic covering. During this process, which occurs over a considerable period of time, the embryo itself is constantly shortening by contraction so that its total length finally corresponds approximately to that of the egg space provided for it within the enveloping follicular epithelium. This contraction permits the complete formation of the dorsal body walls before all of the internal organs have finished their ultimate differentiation. Early in the second postrevolution stage the hypodermis starts to secrete a cuticle over the body and the appendages (Fig. 146*l*).

Destruction of the Envelopes.—The constantly contracting serosa and the amnion gather into an elongate cylindrical, hollow tube along the dorsal side of the egg. Its mass is added to as the growing lateral walls of the embryo still further encroach on the territory formerly occupied by them. However, these membranes show signs of vacuolization and disintegration very early in their present position, so that their substance is no doubt being employed as nutriment by the embryo (Witlaczil, 1884). Both Uichanco (1924) and Tóth (1933) seem to agree that the original yolk cells are all occupied with other functions so that none are free to engage in trophocytic activity at this time. The writer is at a loss for suggestions as to just how this dissolution of the envelopes is accomplished unless it is because of phagocytic activity of the young blood cells. Eventually, the remnants of the embryonic membranes are enclosed within the body through a small opening in the embryonic ectoderm just prior to the complete fusion of this tissue in the dorsal mid-line.

The Appendages.—The appendages evolve from the continued evagination of lateral portions of the intrasegmental areas of the germ band and include a core of mesodermal tissue in each from the earliest steps of the process. Uichanco (1924) and Witlaczil (1884) show in their figures the presence of the preoral antennae, the mandibular, maxillary, and labial appendages and three pairs of thoracic limbs. Will asserts that the thoracic appendages are first to arise with the buccal following, and the antennal last in point of time. The labial appendages grow to be very long and limb-like. The abdominal appendages are represented solely by slight ectodermal swellings which later subside. The intrasegmental masses of mesoderm which largely invade the interior of the forming appendages show, at an early stage, cavities within them. These are the coelomic pouches.

During and after katatrepsis the appendages are directed posteriorly along the ventral surface of the embryo. The antennae are only slightly longer than the second maxillae or labial appendages prior to this time, but shortly after revolution the former constantly grow longer while the latter continually shorten, both thus tending to assume their definitive form. The first maxillae remain short, and after revolution definitely show the palpi growing laterally from them. As the limbs start segmenting in the second postrevolution stage, the mouth parts initiate their final differentiation. This begins by the gradual sinking of the mandibles and maxillae into the body ectoderm and retreat of the mesoderm from their extremities. Their inner ends elongate into the head to form enlarged "retort organs" mentioned by Metschnikoff (1866b), Witlaczil (1882), Zacharias (1884), and Uichanco (1924), but whose function is still unknown. The labia approach each other and fuse medianly. The labium becomes three-jointed with the distal segment acutely pointed. The anterior margin of the head elongates, becomes thinner, and forms the labrum. All of the oral segments contract so that the labrum and labium approach each other very closely to form the external boundaries of the buccal cavity over the pharyngeal opening.

After rotation, the thoracic limbs are slightly less than half their ultimate length, but continue to grow posteriorly. The prothoracic pair do not reach the end of the abdomen but the mesothoracic pair do in the second postrevolution stage, where they turn slightly inward toward the ventral mid-line over the penultimate segment. The third pair extend to the tip of the abdomen, turn medianly and cross to the opposite sides of the body, where they bend slightly anteriorly over the last ventral segment. About the time the metathoracic pair first reach the tip of the abdomen, in the second postrevolution stage, all of the legs show definite constrictions, presaging their segmentation and differentiation into true limbs. The cornicles develop on the fifth abdominal tergite in the second postrevolution stage. These are, at first, only slight elevations of the ectoderm which later, by continued differentiation, assume their characteristic shape. The internal structure involves the mesoderm tissue, as well, for cells from this layer constitute the secretory elements of the organs according to Witlaczil (1884), a conclusion that has been confirmed by Hottes (1928).

The Concentration of the Nervous System.—Now to consider the internal organs and their further growth after revolution. The nervous system, which is the largest and most conspicuous organ in later development, is exceeded in size immediately after katatrepsis only by the large mycetom body. It has previously shown evidences of contraction and anterior aggregation, and the ganglia individually tend to become less distinctly recognizable. Eventually the lobes of the brain form a single unit. The buccal ganglia also fuse to become the suboesophageal ganglion, while the thoracic ganglia unite into a common ganglion and those in the abdomen are drawn forward into an elongate, single ganglionic mass which tapers to a point about two thirds the length of the abdomen. In the second postrevolution stage the eyes begin to differentiate into their final form. An outer thin layer separates from a thicker layer of very narrow, tall cells beneath. The former becomes the corneal outer portion while the cells of the latter represent the retinal layer. Entally, the nerves lead directly to the brain.

The Salivary Glands.—Prior to rotation but after the appearance of the appendages, the salivary glands commence their development. No earlier mention was made of them because most of their growth occurs when rotation is safely passed. These paired organs start as simple, lateral, ectodermal invaginations near the posterior basal margins of the labial appendages. The inner ends bifurcate into two short branches as they penetrate the underlying mesoderm. By the end of the first postrevolution stage they have invaded the thoracic region. During the early part of the following stage the invaginations are converted into exceedingly thin ducts whose distal inner ends are transformed into the highly glandular portions. The paired ducts eventually migrate toward the median line where they fuse into one common duct near the buccal cavity, into which their secretions are discharged.

The Tracheal System.—The tracheal system arises shortly after revolution as serially arranged, bilateral invaginations of the ectoderm. Witlaczil found two pairs in the thorax and seven in the abdomen, but suspected the presence of one more in the thorax and possibly one in the eighth abdominal segment, though these were invisible to him. Their blind, inner ends form dorsal and ventral diverticula during the second postrevolution stage, and these grow toward the median line. Before arriving at the longitudinal axis of the embryo, however, further growth in this direction ceases. Instead, an anterior and a posterior branch from each terminus extend forward and backward respectively until they meet and fuse with similar strands from adjacent segments. The anterior pair project forward into the head and the caudal end is supplied from the posterior abdominal pair. In this manner the four main longitudinal tracheal trunks are established.

The Reproductive System.—Early in the second postrevolution stage the vagina of the reproductive system is perceptible as a rather broad invagination of the ectoderm just ventral to the proctodaeum. From the beginning of its inward growth it is covered by mesoderm, for cells of the latter layer are pushed internally with it as it elongates. Continuing forward and upward, it finally fuses with the approaching posterior ends of the paired oviducts. The discharge of young ova into the embryo's ovarioles commences shortly after this stage is reached, as has already been discussed under paedogenesis.

The Mesodermal Derivatives.—Prior to blastokinesis the mesoderm had achieved a bilateral, segmental condition with coelomic pouches within the two strands. The dorsal growth of the lateral body walls after rotation was also described, but no further consideration of the behavior of the mesodermal tissue was given at either time. It is now expedient to resume our discussion of the growth and differentiation of the mesoderm. The mesodermal somites enlarge and elongate, especially at the bases of the appendages, where they project far into the lumens of these ectodermal evaginations. Here the mesoderm forms into strands of cells which in the second postrevolution stage develop into appendicular muscles. There is a more or less pronounced retreat of the mesoderm, however, from the mandibular and maxillary organs as was mentioned while discussing the mouth parts and their development. Nevertheless, muscles for activating even these parts are formed by the retracting mesoderm. In the legs, the mesodermal strands are persistent and their gradual metamorphosis into typical voluntary muscles can plainly be followed.

Entally, the coelomic cavities also enlarge until they touch each other and finally the walls break through anteriorly and posteriorly so that a single pair of cavities extends along the body, one on each side. As the body ectoderm proceeds dorsally after rotation, the mesoderm accompanies it in its progress. The dorsal portion, above the ruptured openings of the coelomic pouches, is closely applied to the ectoderm and eventually becomes the somatopleure. The median part of the mesodermal somites is splanchnopleure. From the ventral surface sheets of mesoderm spread over the ventral part of the embryo. The upward growing mesoderm carries at its advancing border certain mesodermal cells destined to be the cardioblasts, which form the heart and aorta. These organs are formed when the mesoderm from the right and left sides of the embryo meet in the dorsal mid-line. Mesodermal cells also form mesothelial sheets around the various organs requiring this support. Blood cells and fat cells are likewise derived from the mesoderm, the latter developing gradually into the fat body which extends over a large part of the haemocoelar walls. Both types of cells arise, it should be noted, before the definite organization of muscles. Hirschler (1912) believes the blood cells are purely entodermal in origin, a view which is shared by others and might be supported by the phagocytic activity of some of the types of cells in this category.

The Digestive Tract.—In describing early segmentation of the germ band the stomodaeal and proctodaeal invaginations were mentioned. Authorities differ materially regarding the significance of certain areas in the digestive tract in the aphids; the subject was therefore left to be treated later in its entirety. Metschnikoff (1866) made only incomplete observations but derived the mid-intestine from entoderm. Witlaczil (1884), like his predecessors, had to content himself with a study of whole specimens. To him the digestive tract seemed to consist only of stomodaeal and proctodaeal invaginations from the ectoderm which, upon meeting in the haemocoele, fuse to form a tube. It lacked any entodermal elements, but was covered with mesoderm. Only the yolk cells were entodermal, according to his view, and these eventually degenerated. Lécaillon (1896) held somewhat similar views. Will's (1883) conception differs from Witlaczil's, for he traced the appearance of an enteron composed of entodermal yolk cells.

Hirschler (1912) devoted considerable effort to an attempt to solve the perplexing problems involved in the formation of the aphid alimentary system. According to him, the stomodaeum and proctodaeum of *Rhopalosiphum* are covered with mesoderm when their invagination begins, except at the inner, blind ends. Entoderm cells have already been mentioned as occurring in the thoracic and posterior abdominal regions between the mesodermal bands. These cells are relatively few in number but they manage to remain in the vicinity of the growing inner ends of the fore- and hind-intestines, although not affixed to the latter, as is said to be the condition in most insects. The stomodaeal and proctodaeal invaginations project between the embryo and the mycetom as they grow in length and finally approach very near each other (Fig. 146*k, l*). During this time the embryo has undergone marked changes in position so that, in relation to the surfaces of the egg, the direction of growth of the two intestinal rudiments has materially altered at intervals. But, in relation to the embryo, they have constantly advanced over its mid-ventral line to the metathoracic or first abdominal segments.

Prior to revolution the entoderm cells join the anterior end of the stomodaeum that is left uncovered by the mesoderm. Following rotation, the embryo shortens so that the tip of the abdomen moves from the anterior egg pole back toward the posterior pole.

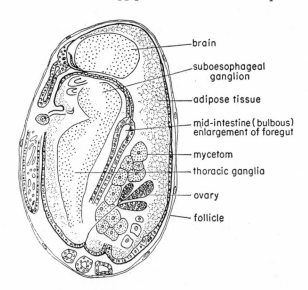

Fig. 147.—*Macrosiphum rosae*. Nearly grown embryo in sagittal section. (After Uichanco, 1924. Courtesy of the Institute of Science, formerly Bureau of Science.)

The entodermal cells now attach themselves to the end of the proctodaeum as they did earlier for the stomodaeum. Hirschler believes they become incorporated with the ectodermal cells in these positions, for he loses them at this stage. The two rudiments then become attached to each other by a very short, solid cord of cells, probably entodermal in nature. A little later the blind ends of the stomodaeal and proctodaeal portions and the entodermal cord open to form a continuous intestinal tube. This occurs just as the tip of the abdomen reaches the end of the egg. At this point of junction between the two intestines a loop develops, involving the mid-intestinal tissue. One or more additional loops later appear in the digestive tract of the mature embryo. Thus the fore- and hind-intestines are exceedingly long in aphids while the enteron is relatively short.

When the alimentary tract has obtained a single lumen running throughout its length, a portion of it over the suboesophageal ganglion enlarges into a bulblike organ with a large lumen (Fig. 147). Its dilation extends posteriorly some distance but the original anterior part is much greater in diameter than the rest of it. The organ finally becomes subpyriform. Its cells, as well as those in the narrower intestine immediately behind it, change to the tall, columnar aspect typical of the mesenteron of other insects. At the anterior end the preceding portion of the tract projects backward somewhat into its lumen as a circular fold which functions as a valve. Since the epithelium lining this enlarged portion so closely resembles mid-intestinal tissue, Hirschler maintains its physiological homology with the enteron of other insects. This explanation of the formation of the digestive system does not seriously conflict with the observations of more recent investigators. Divergence of opinion appears, however, in the interpretation of the various areas included in it. Most investigators are agreed that endothelial tissue constitutes relatively little of its length. Yet many regard the bulbous enlargement and adjacent posterior region as strictly entodermal in nature rather than confining entoderm only to the first intestinal loop. No Malpighian tubules are present.

The Mycetom.—While the embryonic rudiment is appearing, the mycetoblast cells are growing larger, probably because of further accumulation of nutrient material in this portion of the embryo and actual multiplication of the symbionts themselves. When the germ band is fully differentiated, the formative mycetom occupies approximately one third of the egg. Its history is shown in Figure 146.

Early in the segmentation stage of the embryo, the nuclei of the formative mycetom enter a period of active mitoses, for their number is increased very quickly. Simultaneously, the cytoplasm with its inclusions constricts into definitive cellular areas, each containing a nucleus. These are now known as mycetocytes of the mycetom.

The mycetocytes comprising the young mycetom remain in a dorsal position during rotation, shifting posteriorly only far enough to settle against the mesoderm in the posterior thoracic and abdominal regions of the embryo. At present the mycetom contains 30 to 40 mycetocytes.

While the digestive tract is forming, the further differentiation of the mycetom has taken place. Even before this period, mitotic activity almost doubled the number of mycetocytes in it and 60 or 70 of these cells may now be seen. Intestinal growth presses against the mid-ventral surface of the mycetom and this organ becomes bilobed, one lobe lying in each side of the body with a mycetocyte bridge uniting the two near its caudal extremity.

The Cuticula and Follicle.—A cuticula is evident when the body wall is erected over the dorsum of the embryo, and setae appear. The whole embryo is compressed dorsoventrally and lies in its final orientation preceding birth. It is exceedingly interesting to note that the follicular epithelium has not disintegrated early, as in most insects, but presumably maintains its functions, at least until the development of a cuticula prevents further absorption of food from it. The functional significance lies in its probable nutritional activity in supplying the food required by the embryo. It has been suggested that the follicle may serve as an egg covering at parturition, in lieu of a chorion or other envelope.

Growth in Size During Development.—One remaining observation is yet to be presented. The shape of the egg of *Macrosiphum* alters materially after leaving the germarium although this fact has not been mentioned before. At first the egg is spherical, but with the addition of nutriment from the follicular cells and the onset of cleavage it assumes an elongate, oval outline. During the later period, involving the formation of the embryonic rudiment, it gradually changes into a broadly oval form. Its length also increases greatly. After extrusion, but before the formation of the polar body, it measures approximately 25 microns in length and 17 microns in width. After the maturation division the egg measures 30 microns in length with a width of 24 microns, and following the first cleavage, it is 43 microns long and 23 wide. Upon completion of the blastoderm the length is 60 microns and the width 30 microns. When the germ band attains perhaps its greatest length in comparison with the length of the egg, the latter measures about 120 microns in length with a diameter of 60 microns. Immediately prior to katatrepsis the egg is 230 to 280 microns in length with a cross-sectional diameter of 130 to 165 microns. Finally, an embryo ready for birth is 840 microns in length, 264 in width, and 240 in thickness. This represents an increase in length during development of more than 33 times its original size when simply a mature egg.

Literature Cited

De Baehr (1910, 1920), Von Baer (1828), Baker and Turner (1916a, 1916b), Balbiani (1866, 1869, 1870, 1871), Blochmann (1887), Bonnet (1743, 1745, 1779), Bouché (1844), Brass (1882), Buchner (1912, 1930), Buckton (1876), Burnett (1850, 1853), Carus (1849), Claparède (1867), Claus (1858, 1864), Comstock (1925), Dufour (1833), Dutrochet (1833), Duvau (1825), Ewing (1916), de Geer (1771), Henneguy (1899), Von Heyden (1857), Hirschler (1911, 1912, 1924), Hottes (1928), Huxley (1859), Johnson (1900), Kaltenbach (1844), Kirby and Spence (1828), Klevenhusen (1927), Korschelt and Heider (1899), Kyber (1815), Lankester (1872, 1919), Lécaillon (1896), Leeuwenhoek (1695), Lemoine (1892, 1893), Leuckart (1851, 1858, 1859, 1874), Leydig (1848, 1850), Lichtenstein (1878), Lubbock (1859, 1867), Metschnikoff (1866a, 1866b), Mordwilko (1907–9), Morren (1836), Newport (1846), Owen (1849, 1854), Paspaleff (1929), Phillips (1903), Plieninger (1849), Radlkofer (1858), Ratzeburg (1844), Réaumur (1737, 1741), Reyger (1754), Sales-Girons (1875), Schleip (1909), Shull (1933), Von Siebold (1839, 1856, 1862, 1871), Steenstrup (1842), Stevens (1905), Stschelkanovzew (1904), Tannreuther (1907), Taschenberg (1892), Tóth (1933, 1935), Trembly (1776), Turner and Baker (1915), Uichanco (1921, 1924), Wheeler (1891, 1893), Will (1883, 1887, 1888), Witlaczil (1882, 1884), Zacharias (1884).

Chapter 14

PSEUDOPLACENTAL VIVIPARITY—HEMIPTERA
(POLYCTENIDAE)

These curious insects of the family Polyctenidae are apparently
entirely ectoparasitic on bats. They are wingless, the eyes are
absent, and the prothoracic appendages are so profoundly modified that it is doubtful whether they can be used for any purpose
other than clinging to the fur of the host.

Of all viviparous insects this group seems to show the greatest
variety of nutritional organs, yet all are present in the embryogenies of insect species in general. The embryos of this family
have employed them as trophic organs while fewer or simpler
modifications have served other pseudoplacental forms.

The distribution of the species must be largely accidental and
probably occurs only when bats rest in numbers in limited areas
or when their bodies are in contact at such times. In spite of this,
the polyctenid population on any individual bat is not large. No
doubt they are usually overlooked by the collector, for they are
still quite rare in collections. Apparently their choice of hosts
is limited for they have been collected from only a few species
of bats.

Order Hemiptera　　　　Family Polyctenidae

The discovery of viviparity in this group was announced by
Jordan (1911a) in a very brief statement. This information was
followed by another note (1911b), while a third paper (Jordan,
1912) contained a figure of the remains of a fully developed
embryo within the abdomen of the mother, together with a
description of its taxonomic characters. Owing to the poor state
of internal preservation, it was impossible for Jordan to supply
further details of the embryogeny. By examining other specimens, he was able to ascertain the fact that there were only two
or three ovarioles in each ovary. Fertilization must take place in
the ovarioles, for the earliest stages of embryonic growth of the
offspring begin there. The young are born singly, and, because

they are so large, there must be a considerable interval of time between them.

More recently, the present writer (Hagan, 1931) contributed additional information on the embryological development of the species *Hesperoctenes fumarius* Westwood, and from this paper the following summary has been prepared.

Female Reproductive System

The Ovary.—Each ovary consists of two ovarioles whose terminal filaments proceed dorsally to independent attachments in the pericardial region. It has not been determined whether they terminate in the fat body or are permanently attached to other organs. The lower end of each terminal filament widens as it encloses the germarium.

The germarium is short compared with the rest of the system, yet is approximately three times as long as it is wide. A single layer of quadrate cells lines its cavity in the lower portion. Higher up, within the enveloping filament, there is no cavity in the germarium, the cells there being transversely arranged and greatly elongated, extending entirely across the interior. In their anteroposterior aspect they thus appear to be very flat and densely packed together. Presumably, the functional germ cells are those most apically situated while the quadrate cells have other destinies, as will be shown.

The transition to the third and lower section of the ovariole, the vitellarium, is abrupt. Not only is this portion of the ovariole longer and broader than the germarium but its epithelial cells are quite granular and follicular in appearance, with vacuolated margins next to the central cavity of the organ.

The Oviducts.—The paired oviducts are long, thin-walled ducts which unite with a large, highly distensible, and long common oviduct heavily encased in muscular tissue. In the absence of offspring in this portion, as in recently sexually matured females, the common oviduct is a straight tube extending through approximately three body segments where it opens to the outside, posterior to the last visible sternite. There are no accessory glandular organs present, such as the seminal receptacle or colleterial glands of other insects. The homologues of the so-called "milk glands" of the adenotrophic type are entirely absent.

During the reproductive period of the female insect the length, breadth, and shape of the various portions of the reproductive tract vary enormously due to the presence of eggs and embryos within them. Ovulation and development of embryos are continuous processes during the reproductive life. Hence, the genital system, which lies free in the haemocoele except for the anterior and posterior attachments, is subject to continual displacement and change in the relative size of all its parts.

Copulation and Fertilization.—In lieu of a seminal receptacle, another method of receiving and caring for the male sexual elements has been employed. This subject presents three alternative possibilities which have been elaborated upon in the original paper but here we shall present only the seemingly most evident procedure. Mating takes place in the usual manner characteristic of insects receiving the spermatozoa directly into the lower end of the common oviduct. Apparently they then migrate to the neighborhood of the paired oviducts, pass through the walls of the reproductive system, and enter the haemocoele. Once in the latter they aggregate into clumps or masses, recalling to mind the agglutination stage of echinoderm and other invertebrate spermatozoa so frequently mentioned by experimental embryologists and physiologists working with gametes in aqueous media. Spermatic clumps are distributed widely through the body cavity but large numbers of them always may be found in the immediate vicinity of the ovarioles. It is thought that some of them penetrate again to the lumen of the reproductive tract in proximity to the ripe ovum and insure its fertilization.

Another suggestive contribution lies in the probability that coitus may antedate physical maturity of the female, for one specimen with an abundant supply of spermatozoa in the oviduct as well as in the haemocoele, had not yet cast the last nymphal cuticle. In this case, however, the new cuticle had formed beneath the old one and the latter was partially or completely freed over the abdomen. There is, of course, nothing new in this type of mating for Rethfeldt (1924) found the sexually immature females of *Chrysomela* were freely mating with males. Among the Ephemeridae subimagoes copulate, and many examples of the mating of an adult male with neotenic females in other orders may be called to mind. Neoteny offers a slightly different aspect of the case, however, for in these instances the individual never acquires the complete, mature, external form. Gros (1923), Haase (1888), Lowne (1871), and de Peyerimhoff (1913) discuss such examples. Trouessart (1895) cites an interesting observation on the mite *Chorioptes auricularum* var. *furionis*. Here the adult male discharges sperm into the posterior end of the intestinal tract of immature individuals of both sexes. He believes a nutritional function is served thereby. Finally, the curious location of the spermatozoa, namely in the haemocoele of *Hesperoctenes,* might readily suggest the presence of some structure analogous to the organs of Berlese and Ribaga (Berlese, 1898–99; Carazzi, 1902; Cragg, 1920; Ribaga, 1897) but Jordan (1922) has been quite unsuccessful in his search for one and the writer, too, has failed.

Paedogenesis.—A third interesting feature in this embryogeny should be mentioned at this point, for it arises from the foregoing statements. Ovulation, fertilization, and embryonic development had already taken place in the apparently physically immature insect cited in the preceding paragraph. It follows, then, that the first few offspring produced by this female are paedogenetic in nature since their development exhibits precisely the same phenomenon discussed by Uichanco (1924) for parthenogenetic aphids, though in a less marked degree.

Development of the Embryo

Ovulation.—The four ovarioles which constitute the two ovaries apparently discharge oöcytes in alternate order; that is, one from the right germarium, one from the left, a third from the second germarium of the right ovary and a fourth from the second germarium of the left ovary. Cycles with this sequence presumably ensue during the entire reproductive period. This sequence insures a continuous series of ten or twelve embryos of various ages in the lumen of the reproductive system. Ovulation presumably follows shortly after the birth of the oldest embryo.

The oöcyte is derived from the epithelium at the upper end of the ovariole. Even before passing into the vitellarium it begins storing a fatlike substance in its cytoplasm, a substance which is apparently derived from the cells forming the wall of the upper end of the vitellarium or the quadrate cells lining the lower end of the germarium. The oöcyte becomes, finally, about eight times as large as it was when first liberated. This gives its cytoplasm a highly vacuolar aspect in which the plasm appears as a coarse reticular meshwork. The enclosed vacuoles are ovate, with the long axes generally corresponding to that of the egg.

The nucleus is situated near the anterior end of the egg. It is slightly oval in shape, measuring about 16 by 25 microns. The nucleoplasm is clear with no apparent linin or nucleoli. The chromomeres are scattered throughout and are unusual in being uniformly spherical, although of widely varying sizes.

The Ovum.—The mature ovum is approximately 48 by 125 microns in size. It fills the portion of the lumen of the ovariole in which it lies and even dilates the tubule somewhat, for the latter is definitely constricted at either end of it. Only the follicular cells of the vitellarium surround it and these at first are not typical of insects either in shape or number. They appear to

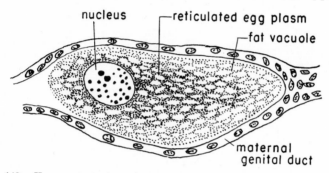

FIG. 148.—*Hesperoctenes fumarius.* Mature ovum with fat vacuoles imbedded in reticular plasm, longitudinal section. (From Jour. Morph. and Physiol., **51**, 1, by H. R. Hagan.)

constitute a flat epithelium around the oöcyte. The egg resembles that of *Hemimerus,* described by Heymons (1912), in possessing no chorion (Fig. 148). It should be emphasized here that no yolk seems to be present in the ovum and the vacuolated stored material is manifestly insufficient to provide for the development and growth of the embryo. Further supplies of nutriment must be furnished from other sources, to be described later.

Blastoderm Formation.—After fertilization, which occurs in the ovariole, the egg gives rise to a thick layer of dense periplasm. Most of the nutrient material, consisting of a fatty substance, remains behind in the interior of the egg. There is, nevertheless, a residuum of cytoplasm which forms a coarse reticulation binding the nutriment into a more or less coherent mass and preserving the structural integrity and continuity of the interior plasm.

Meanwhile, at the upper end of the egg there has accumulated a mass of nutrient cells, conveniently termed the nurse cell body, that is probably derived from the follicular epithelium. This is thought to be the homologue of the customary follicle which normally surrounds the egg of most insects, providing it with yolk and other nutriment as well as a chorionic envelope. This nurse cell body never surrounds the egg but follows after it and rather quickly disintegrates. The resultant assimilable material is taken into the upper end of the egg as fast as it is formed. The ovariole is so contracted between egg and nutrient mass that only a very small lumen persists. This lumen, however, is filled with the product of nutrient cell disintegration and makes the egg appear to be united to the original nutrient mass by a nutrient cord. That the material is actually entering the egg may be verified by inspection of Figure 149, which shows an egg in the metaphase of the second nuclear cleavage stage. As it first enters the egg, the material is a granular fluid substance. It very quickly becomes organized into vacuoles which are distributed gradually throughout the interior of the egg. Nuclear division continues and the germ band is well formed, with early segmentation present, before all of the nutrient cell mass has been absorbed. There is no migration of nuclei toward the periphery of the egg until after at least four nuclei are formed. At some later phase of nuclear multiplication, however, migration begins and nuclei are then found in the anterior, anterodorsal and anteroventral portions of the egg. The last-mentioned area lags behind the others in receiving its supply of nuclei. No stage showing the complete formation of a blastoderm was seen. Apparently certain nuclei remain behind in a more central position to form trophocytes.

As each nucleus attains a definitive position at the periphery of the egg the adjacent periplasm condenses around it and a cell is formed at once. These cells are at first quite large but areas of them later become much reduced in size in the formation of the embryo. The serosal portion always contains large cells somewhat resembling these early cleavage cells.

In contrast to the preceding remarks about the nurse cell body, it may be interesting to point out that although the nurse cells of *Hemimerus* are few in number, each is very large. Of course, they were probably germ cells originally. *Hesperoctenes* presumably possesses none of these for none have been found. The follicular cells of *Hemimerus* also form anterior and posterior pseudoplacental masses for the subsequent nourishment of the embryo, and continue their activity through most of the embryonic life of the offspring. *Hesperoctenes* has but one mass of follicular cells, which is entirely absorbed into the egg. These follicular nutrient cells are probably mesodermal in origin, being derived from the vitellarium of the maternal reproductive system.

As blastoderm formation continues, the cytoplasm in the interior of the egg accumulates around the trophocytes. These cytoplasmic masses are stellate, their attenuated processes uniting them into one reticulate syncytial unit (Fig. 150).

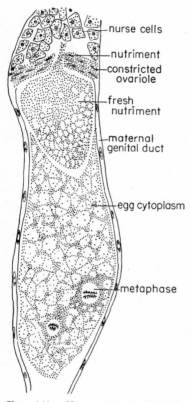

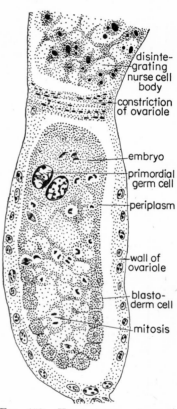

FIG. 149.—*Hesperoctenes fumarius.* Egg in second metaphase, with forming nurse cell body following. Nutriment is flowing into the egg through the constricted lumen of the ovariole, longitudinal section. (From Jour. Morph. and Physiol., **51**, 1, by H. R. Hagan.)

FIG. 150.—*Hesperoctenes fumarius.* Early blastoderm formation, accompanying nurse cell body and two nuclei of primordial germ cells, longitudinal section. (From Jour. Morph. and Physiol., **51**, 1, by H. R. Hagan.)

Primordial Germ Cells.—Primordial germ cells are seen for the first time in the early stages of blastoderm formation. They consist of two enormous, ovate nuclei with polygonally distributed linin and irregularly shaped, flakelike chromomeres, sometimes solitary, but more often aggregated into large masses. Both appear to be entirely peripheral in position. The cytoplasm immediately surrounding them is indistinguishable from that of the egg generally and no cellular membranes are visible. There is a marked contrast in structure between these primordial germ cell nuclei and the egg pronucleus that has already been described. They are about three times the size of the somatic nuclei of the blastoderm.

Anatrepsis, Segmentation, and the Appendages.—The formation of the embryonic rudiment, the mesoderm, and early germ band were not observed. The later germ band stage seems to

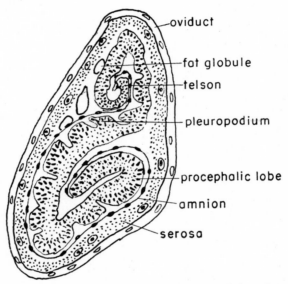

Fig. 151.—*Hesperoctenes fumarius.* Germ band showing early segmentation and typical hemipteran curvature of the invaginate type though no yolk is present, longitudinal section. (From Jour. Morph. and Physiol., 51, 1, by H. R. Hagan.)

have a multilaminar ectoderm or a single layer of very elongate crowded cells, for their minute nuclei are arranged roughly in two layers, an inner and an outer. Cell membranes are not visible. Alternate thin and thickened portions of it indicate the various segments and their approximate boundaries. The embryo is quite long in proportion to the space encompassed by the serosa, so that it is flexed at both extremities in the manner characteristic of aphids and other Hemiptera with the involute type of germ band, although the yolk is absent and other nutriment scanty in amount (Fig. 151). The embryonic cephalic region is folded dorsally over the mandibular segments and the terminal portion of the abdomen is drawn ventrally in front of its anterior half. The embryo at this stage is narrower throughout its entire length than is the case for many insects, the head and thoracic segments being only about twice as wide as those of the abdomen. The completion of the germ band stage leaves the anterior end of the embryo directed posteriorly. This position represents the condition following anatrepsis. Prior to this time the mesoderm has arisen, perhaps by delamination from the ectoderm, and comes to lie as a dorsal, unbroken sheet of cells above the ectoderm. The process was not observed.

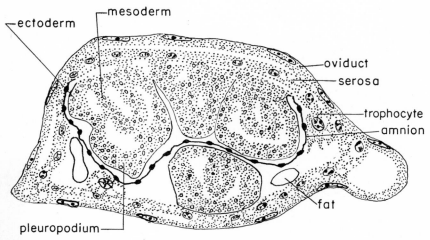

FIG. 152.—*Hesperoctenes fumarius.* Embryo in cross section through first abdominal segment showing the evaginate pleuropodium and the close approximation of dorsal part of embryo and serosa. Space between wall of maternal oviduct and serosa emphasized slightly to differentiate tissues. Trophocytes are largely aggregated in dorsal thoracic region. (From Jour. Morph. and Physiol., **51**, 1, by H. R. Hagan.)

Segmentation is typical, furrows first appearing anteriorly, then posteriorly, though the exact sequence has not been observed. The abdominal segments, especially the more caudally situated ones, are not so sharply defined as those found more anteriorly. The ectoderm of the segments becomes more definitely multilaminar as the primordia of appendages evaginate. These are paired ectodermal thickenings arising first on the anterior segments. The oral, thoracic, and first abdominal or pleuropodial evaginations are most conspicuous from the beginning although the prothoracic pair seem to be individually the most prominent. They are at first quite broad at the tip and blunt, but with continued growth gradually assume a more elongate, slender outline. The pleuropodia, on the contrary, remain almost as large at the tips as at their bases. The other abdominal evaginations in general remain as swellings for a time then slowly subside to the level of the pleural areas. Growth of the thoracic appendages continues as they extend outward toward the amnion and then bend posteriorly parallel to the ventral surface of the embryo. The pleuropodia at this stage are of the evaginate, limblike type. They project directly from the ectoderm of the first abdominal segment and finally come almost in contact with the amnion (Fig. 152).

Mesoblast cells invade the lumen of all the appendages very early, forming at first irregular masses of cells. Later on, they differentiate into elongate strands of syncytial cytoplasm with the nuclei arranged in linear fashion. These are the primordia of the musculature. Their inner portions appear to be continuous with the internal mesoderm rudiment and no coelomic pouches could be seen. The mesoderm apparently takes no active part in the early process of segmentation.

The Extraembryonic Envelopes and the Trophocytes.—The amnion is a narrow, elongate envelope covering the ventral portion of the embryo and attached to the latter at its margins. The posterior portion is separated from the serosa because of the flexed position of the embryo but elsewhere it lies adjacent to the latter, except for the presence of a very small amount of nutriment situated posteriorly.

The amnion is thin, with scattered nuclei whose thickness causes them to appear as swellings when this membrane is viewed in section. The chromomeres are largely accumulated at the ends of the flattened, oval nuclei but linin strands connect them.

Attention may well be directed for a moment to the apparent functions of the thickened serosa. Since there is almost no nutriment visible near the embryo, the serosa lies adjacent to the mesodermal, or dorsal, surface of the latter. A few trophocytes are present at intervals between the two, though these are largely aggregated over the thoracic region. It will further be recalled that an abundant source of food, the degenerating nurse cell body, is available immediately outside the posterior end of the serosa. In separating the embryo from its nutriment, this membrane or tissue has apparently assumed a trophic function, for certainly the embryo continues to grow in size, to acquire its nymphal structures, and is finally born (Fig. 153). At the same time the nutrient, nurse cell mass disintegrates and slowly disappears. It cannot go past the embryo for the latter, surrounded by the serosa, effectively plugs the lumen of the oviduct.

It is also quite possible that nutriment is obtained by the serosa, or trophserosa, directly from the mother by osmosis or diffusion through the wall of the oviduct. These two tissues are closely appressed and both are highly vacuolar. The vacuoles indicate physiological activity and an excess of some substance which is assumed to be nutrient in nature, especially since the vacuoles are larger in the inner portion of the serosa next to the serosal lumen in which the embryo lies.

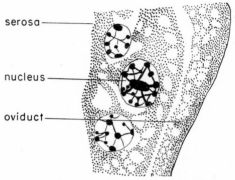

Fig. 153.—*Hesperoctenes fumarius.* Section through wall of maternal genital tract and serosa to reveal vacuoles suggesting metabolic activity in these tissues. (From Jour. Morph. and Physiol., 51, 1, by H. R. Hagan.)

It is probable that the trophocytes, dorsal to the embryo, serve as a medium for further reducing the introduced food to a more assimilable form. That an excess of some substance over the requirements of the embryo is constantly present is beyond question. An exceedingly small amount of the original fatlike contents of the egg has been mentioned as being located near the posterior end of the embryo. During further development of the latter within the serosa a very few, large, clear, elongate vacuoles appear beside the embryo. These are invariably found between the embryo and the serosa and were never noticed within the amniotic cavity. Of course, it might be assumed that these vacuoles are excretion, or waste products, but such an assumption leaves the larger problem of food supply unanswered. If these vacuoles be nutritive in nature then the disposal of waste materials, gaseous as well as liquid, oxygenation, etc., may all be functions of the serosa as well. Reference was made to a possible function of the trophocytes earlier in this paragraph and it might be well to consider them a little more in detail at this point. Following Heymon's (1912) suggestion, the word vitellophag is not used, for such cells are thought to confine their activity to the yolk within the egg. Trophocytes are active in converting foreign substances into nutrient material. These cells are few in number, stellate, apparently amoeboid and highly vacuolated, and possess exceedingly large nuclei. They lie dorsal to the mesoderm of the young embryo in the anterior region. Two or three are typically present in the immediate vicinity of the remains of the fatlike substance of the egg which lies at the posterior end of the embryo. The nuclei contain many chromomeres, some of which form occasional large masses and linin connects these formed structures in the nuclear body. One or more nucleoli seem to be present.

The trophocytes are active agents in the destruction of the embryonic membranes after blastokinesis, when they are found in close association with the ruptured serosa and amnion in the developing enteron. It is probable that they, too, finally disintegrate and are consumed after the embryonic membranes are absorbed.

Prerevolution Stage.—The ventral portion of the embryo, to the posterior abdominal segments, has rounded up because of the dorsal extension of its lateral walls. It has also straightened out anteriorly but the extreme posterior end is still flexed. Ventrally, the ectoderm has assumed the typical one-layered condition of a hypodermis but this is not true of the lateral overgrowth which shows an irregular spacing of the nuclei. The ectoderm of the limbs is likewise more than one cell layer in thickness although some thinning out of this tissue is evident.

The mesoblast cells in the thoracic appendages are arranged in two or three elongate groups which fuse together near the tip of each limb. In the region of the future haemocoele the mesoblast cells lie in scattered masses. The trophocytes are very much less numerous than the mesoblast cells but are readily discovered, because of their large size, in the space between the dorsal portion of the embryo and the adjacent serosa.

The pleuropodia at this time undergo a very peculiar partial invagination into the area of the future haemocoele. This seems to be typical for Hemiptera for Hussey (1926) has called attention to this behavior in the review of the literature and in the embryogenies of the species with which she worked. The blunt distal ends are directed vertically and project beyond the body wall almost to the amnion while their inner ends project inward to the mid-line of the embryo, just above the nerve trunk. These proximal ends enlarge and become bulbous in shape, with all of the pleuropodial nuclei distributed about their inner margins. No nuclei can now be distinguished in the outwardly projecting portions. Laterally, of course, the cells of the pleuropodia merge into the body ectoderm since they were derived from this tissue.

The nervous system extends the length of the body and forms, at this time, its largest internal structure. Specialization now occurs too, for in cross section one can see that two central areas or cores of the cord are restricted to longitudinal fibers while the nuclei are all distributed in the peripheral tissue surrounding them. Enlargements at intervals, larger anteriorly, delimit the ganglionic masses but the nerve trunks have not become structurally distinguishable from the ganglionic areas. The abdominal ganglia later become independently distinct while the thoracic ganglia tend to remain together in a compact mass.

The proctodaeal invagination can readily be seen as a rather large lumen in a cross section of the posterior end of a late germ band stage. The early stomodaeum was not found.

Katatrepsis.—With continued growth of the lateral body walls the embryo becomes increasingly cylindrical in shape along the ventral surface but is wider dorsally and at the same time somewhat shorter because of the closer union of the various segments. Some of them, indeed, tend to coalesce and are no longer externally visible. The prothoracic limbs have become about half as long as the body and are directed posteriorly, as are also the other limbs. Evidently the peculiar modification of the typical hemipteran prothoracic limb to form the curiously shaped and highly specialized hair-grasping organ of the adult polyctenid is a postnatal event that cannot be traced far back in prenatal stages. Studying the nymphal alterations of these appendages should be most interesting. The ventral ectoderm is clearly a one-layered definitive hypodermis, with the mesodermal tissue closely applied to its inner surface. The nervous system is large and occupies all of the interior ventral space with the invaginated basal ends of the pleuropodia extending into the mid-line above it. Dorsally, cells of the formative entoderm will be found just beginning to assume their definitive position in the embryo (Fig. 154).

As previously mentioned, the pleuropodia possess only basally situated nuclei, which have recently oriented themselves in their new location. Beyond them, the granular cytoplasm of these organs protrudes beyond the contours of the embryo to the amnion, which is now closely applied to the serosal envelope. Cell membranes are not distinguishable in the pleuropodia, only the right one of which is shown, while on the left of the figure in this somewhat oblique section is the margin of the metathoracic limb (Fig. 154).

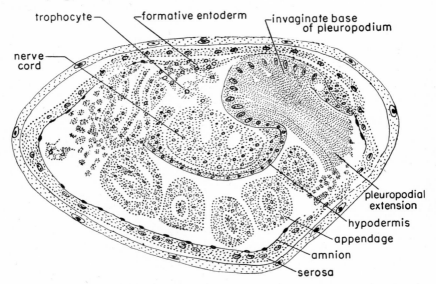

FIG. 154.—*Hesperoctenes fumarius*. Embryo in cross section prior to katatrepsis, cut diagonally through metathoracic leg on left and pleuropodium on right where the amnion has disintegrated. (From Jour. Morph. and Physiol., 51, 1, by H. R. Hagan.)

The amnion, opposite the pleuropodium that touches it, has apparently disappeared although it is intact elsewhere at this time. It is thought that this disintegration is the result of pleuropodial activity and is the first step in the destruction of both membranes, although only the initial rupture of the amnion can be seen here. The membranes of *Tenebrio* also probably undergo their initial degeneration through pleuropodial activity, according to de Selys Longchamps (1904). Whatever the cause may be at this time, the membranes cease their function. They rupture and are crowded to an anterior, dorsal position over the embryo as it undergoes katatrepsis.

The embryos seem to reverse their orientation just as they are leaving the ovarioles or are in the upper ends of the paired oviducts. Those observed had assumed a transverse position in the maternal body but at the close of this stage are so disposed that their anterior and posterior axes coincide with those of the mother. However, their dorsoventral line may be, and usually is, directed laterally in relation to the maternal position. It is only later, shortly before birth in fact, that they no longer lie on their sides. This condition is probably due to the crowding of other embryos in various stages of development.

The stomodaeum and proctodaeum are long cylindrical in-growths and the latter shows the presence of four Malpighian tubules at the inner end. Cellular aggregations between the fore- and hind-intestines presage the entoderm, as mentioned earlier.

Postrevolution Stage.—The lateral walls of ectoderm, followed by a mesodermal sheet, grow dorsally and fuse in the mid-line. This completes the external body form except in the anterodorsal region where the embryonic ectoderm has not yet encompassed the now folded and partially absorbed embryonic envelopes (Fig. 155). Aiding in the breaking down of these membranes,

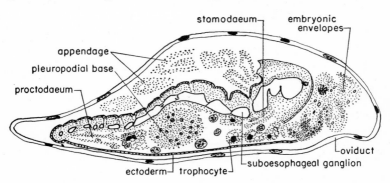

Fig. 155.—*Hesperoctenes fumarius.* Embryo after katatrepsis prior to dorsal closure with amnion and serosa ready for investment. Base of pleuropodium sectioned but extension has been omitted, longitudinal section. (From Jour. Morph. and Physiol., 51, 1, by H. R. Hagan.)

the trophocytes may be seen disposed mainly at their most posterior and posterolateral margins. Indeed, these useless organs now constitute the only apparent source of available food at this time. A weakly developed dorsal organ is visible in the serosa just anterior to the occiput of the embryo, but its function probably is quite limited for the entire mass of residual amnion and serosa is rapidly being overgrown by the embryonic ectoderm. The whole embryo now lies straightened out or only slightly curved ventrally. It will be recalled that no chorion surrounds the egg nor was there a typical follicular epithelium around it. The serosa and amnion no longer intervene between the embryo and the maternal oviduct to serve either as nutrient or protective organs. The embryo lies free in the oviduct. This remarkable condition exists, however, for only a brief period. During kata-trepsis, the pleuropodia continue their growth and extension at their distal ends. The ends of the pleuropodial extensions, in elongating, do not form solid, limblike structures but spread out as membranous sheets of tissue over the embryo. Their antero-posterior development seems to proceed faster than their lateral enveloping growth around the embryo.

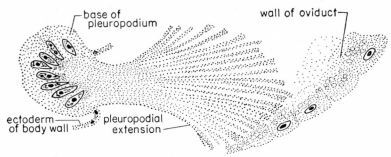

FIG. 156.—*Hesperoctenes fumarius.* Pleuropodium and its extension of cell tips toward the maternal oviduct. The more distal portion, circumscribing the embryo, is omitted. Composite drawing, longitudinal section. (From Jour. Morph. and Physiol., 51, 1, by H. R. Hagan.)

In a short time the pleuropodial extensions surround the embryo and fuse together along their distal margins, thus enclos-ing it in a new protective cytoplasmic envelope. The nuclei still remain at the proximal ends of the pleuropodia. This pleuro-podial membrane seems to consist of long cytoplasmic extensions of the individual cells though again no cell membranes could be distinguished in them. A number of authors (see Hussey, 1926) have described the pleuropodial extensions of embryos under their observation as consisting of granular cytoplasm, a statement which applies also to the organs in this insect. Some have declared cell membranes were visible also but none could be seen in *Hesperoctenes.* Yet the cell boundaries were apparently dis-cernible in the vertical portion, possibly because of shrinkage phe-nomena, shown in Figure 156, where a single pleuropodium is shown in longitudinal section as it touches the maternal oviduct. The pleuropodial extensions enveloping the embryo seem to have no distinguishable cellular structure and the entire envelope, devoid of nuclei, appears to be a membranous sheet of vacuolated, granular cytoplasm.

When the pleuropodia have completely surrounded the embryo they appear as shown in Figure 157. It will be recognized, in spite of the evident distortion of the symmetry of the figure due to pressure of adjacent embryos, that the embryo is broader, the dorsal wall at this point is complete, and the hypodermis is lined internally by embryonic mesoderm. Oenocytes have appeared in the dorsolateral region; the inner ends of the pleuropodia are no longer adjacent and the intervening space is occupied by the newly formed enteron. The trophocytes and embryonic envelopes are enclosed within the enteron, where they serve as nourishment for the embryo.

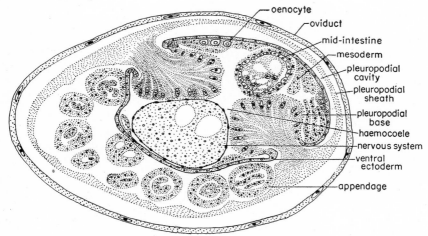

FIG. 157.—*Hesperoctenes fumarius*. Embryo in cross section, and long section of the pleuropodia, after katatrepsis. Amnion and serosa lie within the mesenteron. (From Jour. Morph. and Physiol., 51, 1, by H. R. Hagan.)

The pleuropodial sheath which completely surrounds the embryo appears to have no cell membranes. Furthermore, the point of fusion of the right and left pleuropodial extensions, which entered into the formation of the sheath, cannot be detected. This sheath is never independent of the embryo but is at all times, until its destruction, attached to the ectoderm of the embryo by the stalks and bases of the two pleuropodia. It is proposed that the envelope itself be termed the *pleuropodial sheath* to distinguish it from the preceding embryonic membranes, and the space enclosed by it may be called the *pleuropodial cavity*. The entire organ may be known as a *pseudoplacenta,* a term which likewise should be applied to the analogous nutrient structure in *Hemimerus*.

A nutritive function has been ascribed to the pleuropodial sheath. Examination of the maternal oviduct shows the epithelial, or mesothelial, cells of the tract to be highly vacuolar. The sheath shows exactly the same condition except that the vacuoles are smaller, becoming larger only on the boundary next the pleuropodial cavity. Along this border, moreover, some of the larger vacuoles actually protrude into the pleuropodial cavity. A rupture of the thin walls of such vacuoles would discharge their contents into the latter (Fig. 158).

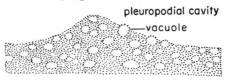

Fig. 158.—*Hesperoctenes fumarius*. Enlarged portion of the pleuropodial sheath to reveal its vacuolated condition. (From Jour. Morph. and Physiol., **51**, 1, by H. R. Hagan.)

Less direct but valuable additional evidence is furnished by the lack of any other apparent source of nourishment except the remains of the amnion and serosa. These are thought to be insufficient to complete development. It is also recalled that epithelium is plastic and serves many useful functions in different animals, one of which is the absorption of nutrient substances. This normally occurs, for example, in the stomach or intestines of animals having these parts, through the trophserosa of certain insect embryos, by the external epithelium of several species of internal parasites with rudimentary or no alimentary tracts, and through the mesothelium of the mammalian placenta. In fact, there is every reason to suppose its absorptive function to be quite analogous to the trophoblast of the very young mammalian embryo. Further, it was maintained that in the absence of yolk the serosa served a trophic function as well as a protective one. Since the serosa has been destroyed, the pleuropodial sheath assumed the latter function, and presumably the former as well, for food requirements still persist and no other intermediary for its transmission to the embryo can be found. The large size and favorable position of the inner ends of the pleuropodia, which remain attached to their extensions in the sheath, render them especially suitable for the distribution of nutriment within the haemocoele, their bulk and position rivaling these features of the intestinal tract. It is further assumed that the pleuropodial sheath serves for the excretion of waste products, the exchange of gases, and as a physical substitute for a chorion.

The thoracic appendages have grown until they reach the posterior end of the body and constrictions at intervals upon their surfaces indicate the future segmentation of these organs. The nervous system has continued its contraction and coalescence. It now consists of three very large ganglia: (1) the supraoesophageal, (2) a suboesophageal united with the first thoracic ganglion, and (3) the meso-metathoracic ganglion which includes all the abdominal ganglia, too, for some of their original boundaries are still visible superficially. The internal histological structure shows the bilateral or paired origin of the nervous system but this is not evident externally. Fat body cells have formed and are disposed in segmental masses. They are large cells because of the three or four vacuoles which distend each one. Myoblast cells, which were simply elongate clusters of cells in earlier stages, are now found to be grouped at first as linear strands of cells, with nuclei almost as great in diameter as the strand itself. A little later the strands become attached at their distal ends and the cytoplasmic portion grows in volume so that the nuclei are superficially placed upon them. The development of the musculature of the appendages lags slightly behind that of the thoracic region.

Precuticular Stage.—An older embryo in this same stage, which is arbitrarily designated the precuticular stage, offers a little additional differentiation. It has practically attained its greatest length prior to hatching. The thoracic appendages extend to the tip of the abdomen where the long meso- and metathoracic legs cross to the opposite lateroventral sides and extend cephalad. The prothoracic pair have not kept pace with the others and consequently are shorter and relatively thick.

The internal musculature is complete in the anterior segments where the large muscle strands have internally placed nuclei in a linear arrangement. The nuclei, however, are globular and have not attained their definitive elongate shape. Cross striations penetrate part way in from the surface but do not as yet occupy the central portion of each muscle fiber. The abdominal muscles are somewhat retarded in development, compared with the foregoing.

Before this stage no trace of stigmatic invaginations was discovered, but spiracular openings are now plainly seen disposed segmentally, with the main longitudinal trunks connected to their branches. The walls of the tracheae are made up of a single layer of flat, long, epithelial cells with flattened nuclei. No tracheoles are yet visible.

During blastoderm formation the primordial germ cells were found and described. In the precuticular stage they may again be seen lying in paired gonads which are elongate, cylindrical bodies whose single-layered mesothelial covering extends anteriorly to form the paired genital ducts. They are situated in the abdomen directly above the anterior portion of the mesenteron. The contents consist of about 50 large nuclei embedded in cytoplasm that reveals no cellular boundaries. They are very large, being second in size only to the nuclei of the active trophocytes of an earlier stage.

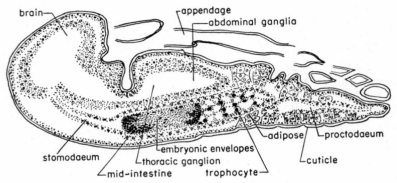

Fig. 159.—*Hesperoctenes fumarius.* Half grown embryo, cuticular stage. The pleuropodial sheath, details of appendages and the maternal oviduct are omitted, longitudinal section. (From Jour. Morph. and Physiol., 51, 1, by H. R. Hagan.)

Cuticular Stage.—The cuticular stage represents the earliest embryo found to be invested with a cuticula, but this structure could not be detected in its alimentary tract (Fig. 159). The embryo has become very large and this increase in size has required another orientation. It no longer lies on its side but has turned over until its dorsoventral axis coincides with that of the mother. Other embryos, and the portion of the maternal reproductive tract enclosing them, have been pushed forward to a position near the head of the large cuticularized embryo.

Sections of the embryo reveal advances internally. The walls of the tracheae are very thin and the lumen is lined with a cuticular layer. The embryonic membranes either have been digested and absorbed, or will be shortly, and even the trophocytes will have practically disappeared. The slight residuum is probably waste material to be evacuated immediately after birth. The epithelial cells of the mesenteron, which in the earliest complete stage were subquadrate and later on flattened and highly vacuolate, have now become columnar in shape with basally situated nuclei. Compared with the fore- and hind-intestines, the mesenteron is very large both in diameter and in length. The hind-intestine is short and coiled and the Malpighian tubules are very long. Since their structure and early ontogeny are typical of other insects, the details are omitted here. The musculature is typical of the hatched nymph except in the intersegmental spaces, where it is slightly retarded in development.

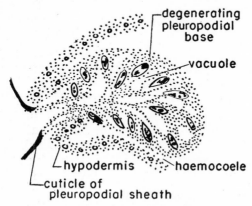

Fig. 160.—*Hesperoctenes fumarius.* Degenerating base of pleuropodium with a portion of the non-chitinous cuticle secreted by the sheath; the last already has been destroyed. Embryonic cuticula omitted, longitudinal section. (From Jour. Morph. and Physiol., **51**, 1, by H. R. Hagan.)

An interesting observation on the origin of the genital system is revealed by this embryo. The ducts from the gonads have grown forward and down, thence posteriorly, as paired narrow tubules, each with a terminal bulbous or clavate mass of cells. At the same time an invaginating portion of the ectoderm near the posterior end of the abdomen has formed a tube of larger diameter which has invaginated anteriorly to meet the two ducts just described. Upon the fusion of all three, the mesodermal paired oviducts will have their lumens open into that of the common oviduct. Hence the mesodermal origin of the paired oviducts and the ectodermal derivation of the common oviduct are plainly shown.

The pleuropodial sheath becomes thin in this stage but still encloses the embryo. It also seems to have differentiated into an outer dense but finely granular layer, a lighter staining and less granular middle layer, and an inner layer composed of ovate or rounded masses which appear to be the first steps in the disintegration of this organ. Externally, the sheath is bounded by a very thin structureless cuticula which appears first in the posterior and anterior regions before finally investing the entire sheath. This cuticula definitely serves to prevent the intimate, direct contact formerly existing between the sheath and the maternal oviduct. Graber (1888) has described such a cuticula formed by the serosa of *Melolontha* on its exterior surface.

The inner ends of the pleuropodia become irregular in shape and smaller in size. The nuclei slip away from their earlier, definite positions and some of them obviously are breaking down (Fig. 160). These steps are accompanied by increased vacuolation in the region of the nuclei and it is evident that the nutrient and protective functions of the pleuropodia are over. The latest observed steps in the process show the invaginated portions of the pleuropodia to be constricted into rather small, elongate cylindrical structures pressed between the circumscribing pleura which project slightly outward around them. The sheath eventually disappears entirely, leaving behind only the cuticula it has recently secreted, which perhaps functions as a protective structure during birth, since the embryo is relatively very large and clothed with numerous stout setae.

It should be emphasized that during this development of the embryo, and in the appearance, growth, functional activity and eventual disintegration of the various nutrient organs, the offspring has migrated down the maternal reproductive tract to its final position in the common oviduct. Its progress presumably was in a series of short downward movements as preceding offspring were born in turn. Just before birth the young nymph lies before the external genital opening with its anteroposterior axis not quite coinciding with that of the mother because of the pressure of another large embryo adjacent to its head. The head is flexed ventrally beneath the prothorax and its appendages are pressed against the body, as outlined previously. At this time its width is about half that of the maternal abdomen and it extends from the genital opening almost to the metathoracic segment.

LITERATURE CITED

Berlese (1898–99), Carazzi (1902), Cragg (1920), Graber (1888), Gros (1923), Haase (1888), Hagan (1931), Heymons (1912), Hussey (1926), Jordan (1911a, 1911b, 1912, 1922), Lowne (1871), de Peyerimhoff (1913), Rethfeldt (1924), Ribaga (1897), de Selys Longchamps (1904), Trouessart (1895), Uichanco (1924).

Chapter 15

APPRAISAL OF VIVIPARITY

The preceding chapters on the four types of viviparity and the embryonic development of insects in relation to them confront one with more unsolved problems and questions than have been answered. In addition, several more are suggested under the general topics discussed in the following pages. They constitute a vital and fruitful field of research for those interested in either the morphological or physiological aspects of insect embryology.

It may be expedient to note again the distribution of the viviparous types among insects. Approximately one third of the orders possess species said to be ovoviviparous. In taxonomic sequence, ovoviviparity starts with the Thysanoptera and appears frequently in other orders, including several of the highest. Adenotrophic and haemocoelic types are confined to Diptera and Strepsiptera. Surprisingly, the pseudoplacental type is represented in five orders and these extend from Dermaptera, a fairly primitive order, to the Homoptera and Hemiptera which are still below five higher orders, most of which show one or more viviparous types. However, no order more primitive than Dermaptera is known to show viviparity.

Modifications Associated with Viviparity

Now that the available histories of the viviparous insects have been reviewed, it remains for us to observe, in summary form, departures from oviparous conditions shown by mother and offspring which seem to accompany this method of reproduction. That such divergences may likewise be expressed to some extent in certain oviparous species is a fact that will be considered later.

1. **Ovoviviparity.**—It should at once be noted that this type of viviparity possesses two subdivisions: occasional or facultative viviparity and obligate viviparity. In the former, viviparity may occur only at the beginning of deposition with eggs appearing later; in the latter, eggs invariably hatch in the maternal repro-

415

ductive tract prior to deposition. As a rule only the obligate insects have been considered although the occasionally viviparous species should be thoroughly investigated experimentally to discover some of the factors controlling their reproductive behavior.

MATERNAL PHYSICAL MODIFICATIONS. Ovarioles may be reduced in number. An egg calyx is wanting and ova descend to the common oviduct which may be greatly enlarged in saccular form, or elongated, to retain the eggs until embryonic development culminates in hatching. Or it may become very short and simply serve as an abbreviated passageway for larvae already developed and seeking liberation before reaching it. There is frequently a characteristic loss of bursa and spermathecae, as well as a modification of the accessory glands. The chorion is usually a delicate membrane around the egg. Likewise, the oötheca or gelatinous matrix enclosing the eggs, if present normally, is thinner, but is often incomplete or absent. Oöcytes frequently mature in the ovariole and spermatozoa, having ascended there, are enabled to penetrate the eggs prior to the formation of the chorion. Embryonic development may thus be initiated in the ovariole.

MATERNAL PHYSIOLOGICAL ADJUSTMENTS. Ovulation may change from a practically simultaneous process for all of the reproductive elements to a serial event with relatively few ova being liberated as functional units at any one time. The gravid female thus usually deposits offspring at intervals, so her active reproductive life may be prolonged far beyond related insects of oviparous habits. Instead of slackening her activities and awaiting death after oviposition, her metabolic rate remains high until she has discovered favorable environments for each of her viviparously produced offspring. Somehow, spermatozoa are nourished elsewhere than in the spermatheca, when this organ is absent, and they are enabled to survive in the ovariole. Finally, and most curious, is the apparent necessity for the mother to secrete some hormone or otherwise insure immunity against attack and destruction of her own tissues by offspring when they are normally predatory in feeding habits.

MATERNAL PSYCHIC ADJUSTMENTS. The maternal nervous system seems to be adjusted to the retention of hatched larvae in her reproductive system and to restrain an earlier reflex to deposit them at once in a mass. Instead of this she maintains solicitous care of each until the proper habitat is discovered, then deposits one or more of them. This often is the rule, regardless of the type of food she seeks for her offspring. As an example, *Sarcophaga kellyi* Aldrich deposits a single larva on each of the host grasshoppers it selects, many of them even in flight. Contrary to the reaction of related oviparous species, the ephemerids thought to be viviparous retain their ova ten days or more to enable the offspring to hatch internally before they are scattered over the water to shift for themselves. There seems to be no doubt that the female producing offspring viviparously must become adjusted in several respects to an added burden in her own economy.

Ovoviviparity is apparently primarily due to modifications of the mother while the embryonic life of the offspring seems to be affected only slightly, or not at all. It is the simplest type of viviparity as well as the most commonly observed. Nevertheless, some observations on larval adjustments are justified. No physical or physiological modifications in the larva are known.

LARVAL PSYCHIC ADJUSTMENTS. The removal of a soft, pliable chorion, constantly moist in the cramped quarters of the maternal reproductive tract, is a distinctly different process than escaping from it when hardened, more brittle and dried by exposure to the atmosphere. Viviparously produced offspring constantly encounter this change successfully. It is not insurmountable by some oviparous offspring who emerge occasionally under similar conditions when the mother dies before the eggs are laid. Also, the offspring of parasitic species are regularly confronted by a similar situation. But this does not lessen the strength of the contention that escape from the chorion is more difficult under this handicap; such species also have this capacity. There must be, also, some psychical adjustment that keeps the larvae immobile or benign parasites, resting quietly in the maternal uterus until deposition comes in turn to each of them. Contrary to reported observations that dissected sarcophagid oviducts revealed wriggling offspring, the writer, in very carefully dissecting two undetermined species, found the contained larvae to be regularly and similarly disposed in the uterus and quiescent. Upon touching the uterus lightly with a probe the larvae twitched readily enough then again lay quiet. However, upon using a hooked microneedle and gently tearing open the delicate uterine wall without touching the larvae, great activity was at once evident among them and they promptly crawled in various directions. Again, it is quite unknown why such larvae, especially when of parasitic or predatory habit, do not consume their mother. As suggested before, it may be due to some maternal secretion, to psychic adjustment, or to a physiological lack of oxygen in the confined space alloted to them. Diffusion through maternal tissues must certainly control the amount of carbon dioxide present but the small quantity of available oxygen may preclude active movements by these offspring.

2. Adenotrophic Viviparity.—While ovoviviparity presents several adaptations to foster viviparity, nearly all these departures from the oviparous condition are confined to the mother insect. Adenotrophic viviparity reveals very profound modifications on the part of the offspring, as well as the adult female. The rapprochement between the two generations is so great there is no possibility of oviparity or ovoviviparity occurring in these insects. Maternal solicitude and nourishment are essential to the larva up to the time of pupation and, in some species, even the site for the pupal stadium is maternally selected.

MATERNAL PHYSICAL MODIFICATIONS. Terminal filaments are very reduced or lacking entirely from ovarioles. The latter have diminished in number to one or two for each ovary and their follicles are limited to not more than five at any one time. The paired oviducts have practically, if not completely, disappeared from the reproductive system. The common oviduct is enlarged, not to accommodate several to many reproductive elements, but to support one huge offspring periodically. This region may be subdivided into an atrium, uterus, and vagina. Spermathecal glands are variable in number, sometimes reduced from three to two (Glossinidae) and their function is frequently entirely altered (Pupipara). The remaining accessory glands have assumed a purely nutrient role and are voluminous in size during gestation. All glands open at the end of a papilla extending into the lumen of the uterus immediately before the larval mouth. Uterus and vagina are unusually muscular and are reinforced by additional muscles extending to the maternal hypodermis both for the support of the organ and to aid in expelling the offspring. The vaginal portion is short and leads to the exterior by means of a large vulva which may be partly open at times for larval respiration.

MATERNAL PHYSIOLOGICAL ADJUSTMENTS. The mother's metabolism must be materially altered to sustain the drain of almost continuously providing sufficient assimilable food for the young individual she is harboring and nourishing and also to fill her own requirements. Further, this nutriment must be elaborated by accessory glands to a form which is suitable for the needs of her offspring. This food is not a yolky substance, but something quite different in physical and chemical properties. In performing this task, the accessory glands have departed from their original function and, in addition, show seasons of periodicity in their activity and extension through the haemocoele that correspond with gestation. The follicular cells continue furnishing yolk for the embryo in the egg in the usual way. The atrium, when present, is physiologically adjusted for the preservation of sperm while the spermathecae have apparently lost that power in such cases. Likewise, the ovarioles exhibit periodicity in ovulation, a function which they now share in alternation.

MATERNAL PSYCHIC ADJUSTMENTS. One of the astonishing characteristics of some species (*Glossina, Melophagus*) is the ability of the female to produce abortions under certain conditions that involve no physical contact or abuse. Examples of such stimuli are exposure to higher temperatures or simply confinement in captivity. While she thus shows some power over the maintenance of the pregnant condition, these manifestations under excessive stimuli do not permit one to assume that larval retention is a "voluntary" act or that abortions are possible under normal circumstances. However, it does reveal an unexpected adjustment of the nervous system which is probably a protective escape mechanism under adverse environments. The retention of the larva over a long period, bulky as it is a considerable part of the time, suggests a nervous adjustment that prevents early deposition until the larva is prepared for pupation. This event then causes the release of another ovum into the uterus just vacated; this, in turn, is followed by the formation of a replacing oöcyte at the upper end of the ovariole. Just which of these events may be due to physiological or psychic adjustments is apparently unknown.

LARVAL PHYSICAL MODIFICATIONS. The egg hatches within a day or two after it reaches the uterus. There the larva escapes from the chorion of the egg and two hypodermal cuticulae as it molts, no small physical feat in a confined space. It resides in the uterus, unable to do more than force food into its storage stomach by means of a highly specialized pumping organ (tongue), twitch the body a little if stimulated, and slightly compress it in respiratory movements. The oral hooks have dis-

appeared. A posterior swelling or ridge develops to enable the
larva to respire without having the stigmata plugged by the
walls of the maternal oviduct. The larvae of some species are
capable of penetrating the soil for pupating, others are practically immobile because almost all musculature has vanished.

The vast storage portion of the mid-intestine is simply a
reservoir for retention of the products of the maternal accessory
glands, a pabulum so nearly the perfect food that the larva has
no salivary glands or gastric caeca. Nor does the larva depend
on a fat body to store reserves after elaboration so this organ is
very scantily represented. Apparently the larva absorbs sufficient food from the mid-intestine for its immediate needs and
stores the balance for pupation. The hind-intestine accumulates
the waste products of metabolism and growth from the Malpighian tubules throughout larval life. The hind-intestine ends
blindly at both ends and acts as a reservoir quite as the stomach
does but this accretion is waste that cannot otherwise be voided.

LARVAL PHYSIOLOGICAL CHANGES. With maternal care and
the loss of muscles, movement, migration, and detection of food
are unnecessary or impossible of achievement. As a generality,
larvae of other species utilize different sources of food than that
which the adult seeks; in this type of viviparity the larva is adjusted to utilize the same, or practically identical, end products
of the mother's food selection. The larva retains the surplus
food, over and above present needs, in a physiologically as well
as physically modified stomach. Excretion remains in the hind-
intestine throughout its uterine life without ill effects. There
are no solid wastes. Lateral spiracles are present but only the
posterior stigmata are used for oxygen intake. Practically all
metabolic activity is associated only with growth requirements,
little energy being used for movement or respiration.

LARVAL PSYCHIC ADJUSTMENTS. Response to stimulation is
primarily limited to feeding from a uterine papilla, respiration,
and molting its larval cuticulae. Aside from these activities the
uterine larva exhibits none of the responses to the environment
characteristic of oviparous larvae, nor does it need to do so. The
larva apparently receives no external environmental stimuli until
after birth.

3. **Haemocoelous Viviparity.**—In this type of viviparity the
reproductive process breaks entirely away from conventional
methods of embryonic development within the confines of a re-

productive system, common to most viviparous species, and from the normal expulsion of eggs in the oviparous forms. Here, reproduction takes place in the maternal haemocoele and offspring must seek other means of leaving to shift for themselves as older, more mature larvae.

MATERNAL PHYSICAL MODIFICATIONS. Parthenogenesis is the rule among Diptera, but in Strepsiptera copulation consists of inserting sperm within the last larval cuticula which remains undiscarded about the female. Females are paedogenetic larvae or they are considered neotenic in the case of the Strepsiptera. The reproductive system is lacking except for the ovaries embedded in the fat body. Having no oviducts, parturition is not conventional but the offspring must either open exits through the body wall or leave by means of special pores which close behind them to prevent their return to the mother's body cavity. Maternal ovaries are readily dissociated and the ova distributed throughout the haemocoele by maternal muscular contractions and by the circulation of the haemolymph.

MATERNAL PHYSIOLOGICAL ADJUSTMENTS. Maternal feeding and storage of surplus food in extensive fat bodies progress rapidly enough so that both she and her offspring may have sufficient food when the reserves are called upon. She apparently suffers no metabolic loss because of the added drain on such reserves even though, in some species, embryonic development is not synchronous and may continue a long time. The nurse cells in some cases (Diptera) appear to be derived from maternal mesoderm. The ability to secrete a chorion over the eggs is lost.

MATERNAL PSYCHIC ADJUSTMENTS. Being devoid of reproductive systems, there is no direct sexual relationship. Nevertheless, the female strepsipteran must secrete some attractant to lure the male and cause him to deposit spermatozoa near her adequate for the needs of her ova. Due to her specialized parasitic habit, she has become largely nothing more than an incubatory sac for her offspring and reveals no observed irritation from the predatory feeding of the young within (*Miastor*, etc.).

LARVAL PHYSICAL AND PHYSIOLOGICAL MODIFICATIONS. The early embryo develops a trophic membrane which contributes the necessary food supply from the maternal tissues. The embryo's own germ cells may develop and be recognizable very early (Diptera) and certain embryonic somatic cells may undergo a marked change in polarity (Strepsiptera) due to altered physiological and physical necessities. Embryonic respiration and disposal of metabolic wastes within the same liquid medium in which the embryo lives must present problems. Accumulated wastes and oxygen deficit might, in part, account for the failure of all offspring to develop successfully. Contrary to preceding types of viviparity, in this type the young haemocoelous larvae are adjusted to active feeding on maternal tissues and cannibalism is normal (*Miastor*, etc.). However, some physiological discrimination must be practiced by the offspring, for the maternal dorsal vessel and nervous system are spared so that the offspring's source of food will not die and disintegrate prior to the completion of their own feeding cycle within. Upon emergence, their food requirements abruptly change. Strepsipteran larvae probably emerge shortly after liberation from the trophic membranes.

LARVAL PSYCHIC ADJUSTMENTS. Dipterous offspring seem to react to some stimulus (possibly hunger or the impending death of the mother) and simultaneously cut exit holes through the maternal cuticula to make their escape; it is no longer a more or less passive submission to uterine expulsion. In the Strepsiptera, each offspring at the proper time, apparently, seeks and discovers an exit tube by which it escapes into the brood canal. From this it leaves through an opening at its anterior end.

4. Pseudoplacental Viviparity.—This type of viviparity differs from the others in that while the mother avoids extreme modifications the embryo is more aggressive in determining the manner in which its nourishment may be obtained. The egg of none of the species possesses sufficient nourishment for development, and to secure it the embryo utilizes structures formerly related to other functions, or which are considered functionless in most insects. Like haemocoelous species, the offspring are born singly or in small numbers. The mother usually reproduces periodically over a comparatively longer time than related oviparous forms.

MATERNAL PHYSICAL MODIFICATIONS. In general terms, the modifications most nearly resemble those noted in adenotrophic females. Ovarioles vary from two to six in the ovary. Seminal receptacles, their glands and accessory glands are absent from some and present in other species. Paired oviducts are variable in length but frequently short, while the common oviduct is divided in some cases into the same enlarged portions as adenotrophic species, or similar spaces for incubatory purposes.

MATERNAL PHYSIOLOGICAL ADJUSTMENTS. In only one species is a chorion secreted around the ovum, so this function has largely disappeared. Ovarial fertilization is the rule except in the parthenogenetic species and *Diploptera*. Embryonic development begins in the ovariole except in *Diploptera*. Yolk is either reduced or quite absent, so the early egg is relatively small. In most cases the eggs are released in alternation from the vitellaria. The ovarioles or oviducts are capable of passing nutriment from the haemocoele to the trophic organ of the embryo. It cannot be said there are any psychic adjustments in the mother beyond those already noted for ovoviviparity except, perhaps, for *Diploptera* where the nervous response to egg retention may more nearly approach conditions in adenotrophic females. This is assumed because the gestation period is long and the retained eggs increase slowly to considerable size.

LARVAL PHYSICAL MODIFICATIONS AND PHYSIOLOGICAL ADJUSTMENTS. In this type of viviparity it is apparently necessary for the offspring to supply the trophic organs. The mother can only place the nutriment she has elaborated in proximity to the developing embryo. More than in preceding types, mother and young must cooperate in food transference, in order that the latter may survive in the midst of plenty. For trophic structures the larva employs various organs, sometimes two or three in succession. Of these *Hemimerus* possesses a special nuchal attachment in the older embryo whereby the posterodorsal side of the head is connected to a maternal "pseudoplacental mass" of follicular cells. Psocids also have, for a short time, a dorsal organ in a position similar to that of *Hemimerus*. All use one or both of the embryonic membranes, the amnion and serosa, to obtain nutriment from the wall of the oviduct. Two use a pseudoplacental organ by reviving and greatly enlarging the pleuropodia and assigning them this task. Trophocytes often seem to play a most important role in converting substances obtained from the mother into assimilable food for the embryo. Possible psychic responses cannot be discussed effectively since the embryos are not retained in the mother after they are fully developed. None are nourished orally.

In outlining these modifications and adjustments to the viviparous condition, there has been no intention of obscuring the fact that oviparous insects, too, may show some of them in scattered instances. Oviparous insects, however, usually do not possess these modifications to such a marked extent, so universally, or with such obvious direct utility as do viviparous insects. The longer, active reproductive life of some viviparous insects is not infrequently matched by certain ovipositing species. Fertilization of the egg in the ovariole is not unknown in oviparous species, nor is reduction of the oötheca and its uterine retention for most of the embryonic period of the offspring. But may not these, and other similar examples occasionally found in oviparous forms, be properly considered as perhaps the first evolutionary steps toward eventual viviparity?

The Problem of Fertilization

The problem of insuring fertilization of the egg is not essentially an embryological one. Yet at one time it must have been, and perhaps still is, a critical stage in the life cycle of many viviparous insects. The greater difficulties in fertilizing the ova of viviparous species are inherent in the very fact that these insects are viviparous. The viviparous condition seems to have been imposed on a genital system originally and primarily equipped for oviparity. It might, therefore, be appropriate to mention briefly a few of these obstacles to fertilization and other variations from oviparous conditions.

The hazards of fertilization of the oviparous egg are apparently reduced to the minimum. Oviparous insects mate and store sperm in receptacula. The oviduct is usually short and the receptacula are conveniently situated near the vulva. The maternal response to the descent of an egg is to discharge some of the stored sperm over the egg as it passes the appropriate orifice. The egg-laying period is brief and death claims the female when her eggs are deposited.

With most of the ovoviviparous insects the problem of egg insemination becomes at once apparent. Ova must be inseminated higher up the oviduct, for the lower end must serve as an incubatory chamber. This means sperm must be delivered, or must migrate, over a longer distance and be stored at a higher elevation in the oviduct. Among Sarcophagidae and Tachinidae, for example, sperm must often pass through a voluminous uterine chamber. Frequently they must ascend very elongate convoluted or coiled uteri, with the receptacula far removed from the vulva. Receptacula are often lacking, as morphologists have frequently remarked from Von Siebold's time to the present, and the sperm supply must be assured in other ways.

When only a few eggs are incubated at a time, ovulation continues for many days, or over periods of weeks or months. In such cases life expectancy of the adult female has been correspondingly prolonged to maintain the population. The duration of the mother's reproductive life is thus related to viviparity and is likewise a factor to be reckoned with in the problem of fertilization of all the eggs to be produced. Accessory factors in the problem enter most obviously here: the number and frequency of mating in relation to ovulation, the reasons for prolonged ovulations, how sperm are cared for, how their viability is maintained, and so on.

A serious problem confronts viviparous Thysanoptera, Homoptera, Chrysomelidae, Corrodentia, Dermaptera, and the Polyctenidae for ovarial fertilization is the rule. Spermathecae are often absent or are not attached to the oviduct. Spermatozoa must ascend the common and paired oviducts, or by some other route arrive at the ovariole in order to reach the oöcytes where embryonic development takes place. The oöcyte rests on a cellular plug which occludes the lumen of the ovariole. Furthermore, in cases where several stages of development may occur simultaneously in each ovariole, all oöcytes in the linear series are separated from one another by a follicular epithelium and occluding cellular plugs in the lumen. In Chrysomelidae, too, not only is development continuing over a long period of time but also a few young are descending the oviducts and being born at 48-hour intervals. Of all these cases, only the situation in the Polyctenidae has been partially revealed, as outlined in Chapter 14.

Adenotrophic species have ingeniously solved the most serious aspects of their problem. The Glossinidae, the Streblidae and Nycteribiidae are said to retain functional spermathecae while *Melophagus* seems to utilize the atrium for the temporary storage of sperm. Ovulation in all these species follows the same pattern in that only one oöcyte is liberated at a time. Availability of the oöcyte is, then, similar to, but more complicated than it is in oviparous species. That the solution is not perfect may be deduced from reports that sperm are occasionally found in the medium surrounding the developing embryo or larva in the maternal uterus. The females of Glossinidae have another interesting reflex to insure a supply of viable spermatozoa, a reflex which might well apply to Pupipara, too, if the facts were known. Ovulation takes place only as a result of the stimulation induced by the inseminated condition of the female (Roubaud, 1909).

Haemocoelous species have met the problem of fertilization differently. Like the pseudoplacental aphids, some of them have avoided the solution, in a sense, by becoming parthenogenetic. This has involved, however, a far more drastic and sweeping change because the process of meiosis has been altered. Perhaps it is much better to state that the alteration of maturation in the oöcyte nucleus has completely obliterated the necessity of utilizing spermatozoa at all. Strepsiptera offer a most peculiar modification of the fertilization problem. Oviducts do not exist in these species. Spermatozoa are deposited on the anterior end of the neotinic female's body within the unshed, last larval cuticle. The spermatozoa must apparently make their way over the hypodermis to the brood canals, thence to the haemocoele, and there find the scattered oöcytes.

One cannot attempt at present to account for the peculiar organs and solutions to the problem of fertilization revealed by viviparous insects. Too little is known concerning this rich field of investigation. At one time Professor G. F. Ferris of Stanford University remarked that a thorough investigation of the problem should prove to be extremely illuminating and a valuable contribution.

The problem and its partial solution are sometimes revealed in most bizarre fashion, even among oviparous insects. One example will be used in closing this discussion because it can be compared with the problem existing in a viviparous family as well. At present no interpretation can be suggested for the necessity of the singular organs of Berlese and Ribaga in *Cimex* where the ordinary method of insemination would appear to be so much more simple, direct, and convenient for this oviparous genus. The Cimicidae and Polyctenidae are related families of insects, the former is oviparous, the latter viviparous. Both have the same type of male genitalia. In some respects their methods of caring for spermatozoa are similar, in others they are very dissimilar. Both methods are distinctive and peculiar to these families.

The Causes of Viviparity

Of the many beliefs expressed as to the influences in nature which are responsible for the appearance of viviparity in insects, only a few need be cited for historical purposes, and these will be listed in summary form. Among those who ascribe viviparity to environmental influences are the following: the influence of summer's heat, Redi (1668); abbreviation of the egg stage to meet a very short summer season, Kusnezov (1909–10), Caillol (1914), Rethfeldt (1924), Henneberg (1927); high temperatures with rich, abundant food, Kyber (1815), Balbiani (1898); coprophagus feeding of larva, Townsend (1911); utilitarian adaptation to contact food supply before it changes, spoils, or is consumed by competitive species, Holmgren (1904), Patton and Cragg (1913), and Portchinski (1910).

To the question as to whether parasitism, in itself, produces viviparity, the answer seems to be negative from the evidence available. Coleopterous platypsyllids are external parasites of beavers and bear a remarkable, superficial resemblance to *Hesperoctenes fumarius*, an hemipteran which lives in the fur of bats. While their mammalian hosts offer quite similar environments to them, and convergent structural appearance would readily confuse many regarding their true taxonomic position, nevertheless the former is oviparous, the latter viviparous. Both are obligate parasites. Likewise, the glossinids are comparable to *Musca stabulans* in feeding yet the latter is oviparous. The genus *Chrysomela* contains phytophagus species, the majority of which are oviparous, while a few are viviparous, as are the aphids on the same plants. Mallophaga, Anoplura, Siphonaptera, and Cimicidae are external oviparous parasites.

Others have suggested genetic and physiological explanations of viviparity and its successful maintenance in insects. John (1923) believes physiological processes are primarily sufficient to explain it, as, also, does Roubaud (1909). The latter adds, significantly, that high temperature and rich food are related to the phenomenon of viviparous reproduction in Glossinidae.

In the light of present knowledge, perhaps no one would seriously object to the assumption that viviparity has resulted from the accumulation of minor cenogenetic modifications that have very gradually supplanted the oviparous method of reproduction. The validity of this assumption is briefly discussed under another topic, the future of viviparity. Theoretically, such steps might be conceived as, first, a heritable capacity for a slightly delayed deposition of eggs while the female seeks favorable environments for them. This might, in turn, be prolonged until internal hatching came to precede extrusion as a regular routine. These may be the result only of physiological and psychic genetic factors whose initial influence on the mother might be relatively mild.

A physical enlargement of the common oviduct would be an aid in such retention and of decided benefit to both mother and offspring in insuring the eventual discovery of suitable habitats by reducing the urgency for deposition. These could be some of the logical and measurable steps leading to ovoviviparity.

Quite independently of the preceding changes, additional alterations of the female reproductive system could occur without, at first, having any marked influence on the reproductive process. Accessory glands might become larger, more active, and alter the nature of their secretions. The reduction of the seminal receptacles or physiologically new secretions elsewhere could lead spermatozoa into the paired oviducts or to the ovary. The reduction of nurse-cell nutrients or diminished contributions from the follicular epithelium would leave the egg impoverished, with resultant dependence of the developing embryo, or the larva, on other sources of nutriment.

A reduction in the number of ovarioles has definitely occurred in some oviparous insects. It is a common phenomenon in viviparous species and is an example of the changes taking place in their reproductive systems, only we are more accustomed to this type of variability and accept the fact with little comment. The examples previously listed are also facts; they all exist. Our only difficulty lies in relating them to viviparity in function, time, and sequence. It is suggested that time and sequence are only important in so far as their presence is required, if the species is to survive, before some critical mutation elsewhere in the reproductive system calls on them in relation to the needs of the young. No doubt, many species at present already possess one or more of these departures from the average without their becoming immediately essential to survival. It must be equally true that many species have perished in the past due to their absence when needed. In the following few pages an attempt will be made to illustrate and analyze some of the modifications that seem pertinent from an evolutionary viewpoint.

Evolutionary Trends Toward Viviparity

Perhaps we should examine more closely some of the inherited modifications of viviparous species in an attempt to discover evolutionary tendencies among them. To do so, the various specific departures from the oviparous condition of these species must be recalled as well as their summary in the pages immediately preceding.

In the Coleoptera, the most significant feature of chrysomelid viviparity appears to be ovarial fertilization of the eggs. This is because it is a condition which applies not only to the viviparous species but to closely related oviparous forms as well. Ovarial fertilization in the latter, followed by genetically based changes leading to egg retention, or the abbreviation of early embryonic development in the egg, and other adjustments, could add more viviparous species to those we know in this family. Chapman (1903) holds this opinion. *Micromalthus*, far removed taxonomically from *Chrysomela*, also reveals ovarial development of the eggs but parthenogenesis and paedogenesis cause this beetle to exhibit what is, perhaps, a tendency toward haemocoelus viviparity. Loss of oviducts and minor physiological adjustments of the offspring could place it in that category.

Those who have discovered viviparous thrips, may-flies, and butterflies offer little evidence of major modifications to distinguish them from related oviparous species. Of these, the maternal physical and physiological and embryonic physiological adjustments are greatest.

Among roaches the preliminary necessary step appears to be the reduction or elimination of the oötheca, in order that the ova may remain in the uterus. There seems to be no evolutionary tendency whatever toward ovarial fertilization as exhibited by Hemimeridae, Polyctenidae, and Coleoptera, nor has the chorion disappeared from the eggs of any of the species. One might conclude the Blattodea are limited to simple ovoviviparity or, in cases of considerable maternal and embryonic modifications, to pseudoplacental viviparity. Adenotrophic and haemocoelous viviparous types seem to be less open to them from the evidence at hand. There may be a tendency toward the elimination of the blattid oötheca. An almost complete series of blattids, selected from various genera, is available to illustrate this tendency. The list could start with species dropping the oötheca early, followed by species retaining a protruded oötheca until shortly before hatching occurs. Then there are species with internally retained oötheca with varying degrees of fragility to *Diploptera* whose oötheca is most delicate and imperfect, and finally ending with species which are said to secrete none at all (Imms, 1925). This list would make no pretense of being an evolutionary series but only an orderly presentation of variability as exhibited by blattids.

Diptera, like the roaches, apparently are not subject to ovarial fertilization and parthenogenesis is exceptional, appearing in a few, closely related species. Most viviparous flies seem to be evolving along two definite lines at present, these are: (1) many eggs retained in an elongate uterus for temporary incubation, in some of which ovoviviparity is almost attained as in the case of *Panzeria rudis*, Prell (1915), and the even more astonishing *Lydella nigripes*, Bowden (1933), and (2) eggs produced singly and stored in a short, enlarged uterus. The larva is retained and the accessory glands are converted into nutrient organs. This has resulted in adenotrophic viviparity. There seems to be no tendency to lose the chorion, except in paedogenetic species, but embryonic life within the egg is definitely abbreviated.

Supporting these two suppositions are the numerous examples of ovoviviparity among Tachinidae and Sarcophagidae, for instance, with Glossinidae and Pupipara to illustrate adenotrophic types. Moreover in ovoviviparous flies, at present, are several examples of evolutionary trends toward adenotrophic types whose course, perhaps, is not yet run to completion. Among these are: *Oestrus ovis* and *Gastrophilus nasalis*; *Hylemyia strigosa, H. variata, Hydrophoria divisa*; *Mesembrina meridiana*; *Theria muscaria, Dasyphora pratorum, Musca larvipara*, and *M. bezzi*. Originally this list was longer but some species have since been ascertained to be still oviparous. Not all of the above have had their viviparity verified by recent, more discriminating observations since the first citation. Patton and Cragg (1913) believe *M. bezzi* embryos receive additional nourishment before deposition.

Of the viviparous flies just listed we may note they all possess some traits in common that appear to indicate their evolutionary convergence may be toward adenotrophic viviparity and that ovoviviparity may be only a step in that direction. The number of ovarioles per ovary has been reduced to approximate or equal those possessed by *Glossina* and the Pupipara. Only a single large oöcyte is liberated at a time. the remainder residing in the ovarioles until its product is fertilized, developed, and expelled. Ovarioles liberate oöcytes in alternation. The maternal uterine conformation corresponds to the dipteran adenotrophic type. It is true that most of these are reported as having their eggs hatch just prior to deposition, but *M. meridiana, australis*, and *humilis* and *H. strigosa* larvae are said to develop to stage II in the egg and to cast the first larval exoskeleton before feeding after birth. Finally, *D. pratorum* gives birth to a larva that has reached its full development (stage III) and feeds only a short time before pupation. It is evident, since these examples are scattered among various genera, that the higher Diptera, at least, appear to differ only in degree toward their viviparous goal, and this seems to be specialization to the adenotrophic type. We, perhaps, are unable to detect several other modifications or adjustments that have already appeared in both mother and offspring that conform to the minimum requirements already outlined for adenotrophic viviparity. This may be because neither parent nor offspring has undergone sufficient total alteration from the oviparous condition to bring them into play. One example of this could be used to illustrate the point: Roubaud (1909) accepts an earlier statement that the accessory glands of *Theria muscaria,* while still simple tubular glands, are more greatly developed than expected for these flies.

This is not the first time attention has been called to this condition in the Diptera for, in considering these flies, Keilin (1916) says in effect that some essential modifications of the female apparatus which characterize "pupiparity" are in part already realized.

If it should be true that certain oviparous higher Diptera are gravitating toward ovoviviparity while others, already ovoviviparous, are veering to the adenotrophic type, this must indicate an evolution having heredity as its basis of change. It is suggested that all observed cases among Diptera seem to point to no other type and indicate that the genes responsible are limited in their kinds of mutations. That other viviparous species should be differently directed is, perhaps, to be expected since the orders were defined so long ago. Ovoviviparity may well be the natural sequence of the first steps toward the other three types that have been reviewed. If we glance backward along any of our assumed evolutionary trails to insects who still exhibit oviparity with eggs bearing more or less well-developed embryos within, there might be visible to us the earliest expressions of a tendency toward eventual viviparity.

Maternal Solicitude

Most insects exhibit care for their reproductive products. Some seek only places of security for their eggs or offspring, most of them endeavor to oviposit on, or near, appropriate food. A few do neither, or this function has been relegated to others as the following examples testify. The walking stick (Phasmidae) is an extreme example of apparent indifference, permitting the eggs, like chips, "to fall as they may," and the *Meloe* triungulin who must steal a ride to its new home on the body of its potential host. The social insects illustrate the second category and here the scope of solicitude is unexcelled by the workers. It seems, however, that the viviparous species, like most parasitic species, are very careful to retain their young until the proper host is discovered and correct deposition of the birth product is assured. Furthermore, maternal solicitude involves more than the mere placement of the egg. It also embraces protection of the hatched product for an indefinite period, as necessitated by the type of viviparity possessed by the mother. The proximity of food is not always the motivating cause of deposition and maternal care may be influenced by other factors, particularly if the offspring is able to fend for itself immediately after it becomes active. To show the scope of the last condition and to illustrate the possible extent of maternal care foreign to the trophic response of most insects, examples will be drawn from the adenotrophic insects.

In examining the activities of the larvae produced by adeno-trophic viviparity one finds this stage of the Pupipara quite incapable of movement except for the compression of the body to aid in respiration. This immobility may be construed as evidence of the great dependence of such larvae upon maternal solicitude and is an indication of further specialization to the viviparous condition. The glossinid larva is nearly as helpless but retains sufficient musculature to force itself into the soil after birth as it seeks shelter for pupation. This the larva of Pupipara cannot do; it is entirely dependent on the mother in finding a retreat. According to Muir (1912), *Ascodipteron speiseriarum* simply drops the mature larva to the ground, where it immediately pupates. *Melophagus ovinus* females abandon their larvae in the fleece of the host to which they adhere because of a viscid coating furnished by the mother upon emergence.

The female of *Eremoctenia (Penicilidia) progressa* retains her larva, almost completely extruded from the vulva, until she is able to find a host to which she firmly presses her offspring, and to which it adheres by virtue of a sticky maternal secretion. Rodhain and Bequaert (1915), however, have observed that *Cyclopodia greeffi* manifests even greater care of the young involving some hazard to the mother. The female of this species, which is wingless, leaves its host to find a suitable substratum on which to place its offspring. Here the larva is born and the mother, standing over it, lowers her body several times to press her offspring firmly to the object she has selected. These are specializations beyond the ability possessed by a glossinid female for the latter, like *Ascodipteron,* merely rests in its shaded retreat and drops its larva to the ground. Its solicitude abruptly ceases after having carefully preserved the egg and nourished the larva throughout its life.

This habit of maternal care of the offspring is quite different in its expression from the eagerness with which so many insects seek food or a host and immediately respond by depositing eggs or larvae. The old trophic response to food supply for a potentially ravenous offspring has been lost, the larva has been retained, and another set of reactions, not previously in force, impel the mother in an entirely new direction. These larvae pupate at once and in a few days are seeking new hosts or find themselves on the host of the mother.

The Future of Viviparity

In conclusion, it is natural to consider whether viviparity in insects is spreading or disappearing. Long ago, Wood-Mason (1878) apparently voiced his opinion for the roaches, at least, when he said, in effect, that the carrying about of an oötheca by the roach might possibly be explained as retention of a vestige of a lost viviparity. Willey (1899) also attempted to trace the serosa of insects back to the trophoblast of viviparous *Peripatus,* which was adapted to the survival of aquatic forms that emerged to terrestrial habitats. He also believed that oviparity with yolk-laden eggs is a secondary acquirement.

Both these views were voiced before the present extent of viviparity was realized, and even yet we are perhaps far from knowing the full range of such variations from the oviparous condition. There seem to be valid reasons for believing that viviparity, as expressed at present, is more recent than oviparity among insects. This view need not conflict with Willey's hypothesis. Turner and Baker (1915) express the opinion that primitive aphids must have been oviparous, reproducing sexually. There is no paleontological evidence to support an assumption that viviparity arose with the hexapods; indeed, the genitalia in known fossil forms appear to indicate oviparous habits were prevalent. If viviparity were the rule, traces of it should be more commonly found in the more generalized orders and in the lower species of each order. Such, however, is not usually the case.

Further contributory facts for the more recent development of viviparity are suggested here for consideration. The primitive reproductive system, or anything approaching it except the

Plectoptera, is never possessed by viviparous insects; on the contrary, they are by comparison greatly specialized. The presence of paired oviducts is a primitive feature while the common oviduct is considered to be a later acquisition. This part of the reproductive tract is typical of oviparous as well as most viviparous species. The loss of the paired and unpaired oviducts in some viviparous insects is a recent loss, and certainly cannot be assumed a condition from which oviducts have been derived in other insects. Their hypothetical hexapod ancestors possessed them in some form. How can one assess their loss in *Miastor* paedogenetic larvae, for example, since they start in the embryo and are later resorbed? Furthermore, they persist as imaginal buds in those larvae that are to produce the adult generation and in the latter the reproductive system is completely formed. In the following generation the larviparous reproductives again lack all but the rudiments of the oviducts. Yolky eggs are considered more primitive than a reduced yolk (Tiegs, 1922). Yolk loss or reduction in the denseness of the chorion, or its complete absence, has not been found in the more generalized present-day insects. Some of these conditions are frequently present in viviparous parasitic insects, and the latter are certainly not primitive species. Viviparity appears in several orders, but in each instance the viviparous species (except *Micromalthus*) possesses more primitive oviparous relatives. It is easier to explain viviparity in *Miastor, Micromalthus,* and *Aphididae* as something new and present only in larval or parthenogenetic forms than to show that the oviparous condition, the presence of complete reproductive systems, and fertilization in adult bisexual generations have been derived by evolution from the former.

Of the Diptera, an order in which by far the greatest number of viviparous species has been reported, viviparity with few exceptions is known only in the Cyclorrhapha. If we should be more precise we could even limit this great number of cases to the Calypterae and the Pupipara. The same condition, with fewer examples, may be seen in Coleoptera, Homoptera, and Hemiptera. It is possible that most species now known to exhibit viviparity had not yet evolved when hexapod forerunners were few and could have conferred this trait on many of the orders or, at least families, that have subsequently appeared. The originally established family Tachinidae, for example, has a very large number of ovoviviparous species, yet geologically it is one of the youngest families of insects. The evidence shows that viviparity (1) occurs relatively infrequently compared with the total number of described species, (2) is widely dispersed through the insects, and (3) offers divergent details of expression even within its four known types. These facts seem to argue for the appearance of a new and successful evolutionary exploration of this field of reproduction rather than the receding vestige of a long-established trait.

Holmgren (1904) cites Swammerdam (1737–38) and Redi (1668) as being among the first to assert viviparity is of value to the offspring of insects. There are cogent reasons for believing viviparity is an important and successful evolutionary advance among some arthropods. It is probably insufficient in itself to insure environmental exploitation for Onychophora or the scorpions, or to overcome the handicaps of other limitations in them such as food habits, negative phototropism, and lack of sclerotization and motility. But for the insects it might open a vista and environmental freedom comparable to those afforded by viviparity in mammals. In fact, it may not be amiss to call attention to the analogy between insects and mammals in exploring the field of viviparity in their respective ecological niches. Insects are pursuing four types of viviparity available to them in evolution, just as mammals have had the prototheria, the primitive (or degenerate) metatheria, and the highly successful eutheria with the latter's evolution of the uterine region.

The chief drains sapping the vitality of oviparous insects appear to be avoiding enemies from the egg stage to the adult, the expenditure of energy required to provide great quantities of yolk for future eggs in addition to food for the mother's needs, and seeking adequate repositories for the eggs. These are only a few of the factors that, together, comprise the formidable sum of the "environmental resistance" which, in turn, determines the death rate.

Anything that reduces environmental resistance automatically increases the population, provided the birth rate remains the same. One of the outstanding features of viviparity in insects is, however, the evident fact that the biotic potential has dropped yet the population has not. So far as we know it remains the same. Therefore, a reduced environmental resistance has permitted a lower biotic potential, both being an economic gain for the species.

It appears to follow, then, that viviparity has been very successful. One might assume environmental resistance has largely been eliminated from the viviparous insect's life in the egg and in some cases as a nymph or larva. The mother stores less food for yolk, has fewer offspring, and takes better care of them. Up to this point, viviparity is an essential saving in the insect's economy. But a static population coupled with a greatly reduced death rate in the immature insect, may imply that environmental resistance has shifted to the viviparously reproducing adult insect. Such checks to the adult insect's survival are problems for the adult to solve in the future. Viviparity, in itself, seems to be an evolutionary advance, a definitely successful improvement on oviparity.

LITERATURE CITED

Balbiani (1898), Bowden (1933), Caillol (1914), Chapman (1903), Henne-berg (1927), Holmgren (1904), Imms (1925), John (1923), Keilin (1916), Kusnezov (1909–10), Kyber (1815), Muir (1912), Patton and Cragg (1913), Portchinsky (1910), Prell (1915), Redi (1668), Rethfeldt (1924), Rodhain and Bequaert (1915), Roubaud (1909), Swammerdam (1737–38), Tiegs (1922), Townsend (1911), Turner and Baker (1915), Willey (1899), Wood-Mason (1878).

BIBLIOGRAPHY

Many of the cited references furnish no embryological information on viviparous insects but are used either to supplement other data or because they
are of historical value. A small number were not consulted directly; among
these a very few are apparently unavailable in the United States.

AGASSIZ, J. L. R. On the classification of insects from embryological data. Smithsonian Contrib. to Knowledge, 2:1–28. 1851.

ALDRICH, J. M. A new genus and two new species of muscoid flies from Guatemala.
Proc. Ent. Soc. Washington, 34:23–25. 1932.

ANONYMOUS. Entomological notes. Psyche, 5:405. 1890.

ARGO, V. N. Braula cœca in Maryland. Jour. Econ. Ent., 19:170–174. 1926.

ARNHART, L. Zur Entwicklungsgeschichte der Braula cœca Nitzsch. Zool. Anz.,
56:193–197. 1923.

ASSMUSS, E. P. Die Parasiten der Honigbeine und die durch dieselben bedingten
Krankheiten dieses Insects. E. Schotte & Co. (Berlin). 1865.

AUSTEN, E. E. Supplementary notes on the tsetse-flies. Brit. Med. Jour., 2:658–662.
1904.

AWATI, P. R. A new larviparous Philaematomyia (Philaematomyia indica, sp. n.).
Indian Jour. Med. Res., 5:529–539. 1918.

——. A note on the genitalia of Portchinsky's species, M. corvina (vivipara)
and M. corvina (ovipara). Ibid., 8:89–92. 1920.

BADEN, V. Embryology of the nervous system in the grasshopper, Melanoplus
differentialis (Acrididae; Orthoptera). Jour. Morphology, 60:159–188. 1936.

BAEHR, V. B. DE. Die Oogenese bei einigen viviparen Aphiden und die Spermato-
genese von Aphis saliceti mit besonderer Berücksichtigung der Chromatin-
verhältnisse. Arch. Zellf., 3:269–333. 1909. Russian dissertation: M. M. Sta-
siulevich Publ. House (St. Petersburg). 1910.

——. Recherches sur la maturation des oeufs parthénogénétiques dans l'Aphis
palmae. La Cellule, 30:317–354. 1920.

BAER, K. E. VON. Über die Entwicklungsgeschichte der Thiere. Verlagsbuchhand-
lung Gebrüder Bornträger (Königsberg). 1828.

——. Bericht über eine neue von Prof. Wagner in Kasan an Dipteren beobach-
tete abweichende Propagationsform. Bull. d. l'acad. imp. d. sci. d. St. Pétersbourg, 6:239–241. 1863. Summary: Novorum Act. Acad. Caesar. Leop.-Carol.
Germanicae Nat. Curios (Dresden), 22(4):51–52. (1863) 1864. Mélanges biol.
d. l'acad. imp. d. sci. d. St. Pétersbourg, 4:307–310. 1864.

——. Über Prof. Nic. Wagner's Entdeckung von Larven, die sich fortpflanzen,
Herrn Ganin's verwandte und ergänzende Beobachtungen und über die Paedogenesis überhaupt. Bull. d. l'acad. imp. d. sci. d. St. Pétersbourg, 9:64–137.
1866. Mélanges biol. tirés du bull. d. l'acad. imp. d. sci. d. St. Pétersbourg,
5:203–308. (1865–1866) 1866.

BAER, W. Die Tachinen als Schmarotzer der schädlichen Insekten. Zeitschr. f.
Angew. Ent. (Berlin), 6:185–246. 1920. 7:97–163. 1920.

BAGNELL, R. S. On Thysanoptera from the Seychelles Islands and Rodriques.
Ann. Mag. Nat. Hist., ser. 9, 7:257–292. 1921.

BAKER, A. C., and TURNER, W. F. Some intermediates in the Aphididae (Hemiptera). Proc. Ent. Soc. Washington, 18:10–14. 1916a.

——. Morphology and biology of the green apple aphis. Jour. Agr. Res.,
5:955–994. 1916b.

BALBIANI, E. G. Sur la reproduction et l'embryogénie des pucerons. Compt. rend. hebd. d. séances d. l'acad. d. sci., 62:1231–1234, 1285–1289, 1390–1394. 1866. Also: Ann. Mag. Nat. Hist., ser. 3, 18:62–65, 65–69, 106–109. 1866. Jour. d. l'anat. et physiol., 3 Ann.:449–464. 1866.

———. Mémoire sur la génération des aphides. Ann. d. sci. nat., Ser. 5, 11:5–89. 1869. Ser. 5, 14, art. 2:1–39, art. 9:1–36. 1870. Ser. 5, 15, art. 1:1–30, art. 4:1–63. 1871.

———. Sur la signification des cellules polaires des insectes. Compt. rend. hebd. d. séances d. l'acad. d. sci., 95:927–929. 1882.

———. Contribution à l'étude de la formation des organes sexuels chez les insectes. Rec. Zool. Suisse, 2:527–588. 1885. Abstract: Jour. Roy. Micr. Soc., (2), 6, Pt. 1:55–56. 1886.

———. Sur les conditions de la sexualité chez les pucerons. Observations et réflexions. Intermédiaire d. Biol., 1:171–174, 1898.

BARBER, H. S. The remarkable life-history of a new family (Micromalthidae) of beetles. Proc. Biol. Soc. Washington, 26:185–190. 1913a.

———. Observations on the life-history of Micromalthus debilis Lec. Proc. Ent. Soc. Washington, 15:31–38. 1913b.

BARNES, H. F. A short note on the viviparity of Chrysocloa gloriosa F. (Coleoptera, Chrysomelidae). Ent. Monthly Mag., 61 (ser. 3, 11):243–245. 1925.

———. Some remarks on paedogenesis in gall-midges (Cecidomyidae). Ibid., 65:138–139. 1929.

BERLESE, A. Fenomeni che accompagnano la fecondazione in taluni Insetti. Riv. di Patol. veg. (Firenze), 6:353–368. 1898. 7:1–18. (1898) 1899. Summary: Zool. Centralbl., 1899:292–296. 1899.

———. Osservazioni su fenomeni che avvengono durante la ninfosi degli insetti metabolici, Parte 1. Ibid., 8:1–155. 1899.

———. Gli Insetti. tom. 1. Societá Editrice Libraria (Milano). 1909.

———. Intorno alle metamorfosi degli insetti. Redia 9:121–137. 1913.

BERNER, L. Ovoviviparous mayflies in Florida. Proc. Florida Acad. Sci., 4:280. (1939) 1940. Florida Ent. (Gainsville), 24:32–34. 1941.

BERNHARD, C. Über die vivipare Ephemeride Chloëon dipterum. Biol. Centralbl., 27:467–479. 1907.

BLANCHARD, É. Über die Embryogenie der Dipteren von der Sippe der Ornithomyier (Pupiparen, Latr.). Froriep's N. Notizen., 37:276–277. 1846a.

———. Sur l'embryogénie des Pupipares. Soc. Philom. de Paris, 1846:6–8. 1846b. Extraits d. procès-verbaux d. séances.

BLEUZE, L. Observations sur une Chrysomèle vivipare. Petites nouv. ent., 1, 6 Ann. (109):435. (1869–1875) 1874. Also: Ent. Monthly Mag. 11(126):135–136. 1874. Feuille d. jeunes nat. (Paris), 5(49):15–16. 1874–1875. Ent. Nachr., 1(1):24–25. 1875.

BLOCHMANN, F. Über die Reifung der Eier bei Ameisen und Wespen. Festschr. d. naturhist. med. Vereins zu Heidelberg, 1886:143–172. 1886.

———. Über die Richtungskörper bei Insekteneiern. Morph. Jahrb., 12:544–574. 1887.

———. Über das regelmässige Vorkommen von bakterienähnlichen Gebilden in den Geweben und Eiern verschiedener Insecten. Zeitschr. f. Biol., 24:1–15. 1888.

BLUNCK, H. Die Entwicklung des Dytiscus marginalis L. vom Ei bis zur Imago. I. Teil. Das Embryonalleben. Zeitschr. f. wiss. Zool., 111(1):76–151. 1914.

BONNET, C. An abstract of some new observations upon insects. Phil. Trans. Roy. Soc. (London), 42:458–488. 1743.

———. Traité d'insectologie ou observations sur les pucerons. I. Durand et Cie (Paris), 1745. Also: Abhandlungen aus der Insektologie. J. J. Gebauers Wittwe und J. J. Gebauer (Halle). 1773.

BONNET, C. Oeuvres d'histoire naturelle et de philosophie. t.1:1–113. Samuel Fauche (Neuchatel). 1779.

BORDAS, L. Les glandes défensives ou odorantes des Blattes. Compt. rend. hebd. d. séances d. l'acad. d. sci., 132:1352–1354. 1901.

——. Recherches anatomiques, histologiques et physiologiques sur les organes appendiculaires de l'appareil reproducteur femelle des Blattes (*Periplaneta orientalis* L.). Ann. d. sci. nat. (Zool.), ser. 9, 9:71–121. 1909.

BORRADAILE, L. A. The Animal and its Environment. Henry Frowde and Hodder & Stoughton (London). 1923.

BOUCHÉ, P., FR. Bemerkungen über die Naturgeschichte der Blattläuse (Aphidina). Stett. Ent. Ztg., 5:81–82. 1844.

BOWDEN, P. B. *Lydella nigripes* and *L. piniariae*, fly parasites of certain tree-defoliating caterpillars (Key No. K–241). Jour. Agr. Res., 46:963–995. 1933.

BRANDT, A. Beiträge zur Entwicklungsgeschichte der Libelluliden und Hemipteren, mit besonderer Berücksichtigung der Embryonalhülle derselben. Mém. d. l'acad. imp. d. sci. d. St. Pétersbourg, ser. 2, 13(1):1–33. 1869.

——. Über die Eiröhren der Blatta (*Periplaneta orientalis*). *Ibid.*, ser. 7, 21(12):1–30. 1874.

BRASS, A. Das Ovarium und die ersten Entwicklungsstadien des Eies der viviparen Aphiden. Zeitschr. f. Naturwiss. (Halle), 55:339–375. 1882.

BREEST, F. Zur Kenntnis der Symbiontenübertragung bei viviparen Cocciden und bei Psylliden. Arch. f. Protistenk. (Jena), 34:263–276. 1914.

BRUCE, D. Further Report on the Tsetse-fly Disease or Nagana in Zululand. Harrison & Sons, Ltd. (London). 1897.

BRUES, C. T. A contribution to our knowledge of the Stylopidae. Zool. Jahrb., Anat. 18:241–270. 1903.

BUCHNER, P. Studien an intracellularen Symbionten. 1. Die intracellularen Symbionten der Hemipteren. Arch. f. Protistenk., 26:1–116. 1912.

——. Tier und Pflanze in Symbiose. Gebrüder Borntraeger (Berlin). 1930.

BUCKTON, G. B. Monograph of the British Aphides. I. Ray Soc. (London). 1876.

BURMEISTER, H. Handbuch der Entomologie. G. Reimer (Berlin). 1836. Transl.: A Manual of Entomology. Edward Churton (London). 1836.

BURNETT, W. I. Facts observed in the generation of the Humble Bee et Aphides, as illustrating some obscure phenomena in the physiology of generation. Proc. Boston Soc. Nat. Hist., 3:262–264. 1850.

——. Researches on the development of viviparous Aphides. Proc. Amer. Assoc. Adv. Sci., 1853:203–223. 1853. Also: Amer. Jour. Sci. and Arts, (2) 17:62–78, 261–262. 1854. Ann. Mag. Nat. Hist., ser. 2, 14:81–98. 1854.

BURR, M. A new species of *Arixenia*. Ent. Monthly Mag. (2) 23:105–106. 1912.

BURR, M., and JORDAN, K. On *Arixenina* Burr, a suborder of Dermaptera. Trans. 2d Internat. Congr. Ent., 1912:398–421. 1912.

CAILLOL, H. Sur le développement anormal d'une espèce de Coléoptère. Bull. d. la soc. linn. d. Provence (Marseille), 2:72–86. (1913) 1914.

CALLONI, S. Viviparità nella *Oreina speciosissima*. Bull. d. soc. ent. ital., 21:46–47. 1889.

CALORI, L. Sulla generazione vivipara della *Cloë diptera* (*Effemera diptera* Linn.). Nuovi ann. d. sci. nat. (Bologna), ser. 2, 9:38–53. 1848. Transl. by Joly, Bull. soc. d'étud. d. sci. nat. d. Nimes., 5(4):65–68. 1877. Note: Archiv. f. Naturgesch., 45, 2:66, 1879.

CARAZZI, D. La borsa di Berlese nella cimice dei letti (*Acanthia lecturlaria* L.). Internat. Monatsschr. f. Anat. u. Physiol. (Leipzig), 19:337–348. 1902.

CARRIÈRE, J. Die Drüsen am ersten Hinterleibsringe der Insektenembryonen. Biol. Centralbl., 11:110–127. 1891.

CARUS, J. V. Zur näheren Kenntnis des Generationswechsels. W. Engelmann (Leipzig). 1849.

CARUS, C. G. Professor Nicolai Wagner's in Kasan Entdeckung von Insekten-Larven, die sich fortpflanzen. Novorum Act. Acad. Caesar. Leop.-Carol. Germanicae Nat. Curios. (Dresden), 25, Heft 5:95–97. (1866) 1867.

CAUSARD, (M.). Sur un Ephémère vivipare. Compt. rend. hebd. d. sci. d. l'acad. d. sci., 123:705–708. 1896. Transl.: Ann. Mag. Nat. Hist., ser. 6, 18:480–482. 1896. Summary: Amer. Nat., 31:165–167. 1897. Zool. Centralbl., 4:251. 1897.

CHAMPION, G. C., and CHAPMAN, T. A. Observations on some species of Orina, a genus of viviparous and ovo-viviparous Beetles. Trans. Ent. Soc. London, 1901:1–18. 1901.

CHAPMAN, T. A. Viviparous and oviparous Oreina. Proc. Ent. Soc. London, 1900:XIV. 1900.

——. A contribution to the life history of Orina (Chrysochloa) tristis Fabr., var. smaragdina Weise. Trans. Ent. Soc. London, 1903:245–261. 1903.

CHEWYREUV. (See Ševyrev.)

CHOLODKOWSKY, N. Die Embryonalentwicklung von Phyllodromia (Blatta) germanica. Mém. d. l'acad. imp. d. sci. d. St. Pétersbourg, ser. 7, 38 (5):1–120. 1891. Also, Trudy Leningradskogo Obshchestva Estestvoispytatelei, 22:39–223. 1892. Rev., Jour. Roy. Micr. Soc., 1892:200–201. 1892.

——. Concerning methods of reproduction and development of viviparous flies. In Russian. Trav. d. la. soc. imp. des nat. d. St. Pétersbourg, 38:100–106. German summary: 106–108. 1907.

——. The female reproductive organs of some viviparous Diptera. In Russian. Ibid., 39:112–119. German summary: 163–164. 1908. German transl.: Zool. Anz., 33:367–376. 1908.

CHOPARD, L. La Biologie des Orthoptères. Encyclop. Ent., ser. A, 20:217–222. 1938.

CLAPARÈDE, É. Note sur la reproduction des pucerons. Ann. d. sci. nat., ser. 5, 7:21–29. 1867. Also: Ann. Mag. Nat. Hist., ser. 3, 19:360–367. 1867.

CLAUS, C. Generationswechsel und Parthenogenesis im Thierreiche. Ein bei Gelegenheit der Habilitation gehaltener Vortrag. N. G. Elwert (Marburg). 1858.

——. Beobachtungen über die Bildung des Insecteneies. Zeitschr. f. wiss. Zool., 14:42–54. 1864.

COLLINGE, W. E. Note on the deposition of the eggs and larvae of Œstrus ovis L. Jour. Econ. Biol., 1:72–73. 1906.

COMSTOCK, J. H. An Introduction to Entomology. Comstock Pub. Co., Inc. (Ithaca). 1925.

CORNELIUS, C. Ernährung und Entwicklung einiger Blattkäfer. Stett. Ent. Ztg., 18:162–171, 392–405. 1857.

CRAGG, F. W. Further observations on the reproductive system of Cimex, with special reference to the behavior of the spermatozoa. Indian Jour. Med. Res., 8(1):32–79. 1920.

CRAWFORD, J. C. Personal correspondence, conversations, etc., with Dr. D. W. Pierce. U. S. Nat. Mus. Bull., 66:1–232. 1909.

DAVIS, W. T. Rearing the young of the viviparous cockroach, Panchlora cubensis. Jour. New York Ent. Soc., 38:85–88. 1930.

DAWYDOFF, C. Traité d'embryologie comparée des invertébrés. Masson et Cie (Paris). 1928.

DIMMOCK, G. On some glands which open externally on insects. Psyche, 3:387–401. 1882.

DINGLER, M. Beiträge zur Kenntnis von Lecanium hesperidum L., besonders seiner Biologie. Zeitschr. f. angew. Ent. (Berlin), 9:191–246. 1923.

DOHRN, A. Über die Bedeutung der fundamentalen Entwicklungsvorgänge in den Insecten-Eiern für die Systematik der Insecten. Stett. Ent. Ztg., 31:244–250. 1870.

DONISTHORPE, H. St. J. K. Mermecophilous notes for 1909. Ent. Record, 21:287–291. 1909.
———. Myrmecophilous notes for 1916. *Ibid.*, 29:48–52. 1916.
———. Viviparity of *Lomechusa strumosa* F. Ent. Monthly Mag., 62, ser. 3 (12):21. 1926.
DRAKE, C. J., and JONES, R. M. The pigeon fly and pigeon malaria in Iowa. Iowa State Coll. Jour. Sci., IV(2):253–261. 1930.
DUFOUR, L. Recherches anatomiques sur l'Hippobosque des chevaux. Ann. d. sci. nat., 6:299–322. 1825.
———. Recherches anatomique et physiologique sur les Hemiptères. Mém. savans étrang., 4:129–462, 1833. Review: Ann. d. sci. nat., 1 (Zool.):232–239. 1834. Froriep's N. Notizen., 42:241–246. 1834.
———. Etudes anatomiques et physiologiques sur les insects diptères de la Famille des Pupipares. Ann. d. sci. nat., ser. 3, 3:49–95. 1845. Extract: Compt. rend. hebd. d. séances d. l'acad. d. sci., 19:1345–1355. 1844.
———. Recherches anatomiques et physiologiques sur les Diptères. Mém. a l'acad. d. sci. d. l'inst. nat. d. France, Math. Phys., 11:171–360. 1851. Separate: J. C. Baillière et fils (Paris). 1850.
DUTROCHET, H. Observations sur les organes de la génération chez les pucerons. Ann. d. sci. nat., 30:204–208. 1833.
DUVAU, A. Nouvelles recherches sur l'histoire naturelle des pucerons. Mém. d. mus. d'hist. nat., 13:126–140. 1825. Summary: Ann. d. sci. nat., 5:224. 1825. Nouv. bull. d. sci. par la soc. Philom. d. Paris, 1825:62–63. 1825. Féruss bull. univ. d. sci. et d. l'indust., (2), 6:303. 1825.
EASTHAM, L. E. S. The formation of germ layers in insects. Cambridge Phil. Soc., Biol. Rev., 5(1):1–29. 1930.
EATON, A. E. A revisional monograph of recent Ephemeridae or mayflies. Trans. Linnean Soc. London, ser. 2, III, 1–6:1–352. 1883–1888.
EDMUNDO, G. F., Jr. Ovoviviparous mayflies of the genus *Callibaetis* (Ephemeroptera: Baetidae). Ent. News (Lancaster), 56:169–171. 1945.
ENTEMAN, M. M. The unpaired ectodermal structures of the Antennata. Zool. Bull., 2(6):275–282. 1899.
EWING, H. E. Eighty-seven generations in a parthenogenetic pure line of *Aphis avenae* Fab. Biol. Bull., 31:53–112. 1916.
FELT, E. P. *Miastor americana* Felt, an account of paedogenesis. New York State Mus. Bull., 147:82–104. (1910) 1911a.
———. *Miastor.* Jour. Econ. Ent., 4:414. 1911b.
———. Biology of *Miastor* and *Oligarces.* Science, 35:278–280. 1912.
FERNANDO, W. The early embryology of a viviparous Psocid. Quart. Jour. Micr. Sci., 77:99–119. 1934.
FERRIS, G. F. Observations on the larvae of some Diptera Pupipara, with description of a new species of Hippoboscidae. Parasitology, 15:54–58. 1923.
FOLSOM, J. W. Entomology with Special Reference to its Ecological Aspects. Blakiston's Son & Co. (Philadelphia). 1922.
GABRITSCHEVSKY, E. Expériences sur le déterminisme et la réversion des caractères polymorphes larvaires de *Miastor metroloas.* Bull. d. la soc. ent. d. France, 1928:75–79. 1928.
———. Sénescence embryonnaire, rajeunissement et déterminisme des formes larvaires de *Miastor metraloas* (Cecidomyidae). Bull. biol. d. la France et Belgique, 62:478–524. 1928.
———. Der umkehrbare Entwicklungscyclus bei *Miastor metroloas.* Roux Arch. f. Entwicklungsmechanik der Organ., 121:450–465. 1930.
GANIN, M. New observations on the reproduction of the larvae of viviparous Diptera. In Russian. Mem. Imp. Acad. Sci., 7:36–56. 1865. (See HANIN, 1865.)
GEDDES, P., and THOMSON, J. A. The Evolution of Sex. Walter Scott (London). 1889.

GEER, C. DE. Mémoires pour servir à l'histoire des insects. t. 2 (1):31–32. 1771. t. 3:27–129. 1773. (Aphididae). t. 6:273–289. 1776. Pierre Hesselberg (Stockholm). German transl.: Abhandlungen zur Naturgeschichte der Insecten. J. A. E. Goeze (Nürnberg). 1780.

GERSTÄCKER, A. Über das Vorkommen von ausstülpbaren Hautanhängen am Hinterleibe von Schaben. Arch. f. Naturgesch. (Berlin), Jg. 27(1):107–115. 1861.

———. Ueber die Fortpflanzungsweise von Miastor. Sitzungsber. Gesellsch. naturf. Freunde zu Berlin, Mai:10. 1865.

GIARD, A. La métamorphose est-elle une crise de maturité génitale? Bull. d. la soc. ent. d. France, 1900:54–57. 1900.

———. La poecilogonie. Bull. sci. d. la France et Belgique, 39:153–187. 1905.

GIER, H. T. The morphology and behavior of the intracellular bacteroids of roaches. Biol. Bull., 71:433–452. 1936.

GRABER, V. Vergleichende Studien über die Keimhüllen und die Rückenbildung der Insekten. Denkschr. d. K. Akad. d. Wiss.. Wien. Math. nat. Cl., 55:109–162. 1888.

———. Vergleichende Studien über die Embryologie der Insecten und insbesondere der Musciden. Ibid., 56:257–314. 1889.

———. Vergleichende Studien am Keimstreif der Insecten. Ibid., 57:621–734. 1890.

GRASSI, B. Anatomia comparata dei Tisanuri e considerazioni generali sull' organizzazione degli insetti. Atti d. reale accad. d. Lincei, Mem., cl. sci. fis., ser. 4, 4:543–606. 1887. French transl.: Arch. ital. d. biol., 11:1–11, 291–337, 389–419. 1889.

GRIMM, O. History of development of Chironomus. In Russian. Convention Soc. Nat. (St. Petersbourg). 1870.

———. The agamic reproduction of the pupa of a species of Chironomus. In Russian. Trans. 2d. meet. Russian nat. at Moscow. (Zool.), 1(1):171–178. (1869) 1870.

———. Die ungeschlechtliche Fortpflanzung einer Chironomus—Art und deren Entwickelung aus dem unbefruchteten Ei. Mém. d. l'acad. imp. d. sci. d. St. Pétersbourg, (7), 15, 8:1–24. 1870. English transl., Ann. Mag. Nat. Hist., (4), 8:31–45, 106–115. 1871. French summary: Horae soc. ent. Rossicae, 9:VII–IX. (1872) 1873.

GROS, M. A. Note sur la reproduction des Ephémères. Ann. d sci. nat. (Zool.), ser. 10, 6:411–413. 1923.

GUYÉNOT, É. Études biologiques sur une mouche, Drosophila ampelophila Löw. vii. Le déterminisme de la ponte. Compt. rend. hebd. d. séances et mém. d. la soc. d. biol., 74:443–445. 1913.

HAASE, E. Zur Kenntnis von Phengodes. Deutsche Ent. Zeitschr., 32:145–167. 1888.

———. Stinkdrüsen der Orthopteren. Sitzungsber. Gesellsch. naturf. Freunde zu Berlin, 1889:57–58. 1889a.

———. Zur Anatomie der Blattidae. Zool. Anz., 12:169–172. 1889b.

HACKER, L. Atome zur Biologie der Käfer. I. Wiener Ent. Ztg., 7(2):49–56. 1888.

HAGAN, H. R. Observations on the embryonic development of the mantid Paratenodera sinensis. Jour. Morphology, 30:223–237. 1917.

———. The embryogeny of the polyctenid, Hesperoctenes fumarius Westwood, with reference to viviparity in insects. Ibid., 51:1–117. 1931.

———. Diploptera dytiscoides, a viviparous roach with elongate pleuropodia. Ann. Ent. Soc. America, 32:264–266. 1939.

———. The general morphology of the female reproductive system of a viviparous roach, Diploptera dytiscoides (Serville). Psyche, 48:1–9. 1941.

HAGEN, H. Specielle Monographie der Termiten. Linnaea Entomologica, 12:4–342. 1858.

HALL, D. G. Biology of *Sarothromyia femoralis* var. *simplex* Aldrich. (Diptera, Calliphoridae). Ann. Ent. Soc. America, 25:641–647. 1932.

HALLEZ, P. Orientation de l'embryon et formation du cocon chez la *Periplaneta orientalis*. Compt. rend. hebd. d. séances d. l'acad. d. sci., 101:444–446. 1885.

———. Loi de l'orientation de l'embryon chez les insectes. *Ibid.*, 103:606–608. 1886. Summary: Jour. Roy. Micr. Soc., 1887:72. 1887.

HANIN, M. Neue Beobachtungen über die Fortpflanzung der viviparen Dipteren-larven. Zeitschr. f. wiss. Zool., 15:375–390. 1865. (See GANIN, 1865.)

HANSEN, H. J. On the structure and habits of *Hemimerus talpoides* Walk. Ent. Tidskr., 15:65–93. 1894.

HARDENBERG, J. D. F. Bijdrage tot de kennis der Pupipara. Drukkerij J. van Boekhoven (Utrecht). 1927. German transl., Beiträge zur Kenntnis der Pupiparen. Zool. Jahrb., (Anat.) 50(4):497–570. 1929.

HARRIS, R. G. Control of the appearance of pupa-larvae in paedogenetic Diptera. Proc. Nat. Acad. Sci. United States, 9:407–413. 1923a.

———. Occurrence, life-cycle and maintenance, under artificial conditions, of *Miastor*. Psyche, 30:95–101. 1923b.

———. Sur la culture des larves de Cécidomyies paedogénétiques (*Miastor*) en milieu artificiel. Compt. rend. hebd. d. séances et mém. d. la soc. d. biol., 88(1):256–258. 1923c.

———. Sex of adult Cecidomyidae (*Oligarces sp.*) arising from larvae produced by paedogenesis. Psyche, 31:148–154. 1924.

———. Further data on the control of the appearance of pupa-larvae in paedogenetic Cecidomyidae. Trav. d. la sta. zool. d. Wimereux (Paris), 9:89–97. 1925a.

———. Reversal of function in a species of *Oligarces*. Biol. Bull., 48:139–144. 1925b.

HARRISON, R. M. Preliminary account of a new organ in *Periplaneta orientalis*. Quart. Jour. Micr. Sci., 50:377–381. 1906.

HASE, A. Zur Frage des "Lebendiggebärens" der Kleiderlaus. Centralbl. f. Bakt. (Jena), Abt. 1. 85:377–379. 1921.

HATHAWAY, C. R. Verificação da viviparidade em Thysanoptera. Mem. do Inst. Oswaldo Cruz (Rio de Janeiro-Manguinhos), 33:357–358. 1938.

HEBERDEY, R. F. Zur Entwicklungsgeschichte, vergleichenden Anatomie und Physiologie der weiblichen Geschlechtsausführwege der Insekten. Zeitschr. f. Morph. u. Ökol. d. Tiere, 22:416–586. 1931.

HEGNER, R. W. The history of the germ cells in the paedogenetic larva of *Miastor*. Science, 36:124–126. 1912.

———. Studies on germ cells. Jour. Morphology, 25:375–509. 1914a.

———. The Germ-cell Cycle in Animals. The Macmillan Co. (New York). 1914b.

———. The genesis of the organization of the insect egg. Amer. Nat., 51:641–661, 705–718. 1917.

HENNEBERG, B. Viviparität bei *Phytodecta rufipes* Fbr. (Coleopt. Chrysomelid.). Ber. d. Oberh. Gesellsch. f. Natur- u. Heilk. zu Giessen, 11:17–20. (1926) 1927.

HENNEGUY, L. F. Les modes de reproduction des insectes. Bull. d. la soc. philom. d. Paris, (9), 1:41–86. 1899.

———. Les insectes. Masson et Cie (Paris). 1904.

HENSON, H. The development of the alimentary canal in *Pieris brassicae* and the endodermal origin of the malpighian tubules of insects. Quart. Jour. Micr. Sci., 75:283–305. 1932.

———. Theoretical aspect of insect metamorphosis. Biol. Review, 21:1–14. 1946.

HEYDEN, C. H. G. VON. Zur Fortpflanzungsgeschichte der Blattläuse. Stett. Ent. Ztg., 18:83–84. 1857.

HEYMONS, R. Die Entwickelung der weiblichen Geschlechtsorgane von *Phyllodromia* (*Blatta*) *germanica*. Zeitschr. f. wiss. Zool., 53:434–530. (1891) 1892.

HEYMONS, R. Die Embryonalentwicklung der Dermapteren und Orthopteren. Gustav Fischer (Jena), 1895.

———— Grundzüge der Entwicklung und des Körperbaues von Odonaten und Ephemeriden. Anhang z. d. Abhandl. d. K. Preuss. Akad. d. Wiss (Berlin), 1896:1–66. 1896.

————. Über den Nachweis der Viviparität bei den Eintagsfliegen. Zool. Anz. 20:205–206. 1897.

————. Eine Plazenta bei einem Insekt (Hemimerus). Verhandl. d. deut. Zool. Gesellsch., 19:97–107. 1909.

————. Über den Genitalapparat und die Entwicklung von Hemimerus talpoides Walker. Zool. Jahrb., Suppl. 15. 2:141–184. 1912.

HIRSCHLER, J. Deux types différents d'embryons dans une même espèce. Etude analytique de la forme et du développement des Aphides. Lwów Ksiega Pamiatkowa ku uczczeniu Prof. J. Nusbauma, 1911:175–195. 1911.

————. Embryologische Untersuchungen an Aphiden nebst theoretischen Erwägungen über den morphologischen Wert der Dotterelemente (Dotterzellen, Vitellophagen, Dotterepithel, Merocyten, Parablast) im allgemeinen. Zeitschr. f. wiss Zool., 100:393–446. 1912.

————. Embryogenese der Insekten. In Schröder's Handbuch der Entomologie. 1:570–824. Gustav Fischer (Jena). (1924) 1928.

HOFENEDER, K. Stylops in copula. Verhandl. d. Zool.-Bot. Gesellsch. in Wien, 73:128–134. 1923.

HOFFMANN, R. W. Zur Embryonalentwicklung der Strepsipteren. Nachr. v. d. K. Gesellsch. d. Wiss z. Göttingen. Math.-Phys. Kl., 3:392–408. 1913.

————. Die embryonalen Vorgänge bei den Strepsipteren und ihre Deutung. Verhandl. d. deut. Zool. Gesellsch, 24:192–216. 1914.

HOLMGREN, N. Ueber vivipare Insecten. Zool. Jahrb. (Syst.), 19(4):431–468. 1903–1904.

HOOD, J. D. Some further new Thysanoptera from Panama. Proc. Biol. Soc. Washington, 47:57–82. 1934.

————. Studies in neotropical Thysanoptera, II. Rev. de Ent., 6:424–460. 1936.

————. Studies in neotropical Thysanoptera. Ibid., 8:161–187. 1938.

————. New North American Thysanoptera, principally from Texas. Ibid., 10:550–619. 1939.

HOTTES, F. C. Concerning the structure, function, and origin of the cornicles of the Family Aphididae. Proc. Biol. Soc. Washington, 41:71–84. 1928.

HUBBARD, H. G. The life history of Xenos. Canadian Ent., 24:257–262. 1892.

HUGHES-SCHRADER, S. Reproduction in Acroschismus wheeleri Pierce. Jour. Morphology, 39:157–205. 1924.

HUSSEY, P. B. Studies on the pleuropodia of Belostoma flumineum Say and Ranatra fusca Palisot de Beauvois, with a discussion of these organs in other insects. Entomologica Americana, 7(1):1–80. 1926.

HUXLEY, T. H. On the agamic reproduction and morphology of Aphis. Trans. Linn. Soc. London, Part I, 22:193–219, Part II, 22:221–236. 1859.

IMMS, A. D. A General Textbook of Entomology. Methuen & Co., Ltd. (London). 1925.

————. Recent Advances in Entomology. Blakiston's Son & Co. (Philadelphia). 1931.

ITO, H. Contribution histologique et physiologique à l'étude des annexes des organes génitaux des Orthoptères. Arch. d'anat. micr., 20:343–460. 1924. Thèse présentée à la Faculté des sciences de l'Université de Montpellier. Masson et Cie (Paris). 1924.

JAHN, T. L. Nature and permeability of the grasshopper egg membranes. I. The EMF across membranes during early diapause. Jour. Cell. Comp. Physiol., 7:23–46. 1935.

JENTSCH, S. Ovoviviparie bei einer einheimischen Copeognathenart (*Hypertes guestphalicus*). Zool. Anz., 116:287–289. 1936.

JOHANNSEN, O. A. Paedogenesis in *Tanytarsus*. Science, 32:768. 1910.

———. Insect notes for 1910. Maine Agr. Exp. Sta. Bull., 187:3–4. (1910) 1911.

———. Some phases in the embryonic development of *Diacrisia virginica* Fabr. (Lepidoptera). Jour. Morphology, 48:493–541. 1929.

JOHANNSEN, O. A., and BUTT, F. H. Embryology of Insects and Myriapods. McGraw-Hill Book Co., Inc. (New York). 1941.

JOHN, O. Fakultative Viviparität bei Thysanopteren. Ent. Mitt., 12(5–6):227–232. 1923.

JOHNSON, W. G. The destructive green-pea louse. Canadian Ent., 32:56–60. 1900.

JOHNSTON, T. H., and BANCROFT, M. J. The life histories of *Musca australis*, Macq. and *M. vetustissima*, Walker. Proc. Roy. Soc. Queensland, 31:181–203. 1920.

JOLY, E. (See CALORI, 1848) 1877.

JORDAN, K. Description of a new kind of apterous earwig, apparently parasitic on a bat. Novitates Zoologicae, 16:313–326. 1909a.

———. Notes on the anatomy of *Hemimerus talpoides*. *Ibid.*, 16:327–330. 1909b.

———. Polyctenidae viviparous. Trans. Ent. Soc. London, 1911:lxiv. 1911a.

———. Contribution to our knowledge of the morphology and systematics of the Polyctenidae, a family of Rhynchota parasitic on bats. Novitates Zoologicae, 18:555–579. 1911b.

———. On viviparity in Polyctenidae. Trans. Internatl. Congr. Ent. (Oxford), 2:342–350. 1912.

———. Note on the distribution of the organ of Berlese in Clinocoridae. Ectoparasites, 1:284–286. 1922.

JORDAN, K. H. Zur Morphologie und Biologie der myrmecophilen Gattungen *Lomechusa* und *Artemeles* und einiger verwandter Formen. Zeitschr. f. wiss. Zool., 107(2):346–386. 1913.

JURINE, L. Observations sur le *Xenos vesparum*. Mem. d. reale accad. d. sci. d. Torino, 23:50–63. 1818. Summary: Oken Isis, 1832:761–764. 1832.

KADYI, H. Beitrag zur Kenntnis der Vorgänge beim Eierlegen der *Blatta orientalis*. Zool. Anz., 2(44):632–636. 1879.

KAHLE, W. Die Paedogenesis der Cecidomyiden. Zoologica (Stuttgart), Bd. 2, Heft 55:(5, 6)1–80. 1908.

KALTENBACH, J. H. Einige Bemerkungen zu Herrn Prof. Dr. Ratzeburg's Agenda hemipterologica. Stett. Ent. Ztg., 5:133–135. 1844.

KARSCH, F. Ueber eine Cecidomyide aus den Rhizomorphen des Kohlen-reviers bei Burgk (Sachsen). Ent. Nachr., 13:198–200. 1887.

KEILIN, D. Sur la viviparité chez les Diptères et sur les larves de Diptères vivipares. Arch d. zool. exp. et gén., 55:393–415. 1916.

KERRICH, G. J. Notes on larviposition in *Polyblastus* (Hym. Ichn. Tryphoninae). Proc. Roy. Ent. Soc. London, (A) 11:108–110. 1936.

KIRBY, W., and SPENCE, W. Introduction to Entomology. 5th ed. Longman, Rees, Orme, Brown and Green (London). 1815–1828.

KLEVENHUSEN, F. Beiträge zur Kenntnis der Aphidensymbiose. Zeitschr. f. Morph. u. Ökol. d. Tiere, 9:97–164. 1927.

KLOTS, A. B. Ovoviviparity in *Colias* ? (Lepid.: Pieridae). Ent. News, 46:58. 1935.

KLUG, J. C. F. Nachricht von einem neuen Schmarotzerinsekt auf einer Andrene. Mag. d. Gesellsch, naturf. Freunde zu Berlin, 4:266–270. 1810.

KLYVER, F. D. Preliminary note on paedogenesis in a Cecidomyiid. Pan-Pacific Ent., 8:9–10. 1931.

KOLENATI, F. A. Beiträge zur Kenntnis der Phthirio-Myiarien. Horae soc. ent. Rossicae 2(2):11–109. (1862) 1863.

KORSCHELT, E. Zur Bildung der Eihüllen, der Mikropylen und Chorionanhänge bei den Insekten. Verhandl. d. K. Leop.-Carol. deutsch. Akad. d. Naturf., 51:183–252. 1887.

KORSCHELT, E. Zur Embryonalentwicklung des *Dytiscus marginalis* L. Zool. Jahrb. (Anat.) Suppl. 15, 2:499–532. 1912.

KORSCHELT, E., and HEIDER, K. Textbook of the Embryology of Invertebrates. Vol. 3. The Macmillan Co. (New York). 1899.

KOWALEVSKY, A. Embryologische Studien an Würmern und Arthropoden. Mém. d. l'acad. imp. d. sci. d. St. Pétersbourg, 7th ser., 16(12):1–70. 1871.

———. Zur embryonalen Entwicklung der Musciden. Biol. Centralbl., 6:49–54. 1886–1887. Summary: Jour. Roy. Micr. Soc., 1886:429–430. 1886.

KRACZKIEWICZ, Z. Nouvelles recherches sur l'oogenèse et la diminution dans les larves paedogénétiques de *Miastor metraloas* (Diptera). Compt. rend. et mém. d. la soc. d. biol (Paris), 119:1201–1205. 1935.

———. De la différence entre les premiers stades de maturation des oocytes parthénogénétiques et des oocytes sexués de *Miastor metraloas* Meinert (Diptera). *Ibid.*, 123:879–883. 1936.

———. Recherches cytologiques sur le cycle évolutif de *Miastor metraloas* Meinert (Cecidomyidae, Diptera). La Cellule, 46:55–74. 1937.

KRASSILSTSCHIK, J. Zur Entwicklungsgeschichte der Phytophthires. Zool. Anz., 16:69–76. 1893.

KUSNEZOV, N. J. (Brief note to the effect that his investigations led him to believe certain lepidopterous species are viviparous.) In Russian. Russian ent. survey, 8:XIII. 1908.

———. On the probable viviparity in some Danaid, i.e. Pierid, butterflies. In Russian. Horae soc. ent. Rossicae, 39:634–651. English Summary: 648–651. 1909–1910.

KYBER, J. F. Einige Erfahrungen und Bemerkungen über Blattläuse. Mag. d. Ent., Germar. 1(2):1–39. 1815.

LANKESTER, E. R. Siebold's new researches in parthenogenesis. Nature, 6:483–485, 523–525. 1872. Also: The Advancement of Science, Ch. 7. The Macmillan Co. (New York). 1890.

———. The terminology of parthenogenesis. Nature, 99:504–505. 1917. Revision: Quar. Jour. Micr. Sci., 63:531–536. 1919.

LASSMANN, G. W. P. The early embryological development of *Melophagus ovinus* L., with special reference to the development of the germ cells. Ann. Ent. Soc. America, 29(3):397–413. 1936.

LATREILLE, P. A. Histoire naturelle, générale et particulière, des Crustacés et des Insectes. F. Dufart (Paris). 1802–1805.

LÉCAILLON, A. Sur l'endoderme des insectes. Bull. d. la soc. philom. d. Paris, ser. 8. 9:103–124. 1896.

———. Sur les enveloppes ovulaires de quelques Chrysomélides. Arch. d'anat. micr. (Paris), 2:89–117. 1898a.

———. Recherches sur l'œuf et sur le développement embryonnaire de quelques Chrysomélides. Thèses presentées à la Faculté des Sciences de Paris, Ser. A, No. 299:1–219. 1898b. Summary: Zool. Centralbl., 5:813–816. 1898.

———. Recherches sur le développement embryonnaire de quelques Chrysomélides. Arch. d'anat. micr. (Paris), 2:118–176, 189–250. 1898c.

LEEUWENHOEK, A. VAN. Arcana Naturae Detecta, 2, Epistola 90. Delphis Batavorum: Henricum a Krooneveld. 1695.

LEMOINE, V. Note on development of Hemiptera. (No title given.) Ann. d. la soc. ent. d. France, 61:CLXIV–CLXV. 1892.

———. Etude comparée du développement de l'oeuf chez le Puceron vivipare et ovipare. *Ibid.*, 62:LXXXIX–XCVII. 1893.

LEUCKART, R. Ueber Metamorphose, ungeschlechtliche Vermehrung, Generationswechsel. Zeitschr. f. wiss Zool., 3:170–188. 1851.

———. Sur le développement des Pupipares. Bull. d. l'acad. roy. d. sci. de Belgique, 21(21):851–853. 1854.

LEUCKART, R. Die Fortpflanzung und Entwicklung der Pupiparen. Nach Beobachtungen an *Melophagus ovinus*. Abhandl. d. Naturf. Gesellsch. zu Halle, 4:147–
226. (1856–1857) 1858.

———. Zur Kenntniss des Generationswechsels und der Parthenogenesis bei den
Insekten. Meidinger Sohn & Comp. (Frankfort a.M), 1858. Also: Moleschott's
Untersuch. zur Naturlehre, 4(21):328–438. 1858.

———. Die Fortpflanzung der Rindenläuse. Ein weiterer Beitrag zur Kenntnis
der Parthenogenesis. Arch. f. Naturgesch., 25(1):208–231. 1859. Also: Ann.
Mag. Nat. Hist., ser. 3, 4:321–327, 411–422. 1859.

———. Ueber die Fortpflanzung der viviparen Cecidomyienlarven;. Nachr. v. d.
K. Gesellsch. d. Wiss. zu Göttingen, 8:215–219. 1865a.

———. Die ungeschlechtliche Fortpflanzung der Cecidomyienlarven. Arch. f.
Naturgesch., 31(1):286–303. 1865b. Transl.: Ann. Mag. Nat. Hist., ser. 3,
17:161–173. 1866.

———. Die Fortpflanzung der Blatt- und Rindenläuse. Mitth. Landw. Inst. Leipzig., Heft 1:116–148. 1874.

LEYDIG, F. Die Dotterfurchung nach ihrem Vorkommen in der Thierwelt und
nach ihrer Bedeutung. Oken Isis, 3:161–193. 1848.

———. Einige Bemerkungen über die Entwicklung der Blattläuse. Zeitschr. f.
wiss. Zool., 2(1):62–66. 1850. Abridged in: Der Keim der Blattläuse. Froriep's
Tagsber. über d. Fortschr. d. Natur- und Heilk. (Zool.), 1(102–3):142–143.
1850.

———. Zur Anatomie von *Coccus hesperidum*. Zeitsch. f. wiss. Zool., 5:1–12. 1854.

LICHTENSTEIN, J. (No title) "M. de Selys-Longchamps demande la parole, et, au
nom de M. Jules Lichtenstein, donne lecture du travail suivant." Ann. d. la
soc. ent. d. Belgique, 21:lxii–lxiii. 1878.

LISTER, M. Letter concerning a kind of viviparous fly. Phil. Trans., 6(72):2170–
2171. 1671.

LOCKWOOD, S. A viviparous fly. American Nat., 7:193–197. 1873.

LOEW, H. Bericht über die lebendiggebärenden Dipteren-Larven, welche in den
letzten Jahren beobachtet worden sind. Berliner Ent. Zeitsch., 8:v–x. 1864.

———. Notiz über eine neuere, die lebendiggebärenden Dipteren-Larven betref-
fende Publication. *Ibid.*, 9:270. 1865.

LOWNE, B. T. Observations on immature sexuality and alternate generation in
insects. Trans. Ent. Soc. London, 1871:193–202. 1871.

———. Anatomy, Physiology, Morphology and Development of the Blow-fly
(*Calliphora erythrocephala*). R. H. Porter (London). 1893–1895.

LUBBOCK, J. On the ova and pseudova of insects. Phil. Trans. Roy. Soc. London,
149:341–369. Abstracts: Proc. Roy. Soc. London, 9:574–583. 1859. Ann. Mag.
Nat. Hist., 3(3):499–506. 1859.

———. On the development of *Chloëon* (*Ephemera*) *dimidiatum*. Part 2. Trans.
Linnean Soc. London, 25:477–492. 1865.

———. President's address. Trans. Ent. Soc. London, ser. 3, 5:lii–lxv. 1865–1867.

MÄKLIN, W. Om vivipara dipter-larver. Öfvers. af. Finska Vetensk.-Soc. Förhandl.
(Helsingsfors), 8:22–32. 1865–1866.

MANEVAL, H. La ponte ovovivipare de *Chrysochloa viridis* Duft. Misc. ent.; rev.
ent. internatl., 39(11):99–101. 1938.

MANI, M. S. A case of ovoviviparousness in adult gall midges (Itonididae). Cur-
rent Sci. (Bangalore), 3:109. Sept. 1934.

MARCHAND, E. Observations sur l'*Echynomyia fera* (Linné) (Accouplement;
Appareil génital; reproduction; mœurs). Bull. d. la soc. d. sci. nat. d. l'ouest d.
la France, 6:119–136. 1896.

MASSONNAT, É. Contribution a l'étude des Pupipares. Ann d. l'Univ. d. Lyon,
n.s. 1, sci., Med., f. 28:1–388. 1909.

MAYET, V. Remarques sur les Coléoptères vivipares. Petites nouv. ent. 6 Ann.
(111):443. 1874.

MEINERT, F. *Miastor metraloas*: yderligere oplysning om den af Prof. Nic. Wagner nyligt beskrevne insektlarve, som formerer sig ved spiredannelse. Naturh. Tidsskr., R. 3. 3:37–43. 1864–1865. German transl.: Zeitschr. f. wiss. Zool., 14:394–399. 1864.

———. Endnu et Par Ord om *Miastor*. Naturh. Tidsskr., R. 3. 3:225–238. 1865a.

———. Om Larvespirernes Oprindelse i Miastorlarven. *Ibid.*, R. 3. 3:83–86. 1865b.

———. Nouvelles observations sur le multiplication des Cécidomyies. Ann. d. sci. nat., ser. 5, 6:16–18. 1866. Transl.: Observations on the reproduction of the Cecidomyidae. Ann. Mag. Nat. Hist., ser. 3, 18:496–498. 1866.

———. Om en ny Slægt med ynglende Larveform af Cecidomyiernes Familie. Naturh. Tidsskr., R. 3, 6:463–466. 1869–1870.

———. Om. Aeggets Anlaeg og Udvikling og om Embryonets første Dannelse i Miastorlarven. *Ibid.*, ser. 3, 8:345–378. 1872–1873.

———. Bidrag til Strepsipterernes Naturhistorie. Ent. Meddel., 5(4):148–182. 1895–1896.

———. Contribution a l'histoire naturelle des Strepsiptères. Overs. over d. K. Danske Videnskab. Selsk., 1896:67–76. 1896b. Summary: Jour. Roy. Micr. Soc., 1896:604. 1896.

METCALFE, M. E. Notes on the structure and development of the female genital system in *Dasyneura leguminicola* Lint. (Cecidomyidae-Diptera). Quart. Jour. Micr. Sci., 76:89–105. 1933.

METSCHNIKOFF, E. Ueber die Entwickelung der Cecidomyienlarve aus dem Pseudovum. Arch. f. Naturgesch., 31(1):304–310. 1865.

———. Untersuchungen über die Embryologie der Hemipteren. Zeitschr. f. wiss. Zool., 16:128–132. 1866a.

———. Embryologische Studien an Insecten. *Ibid.*, 16:389–500. 1866b. Also: W. Engelmann (Leipzig). 1866.

MINCHIN, E. A. Notes on a new organ, and on the structure of the hypodermis in *Periplaneta orientalis*. Quart. Jour. Micr. Sci., 29:229–233. (1888) 1889.

———. Report on the anatomy of the tsetse-fly (*Glossina palpalis*). Proc. Roy. Soc. London, ser. B, 76:531–547. 1905. Also: Reports of the Sleeping Sickness Commission of the Royal Society, 8:106–122. 1907.

MOLLISON, T. Die ernährende Tätigkeit des Follikelepithels im Ovarium von *Melolontha vulgaris*. Zeitschr. f. wiss. Zool., 77:529–545. 1904. Abstract: Zool. Centralbl., 1905:35. 1905.

MONIEZ, R. Les mâles du *Lecanium hesperidum* et la parthénogénèse. Compt. rend. hebd. d. séances d. l'acad. d. sci., 104:449–451. 1887.

MORDWILKO, A. Beiträge zur Biologie der Pflanzenläuse, Aphididae Passerini. Die zyklische Fortpflanzung der Pflanzenläuse. Biol., Centralbl., 27(1907); 28(1908); 29(1909). 1907–1909.

MORSE, M. The nuclear components of the sex cells of four species of cockroaches. Arch. Zellf., 3:483–520. 1909.

MORREN, C. Mémoire sur l'émigration du puceron du pêcher (*Aphis persicae*), et sur les caractères et l'anatomie de cette espèce. Ann. d. sci. nat., 6(2): 65–93. 1836. Also: Bull. d. l'acad. roy. d. Belgique, 2:75–104. 1836.

MÜGGENBURG, F. H. Der Rüssel der Diptera pupipara. Arch. f. Naturgesch., Jg. 58, 1:287–332. 1892.

MUIR, F. Notes on Stylopid and dipterous parasites in Fiji. (1) *Elenchus tenuicornis*. Hawaiian Sugar Planter's Assoc., Ent. Bull. 2:6–10. 1906.

———. Two new species of *Ascodipteron*. Mus. Comp. Zool., Bull. 54(11):351–366. 1912.

MÜLLER, F. Exhibition by Mr. R. Meldola. Trans. Ent. Soc. London, Proceedings, Parts 4 & 5, XXII. 1882.

MÜLLER, G. W. Beobachtungen an pädogenetischen Miastorlarven. Zool. Anz., 40:172–176. 1912.

NASSONOV, N. V. Position des Strepsiptères dans le système selon les données, du développement postembryonal et de l'anatomie. Congr. internatl. d. Zool. à Moscou, Sess. 2(1):174–184. 1892.

———. Untersuchungen zur Naturgeschichte der Strepsipteren. Ber. d. Naturwiss.- Med. Vereines in Innsbruck, 33:1–206. 1910.

NEEDHAM, J. G., and MURPHY, H. E. Neotropical mayflies. Bull. Lloyd Lib., 24, Ent. ser. 4:1–79. 1924.

NEEDHAM, J. G., TRAVER, J. R., and HSU, Y. The Biology of Mayflies. Comstock Publ. Co., Inc. (Ithaca), 1935.

NELSON, J. A. The Embryology of the Honey Bee. Princeton Univ. Press. 1915.

NEWPORT, G. On the generation of aphids. Proc. Linnean Soc. London, 1:292–293. 1846. Also: Zoologist, 6:2002–2004. 1848. Trans. Linnean Soc. London, 20:281–283. 1851.

———. On the natural history, anatomy and development of the oil beetle, Meloë, more especially of Meloë cicatricosus Leach. Parts I and II. Trans. Linnean Soc. London, 20:297–357. 1851.

NEWSTEAD, R. Polypneustic lobes in the larvae of tsetse-flies (Glossina) and forest-flies (Hippoboscidae). Ann. Trop. Med. and Parasit, 12:93–107. 1918.

NEWSTEAD, R., EVANS, A. M., and POTTS, W. H. Guide to the Study of Tsetse-flies. Univ. Press, Ltd. (Liverpool). 1924.

NOACK, W. Beiträge zur Entwicklungsgeschichte der Musciden. Zeitschr. f. wiss. Zool., 70:1–57. 1901.

NOSKIEWICZ, J., and POLUSZYŃSKI, G. Un nouveau cas de polyembryonie chez les insectes (Strepsiptères). Compt. rend. hebd. d. séances et mém. d. la soc. d. biol., Année 1924, 1:896–898. 1924.

———. Embryologische Untersuchungen an Strepsipteren. I. Teil. Embryogenesis der Gattung Stylops Kirby. Bull. internatl. d. l'acad. polonaise d. sci. et d. let. Cl. sci. math., Ser. B: Sci. Nat. (Cracovie), No. 8–10B:1093–1227. 1927.

———. Embryologische Untersuchungen an Strepsipteren. II. Teil. Polyembryonie. Zool. Poloniae (Lwów), 1(1):53–94. 1935.

NOTMAN, H. Concerning species, with notes on Phytodecta affinis Gyll. and pallidus Linn. Bull. Brooklyn Ent. Soc., 16:75–78. 1921.

OETTINGER, R. Über die Drüsentaschen am Abdomen von Periplaneta orientalis und Phyllodromia germanica. Zool. Anz., 30:338–349. 1906.

OSTEN-SACKEN, C. R. On the larva of Nycteribia. Trans. Ent. Soc. London. 1881:359–361. 1881.

———. On Mr. Portchinski's publications on the larvae of Muscidae. Berlin Ent. Zeitschr., 31(1):17–28. 1887.

OWEN, R. On Parthenogenesis, or the Successive Production of Procreating Individuals from a Single Ovum. John Van Voorst (London). 1849.

———. On metamorphosis and metagenesis. Proc. Roy. Instn., 1:9–16. 1851–1854.

PAGENSTECHER, H. A. Die ungeschlechtliche Vermehrung der Fliegenlarven. Zeitschr. f. wiss. Zool., 14:400–416. 1864. Abstract: Verhandl. d. naturhist.-med. Vereins zu Heidelberg, 3:157. (1862–1865) 1865.

PALMÉN, J. A. Über paarige Ausführungsgänge der Geschlechtsorgane bei Insecten. W. Engelmann (Leipzig). 1884.

PANTEL, J. Recherches sur les Diptères à larves entomobies, Part 1. La Cellule, 26:25–216. 1910. Review: Ent. Soc. Washington, 13:151–166. 1911.

———. Recherches sur les Diptères à larves entomobies, Part 2. Ibid., 29:1–289. 1913.

PARKER, G. H. Possible pedogenesis in the blow-fly, Calliphora erythrocephala Meigen. Psyche, 29:127–131. 1922.

PASPALEFF, G. W. Ovarialschläuche und Ooziten bei den parthenogenetischen Generationen von Aphis rosae, Koch und Siphonophora rosarum, Koch. (Bulgarian with German summary). Ann. Univ. Sofia, 2 Fac. phys.-mat., 25(3):238–272. 1929.

PATERSON, N. F. A contribution to the embryological development of *Euryope terminalis* Baly (Chrysomelidae). South African Jour. Sci. (Johannesburg). Part 1, Early development. 28:344–371. 1931. Part 2, Organogeny. 29:414–448. 1932.

PATTON, W. S., and CRAGG, F. W. A Textbook of Medical Entomology. Christian Literature Society for India (London). 1913.

PAYNE, F. A study of the cytoplasm in insect ova. Jour. Morphology, 53:523–591. 1932.

PERKINS, R. C. L. The assembling and pairing of *Stylops*. Ent. Monthly Mag., 54:129–131. 1918.

PERROUD, B. P. Notice sur la viviparité ou l'ovoviviparité des *Oreina speciosa* Panzer et *superba* Olivier, avec la description de la larve de cette dernière espèce. Ann. d. la. soc. Linn. d. Lyon, n. s. 2:402–408. 1854–1855. Also: Mélanges Ent. (Lyon), 3:82–88. 1855.

PEYERIMHOFF, P. DE. Paedogénèse et néoténie chez les Coléoptères. Bull. d. la soc. ent. d. France, 16:392–395. 1913.

———. Les larves des Coléoptères d'après A. G. Bøving et F. C. Craighead et les grands critériums de l'ordre. Ann. d. la soc. ent. d. France, 102:77–106. 1933.

PHILIPTSCHENKO, J. Beiträge zur Kenntnis der Apterygoten. III. Die Embryonalentwicklung von *Isotoma cinerea*. Zeitschr. f. wiss. Zool., 103:519–660. 1912.

PHILLIPS, E. F. A review of parthenogenesis. Proc. American Phil. Soc., 42:275–345. 1903.

PIERANTONI, U. Struttura ed evoluzione dell'organo simbiotico di *Pseudococcus citri* Risso, e ciclo biologico del *Coccidomyces dactylopii* Buchner. Arch. f. Protistenk., 31:300–316. 1913.

PIERCE, F. N. Viviparity in Lepidoptera. Entomologist, 44:309–310. 1911.

PIERCE, W. D. A monographic revision of the twisted winged insects comprising the order Strepsiptera Kirby. Smithsonian Inst., Nat. Mus. Bull., 66:1–232. 1909.

———. The comparative morphology of the order Strepsiptera together with records and descriptions of insects. Proc. United States Nat. Mus., 54:391–501. 1918.

PLIENINGER, T. W. H. Superfoetation bei Insecten. Jahresb. d. Vereins f. vaterländ. Naturk. in Württemberg (Stuttgart), 4:108–109. 1849. Also: Froriep's N. Notizen, 3(7):232. 1848.

POLUSZYŃSKI, G. Von der Bildung des unteren Blattes, der Genitalanlage und von der Blastokinese bei den Cocciden. In Polish. Ksiega pam. XI. zjezdu Lek. i. Przyrod. Polsk. Kraków. 1911.

PORTCHINSKI, J. A. On the different forms of reproduction and on the abbreviation of development in some of the most common species of flies. In Russian. Horae soc. ent. Rossicae, 19:210–244. 1885. Review: Berlinen ent. Zeitschr., 31:17–28. 1887. Ent. Soc. Washington, 13:166–170. 1911.

———. Investigations on the Russian Diptera. In Russian. Horae soc. ent. Rossicae, 26:63–131. 1891.

———. Recherches biologiques sur le *Stomoxys calcitrans* L. et biologie comparé des mouches coprophagues. In Russian. Trav. du bur. ent. du comité sci. du minist. d'agr. et d. domaines (St. Pétersbourg), 8(8):1–90. 1910.

PRATT, H. S. Beiträge zur Kenntnis der Pupiparen. Arch. f. Naturgesch., Jg. 59. 1:151–200. 1893.

———. Imaginal discs in insects. Psyche, 8:15–30. 1897.

———. The anatomy of the female genital tract of the Pupipara as observed in *Melophagus ovinus*. Zeitschr. f. wiss. Zool., 66(1):16–42. 1899.

———. The embryonic history of imaginal discs in *Melophagus ovinus* L., together with an account of the earlier stages in the development of the insect. Proc. Boston Soc. Nat. Hist., 29(13):241–272. 1900. Review: Zool. Centralbl., 8:245–248. 1901.

PRELL, H. Zur Biologie der Tachinen *Parasetigena segregata* Rdi. und *Panzeria rudis* Fall. Zeitschr. f. angew. Ent. (Berlin), 2:57–148. 1915.

PRINGLE, J. A. A contribution to the knowledge of *Micromalthus debilis* Le C. (Coleoptera). Trans. Roy. Ent. Soc. London, 87:271–290. 1938.

PUTNAM, J. D. Biological and other notes on Coccidae. I. *Pulvinaria innumerabilis*. II. *Aspidiotus ancylus*. Proc. Davenport Acad. Nat. Sci., 2(2):293–347. (July 1877–Dec. 1878). 1880.

PYROR, M. G. M. On the hardening of the ootheca of *Blatta orientalis*. Proc. Roy. Soc. London, Ser. B, 128:379–393. 1940.

RADLKOFER, L. A. T. Ueber das Verhältniss der Parthenogenesis zu den anderen Fortpflanzungsarten. W. Engelmann (Leipzig). 1858.

RATZEBURG, J. T. C. Agenda hemipterologica. Stett. Ent. Ztg., 5:9–14. 1844.

RAU, G. J. Two apparently undescribed mealybugs (Hemiptera: Pseudococcidae) from New York State. Bull. Brooklyn Ent. Soc., 32:195–201. 1937.

RÉAUMUR, R. A. F. DE. Mémoires pour servir à l'histoire des insectes. A Paris de l'Imprimerie Royale (Paris). 1734–1742.

———. Observations sur les insectes qui se multiplient sans accouplement et par la seule fécondité de chaque individu. Hist. d. l'acad. roy. d. sci. (Amsterdam), 73:44–45. 1741. Also: Mém. pour l'hist. d. sci. et d. beaux-arts. Trévoux (Paris). (1741):32–33. 1744.

REDI, F. Experiments on the Generation of Insects. 1668. Bigelow transl. of Italian, 5th ed. (1688). The Open Court Pub. Co. (Chicago). 1909.

REITBERGER, A. Des Verhalten der Chromosomen bei der paedogenetischen Entwicklung der Cecidomyide *Oligarces paradoxus*, mit besonderer Berücksichtigung der Chromosomen-Elimination. Verhandl. d. schweiz. naturf. Gesellsch. (Zürich), 115:359–360. 1934.

RETHFELDT, C. Die Viviparität bei *Chrysomela varians* Schaller. Zool. Jahrb., (Anat.), 46(2):245–302. 1924.

REYGER, G. Von der Erzeugung der Blattläuse. Versuche u. Abhandl. d. naturf. Gesellsch. in Danzig, 2:294–301. 1754.

RIBAGA, C. Sopra un organo particolare delle Cimici dei letti (*Cimex lectularius* L.). Riv. di patol. veg. (Firenze), 5:343–353. (1896) 1897.

RICHARDS, A. G. Comments on the origin of the midgut in insects. Jour. Morphology, 53:433–437. 1932.

RILEY, C. V. A viviparous cockroach. Proc. Ent. Soc. Washington, 2:129–130. 1890.

———. A viviparous cockroach. Insect Life, 3:443–444. 1891a.

———. Further notes on *Panchlora*. *Ibid.*, 4:119–120. 1891b.

ROBERT, E. Note sur quelques recherches zoologiques pendant un voyage au Sénégal. (Une Blatte vivipare). L'Écho du monde savant, 3 Ann. (126) 2 Div: 77. 1 Mai. 1836.

ROBINEAU-DESVOIDY, A. J. B. Observation sur la genre *Trixa* comme vivipare. Bull. d. la soc. ent. d. France, Ser. 2. 8:VIII. 1850. *Ibid.*, Ser. 3. 3:XCV. 1855.

RODHAIN, J., and BEQUAERT, J. Observations sur la biologie de *Cyclopodia greeffi* Karsch (Dipt.), Nycteribiide parasite d'une chauve-souris congolaise. Bull. d. la soc. zool. d. France (Paris), 40:248–262. 1915.

ROONWAL, M. L. Studies on the embryology of the African migratory locust, *Locusta migratoria migratorioides* R. and F. 1. The early development, with a new theory of multi-phased gastrulation among insects. Phil. Trans. Roy. Soc. London, Ser. B, 226:391–421. 1936.

———. Some recent advances in insect embryology, with a complete bibliography of the subject. Jour. Roy. Asiatic Soc. Bengal. Science, 4(2):17–105. (1938) 1939.

ROOT, DR. A case of intra-uterine pupation in the sheep tick. Jour. Parasitology (Urbana), 7:190. 1921.

ROUBAUD, E. Sur la reproduction et les variations du développement dans la *Glossina palpalis* R.-Desv. Compt. rend. hebd. d. séances d. l'acad. d. sci., 146:362–365. 1908.

———. La *Glossina palpalis*. Thèses. L. Barnéoud et Cie (Paris). 1909a.

Roubaud, E. Recherches biologiques sur les conditions de viviparité et de vie larvaire de *Glossina palpalis* R. Desv. Compt. rend. hebd. d. séances d. l'acad. d. sci., 148:195–197. 1909b.

———. Les particularités de la nutrition et la vie symbiotique chez les mouches tsétsés. Ann. d. l'inst. Pasteur (Paris), 33:489–536. 1919.

Rupertsberger, M. Biologische Beobachtungen. Coleopteren. Verhandl. d. K. K. zool.-bot. Gesellsch. in Wien, 20:835–842. 1870.

Sachs, J. Physiologische Notizen. II. Beiträge zur Zellentheorie. Flora (Allg. Bot. Ztg.), 75(1):57–63. 1892.

Sagemehl, M. Ein Paar von *Stylops* sp. in der Begattung. Sitzungsb. Naturf.-Gesellsch. bei d. Univ. Dorpat, 6(2):399–400. 1882.

Sales-Girons, Dr. Sur la parthénogénèse ou la génération virginale des insectes. Rev. med. franç. et étrang. (Paris), 1:137–141. 1875.

Saupe, R. Zur Kenntnis der Lebensweise der Riesenschabe *Blabera fusca* Brunner und der Gewächshausschabe *Pycnoscelus surinamensis* L. Zeitschr. f. angew. Ent., 14:461–500. 1929.

Schenkling, C. Zum Fortpflanzungsgeschäft von *Chrysomela varians* Schall. Illustr. Zeitschr. f. Ent., 5:7–9. 1900.

Schiödte, J. M. C. On some Staphylinidae, found in the nests of termites. Proc. Zool. Soc. London, 21:101–102. 1853.

———. Observations sur des Staphylins vivipares qui habitent chez les Termites. Det K. Danske Videnskab. Selsk. Skrift. Nat. Math., (5) 4:41–59. 1856. Transl., Ann. d. sci. nat., (4) 5:169–183. 1856.

Schleip, W. Die Reifung des Eies von *Rhodites rosae* L. und einige allgemeine Bemerkungen über die Chromosomen bei parthenogenetischer Fortpflanzung. Zool. Anz., 35:203–213. 1909.

Schmitz, H. Zur Lebensweise von *Helicobosca muscaria* Mg. Zeitschr. f. wiss. Insektenbiol., 6:107–109. 1910.

———. Eine auf der afrikanischen Honigbeine schmarotzende neue *Braula* Art. Arch. zool. (Paris), 54:121–123. 1914.

Schneider, A. *Chironomus grimmii* und seine Parthenogenesis. Zool. Beitr. (Breslau), 1(3):301–302. 1885.

Schrader, F. Notes on reproduction of *Aspidiotus hederae* (Coccidae). Psyche, 36:232–236. 1929.

Schwabe, H. Ueber ungeschlechtliche Fortpflanzung der Maden von Zweiflüglern. Das Ausland, 39:166–168. 1866.

Scott, A. C. Haploidy and aberrant spermatogenesis in a coleopteran, *Micromalthus debilis* Leconte. Jour. Morphology, 59:485–515. 1936.

———. Paedogenesis in the Coleoptera. Zeitschr. f. Morph. u. Ökol. d. Tiere, 33(4):633–653. 1938.

Scott, A. W. Description of an ovo-viviparous moth, belonging to the genus *Tinea*. Trans. Ent. Soc. New South Wales, 1:33–36. 1863.

Scott, H. Notes on Nycteribiidae, with descriptions of two new genera. Parasitology, 9(4):593–610. 1916–1917.

Seidel, F. Untersuchungen über das Bildungsprinzip der Keimanlage im Ei der Libelle *Platycnemis pennipes* 1–V. Arch. f. Entwicklungsmechanik d. Organ. (Berlin), 119:322–440. 1929.

Selys-Longchamps, M. de. Recherches sur le développement embryonnaire de l'appendice du premier segment abdominal chez *Tenebrio molitor* (Communication préliminaire). Bull. d. la cl. d. sci. l'acad. roy. d. Belgique, 4:413–447. 1904.

Ševyrev, Iv. (Shevyrev, Chewyreuv). Parasites and hyperparasites among insects. Part I. Investigations of the parasites of *Agrotis segetum*. In Russian. Reports of the Forest Department on the investigation of harmful insects. 3d ed. Public Utility, 1912. (St. Petersburg). Jour. Agric. and Forestry (1911). 1912. In part, Entomologicheskii Viestnik (Messager Ent.), 1:1–77. (1912) 1913.